Cover Photo
Health Valley Sesame Chicken With Broccoli (Chicken Recipes)

Healthier Eating

GUIDE
& COOKBOOK

Healthier Eating Guide & Cookbook
© 1987 Health Valley Foods
700 Union St., Montebello, CA 90640

Library of Congress
catalog card number
TX 1-446-977

Healthier Eating

GUIDE & COOKBOOK

GEORGE MATELJAN, HEALTH VALLEY FOODS

NEW REVISED SECOND EDITION

Published by
Health Valley Foods
700 Union St., Montebello, CA 90640

Printed in the United States of America

Acknowledgments

This book could not have been completed without the hard work and dedication of many knowledgable people at Health Valley who assisted and encouraged me. I'd like to thank and acknowledge some of them.

My special thanks to Harry M. Urist, who worked closely with me in the research, writing and editing of this book. Without his patience and attention to detail, this book would never have been completed. Dr. Bernie Landes provided his expertise on nutrition and health, and did all of the calculations and much of the research necessary. Rita Schwarz worked with me in developing and testing the recipes over many months. Terry Taketa provided editorial assistance, making many valuable suggestions. Michael Clayton and Lessa Woods did a beautiful job of designing and executing the graphic elements of this book, making it attractive and easy to use. I also want to thank Charles Brockett, Earl Crossley, Vicky Earhart, Joy McFerrin, Sheldon Price, Bill Rice and Kate Zurak for their various contributions.

All of these people worked tirelessly and patiently, and I appreciate their efforts.

George Mateljan

Dedication

This book is dedicated to you, and all health-minded individuals who are looking for a better, more practical way to eat healthy. It is my way of thanking you for supporting our Health Valley foods, and making our work possible.

A Message
from the Author

How healthier eating changed my life,
and why I think it can change yours.

It's unfortunate that we only really appreciate what it means to feel good, when we're not feeling that way.

I know, because for many years, I didn't feel very good at all. I was at least 50 pounds overweight, and had little success in trying to lose the excess weight and keep it off. But worst of all, I didn't have much energy, and I seemed to get tired very easily.

Like many people, I went looking for some "miracle cure," but nothing really helped for long.

So finally, in desperation, I began to read and study everything I could find on the subject of health. Eventually, I discovered the problem was caused by the foods I ate.

I learned that a major contributing factor to many of my health problems was all the thick steaks, sugary desserts, and lots of butter and cream, as well as the other high-fat foods that made it impossible for me to maintain my proper weight. My "typical American diet" made me fat, yet left my body lacking in many essential nutrients, including the vitamins, minerals and fiber needed to have energy and vitality.

Finally, I was convinced enough to change the way I ate. And I was pleasantly surprised at what a tremendous change it made, both in the way I felt, and the way I looked. My mental and physical health improved radically when I began to eat a diet with more fiber and less fat, cholesterol, salt and refined sugar.

And by eating in a healthy way, I was able to experience firsthand the fact that true good health is much more than just the absence of disease, it is an active state of feeling good. In fact, I now believe that of all the things we can control, choosing the right foods to eat has the greatest impact on how healthy we are and how long we live. And I feel so strongly that we all have the opportunity to control our own health and well-being that I wrote this book to share the information with you.

Most cookbooks published by food companies are created primarily as a way to help sell the company's products by featuring recipes and serving suggestions that include their food.

But that's not the reason I wrote this book. I strongly believe that Health Valley makes the best tasting healthy foods in the world. But I also believe that Health Valley has a responsibility to provide more for you than just healthy foods. We must also provide the information you need to use these foods as part of a healthier diet that will maximize your health and well-being.

I am anxious to share our knowledge and experience with as many health-conscious people as possible, so that you can enjoy the great benefits of eating the right foods and avoid the wrong ones. Indeed, there is now irrefutable evidence that eating the healthier way can significantly reduce our risk of such serious degenerative diseases as cancer, diabetes, and atherosclerosis (which can lead to heart attack and stroke), as well as greatly reducing the risk of conditions such as high blood pressure and obesity, which can contribute to the development of degenerative diseases.

We also feel a strong responsibility to provide the information needed by caring parents to protect and safeguard the health and well-being of their children. That includes warning parents about the risks of feeding children pre-sweetened cereals that contain more sugar, ounce for ounce, than candy bars, and more salt, ounce for ounce, than potato chips. We believe that teaching children good eating habits is one of the most important, most loving gifts we can give them, because it can benefit them for the rest of their lives.

Because to a large extent, we are the product of our own choices, we can take control over the quality of our lives and our own health, simply by choosing to eat in a healthier way. This is a very exciting prospect. So please invest the time to read enough of this book so you can get all the benefits it offers you. This book is unique in that it is a guide to healthier eating, not just another cookbook. So the most effective way to use it is to read enough of it so that you understand the concept of how to eat healthier, rather than simply picking out a few recipes to try on their own. For the first time, you have access to a complete plan, including recipes and cooking methods, for implementing the current dietary guidelines of America's most respected health-promoting organizations. Not only can you learn what these guidelines are, you can also learn in a clear, concise, step-by-step manner how to implement them with meals that are tasty, satisfying, easy-to-prepare, and convenient. This plan is presented in the **Week of Healthier Eating** from Health Valley. It is the most successful plan yet developed for getting complete, balanced nutrition without sacrificing the convenience, flexibility and practicality you need in today's busy world.

Please try the **Week of Healthier Eating.** I believe you will find it delicious, convenient and highly beneficial. And when you do, please write to me and let me know how it worked for you. The greatest reward I could ever hope to get by publishing this book is the knowledge that through it I have contributed to improving your life, the same way I improved my own.

10

Finally, I want to thank you for purchasing this "Healthier Eating Guide and Cookbook." This is the third book we've written, and we believe it is our best, because it offers you the greatest potential to benefit from a healthier way of eating. We are proud to be able to give you this information, and we're honored that you have supported our efforts by supporting our products with your continued patronage. We pledge to continue to work on your behalf, and to maintain the uncompromising high standards for quality and integrity that are reflected in each and every Health Valley food. And we hope that if you like what we are doing, you will recommend us to your family and friends.

Let's all work together to make this world a better, healthier place.

Yours in good health!

George Mateljan

How to Use this Guide for the Greatest Benefits

You can get the most from this book by using it as your complete Guide to Healthier Eating, rather than treating it like just another cookbook.

1. Start with the **Week of Healthier Eating** section. You'll get a full week of menus and recipes that comply with the dietary guidelines issued by the leading health-promoting organizations. You'll also get 100% of all the key nutrients you need, with a daily average of only 17% of your calories from fat, compared with over 40% in the typical American diet.

2. Consult the charts at the back of the book to find a complete nutritional analysis of every recipe in the book. If you have special dietary needs, such as getting more calcium or fiber into your diet, you'll also find easy-to-use charts listing the richest sources of 21 key nutrients.

3. Read the **3 Golden Rules of Healthier Eating.** You'll learn the latest information about how to eat healthier and why. You'll learn how to use food to reduce your risk of obesity, high blood pressure, diabetes, heart disease and cancer.

4. Enjoy the recipe sections. You'll find over 130 recipes that are practical, easy-to-prepare, tasty, and satisfying, and that comply with the dietary guidelines issued by the leading health-promoting organizations. Every one of these recipes contains less than 30% of calories from fat, and no added salt or refined sugar.

By following these four steps, you can get the greatest benefits from this book.

Table of Contents

Important Note:

The recipes, meal plans, and information presented in this ***"Healthier Eating Guide and Cookbook"*** *are in complete compliance with the latest published dietary guidelines of the following health promoting organizations:*

The American Cancer Society
The American Heart Association
The National Academy of Sciences
The National Cancer Institute

This is intended as a guide to the practical application of the most current accepted nutritional guidelines for healthier eating issued by the leading health-promoting organizations, but this does not imply their endorsement of this book.

Introduction

How this Healthier Eating Guide & Cookbook can benefit you.

You *can* eat healthier, even if your busy schedule leaves you very little time to prepare foods.

You can control your weight, without depriving yourself of flavorful, satisfying meals.

And you can select foods that provide you with more energy without extra calories, so you can stay slim, feel your best, and also significantly reduce your risk of developing obesity and high blood pressure, and serious degenerative diseases, such as diabetes, heart disease and cancer.

Best of all, you will have all the information in an easy-to-use chart form so that you can select the recipes that provide the specific nutrients you need to meet your individual dietary goals. These charts list the best source of fiber, calcium, vitamins A and C, as well as potassium, zinc, magnesium, and other essential nutrients.

All of this information is available to you in this book.

Eating healthier without sacrificing flavor or convenience.

You'll find a complete menu plan for a **Week of Healthier Eating** that is tasty, satisfying, and easy to prepare, and that provides you with all the fiber, calcium, vitamins A and C, complex carbohydrates, as well as all the other essential nutrients you need for good health.

You'll find that with the **Week of Healthier Eating,** you can enjoy breakfasts and lunches that require little or no cooking, and dinners that can be prepared in no more than an hour. And for extra busy days, you'll find a section with healthy meals you can prepare in 10 minutes or less.

All your meals will be light and flavorful, yet prepared with no added refined sugar or salt. And on an average day, only 17% of your total calories will come from fat, compared to an average of over 40% in the typical American diet.

If you have special dietary needs, this **Guide & Cookbook** can show you how to meet them.

For example, if you want to control your weight, the **Week of Healthier Eating** provides both a 1,900 calorie-a-day meal plan and a 1,200 calorie-a-day plan. The 1,900 calorie plan provides 100% of all the essential nutrients you need each day. So by rotating between the two calorie plans, you can lose weight safely, and get all the nutrients you need without taking supplements.

If you have special needs for iron, calcium, or any other nutrient, you'll find tips on how to get them from foods, rather than from supplements.

You'll also learn how to maintain your healthier way of eating even when you're dining in a restaurant.

This book also tells you what you need to know about fat, saturated fat and cholesterol, including how much you should be eating, and how to avoid excess amounts in your diet.

You'll also learn the facts about refined sugar and sodium, including how to stay away from the "hidden" sources of these ingredients in processed foods.

And you'll learn the shocking secrets of how "pure vegetable oils," such as coconut oil and palm kernel oil actually contain 30% more saturated fat than lard!

Finally, this book contains over 100 recipes that have all been developed to fulfill the dietary guidelines of the National Cancer Institute, the American Heart Association and the American Cancer Society. None of the recipes supplies more than 30% of the calories from fat, so you can use any of them as part of the **Week of Healthier Eating.**

Why you need to eat the healthier way.

Food is something we all need every day. But because there is an abundant supply of it in our country, we often give very little thought to what we eat, beyond choosing foods that offer us convenience, and appeal to our tastes.

Unfortunately, that means that most of us don't give enough thought to food from a nutritional standpoint. But if you stop to think about it, virtually all the materials needed to build and maintain our bodies come from the foods we eat.

Our bodies are amazingly adaptable. So they can continue to function even when we don't provide all the right nutrients needed for optimum good health. But if you don't eat enough of the right foods, your body eventually begins to break down or degenerate. And this degeneration is what causes degenerative diseases. Depending upon which nutrients you are lacking, which ones you consume in excess, and your own biochemistry, the specific degenerative disease you are at risk for will vary.

And the most effective way to deal with degenerative diseases is to reduce the risk of them occurring in the first place.

For example, it is more effective and substantially less expensive to prevent cardiovascular heart disease through proper nutrition and lifestyle practices than it is to try and treat it with bypass surgery or other interventionary techniques.

As the name implies, "bypass" surgery doesn't cure the problem, it only bypasses it. But if you maintain a healthy heart and cardiovascular system, you enjoy many positive benefits, such as having more stamina and less of a tendency toward fatigue, that go well beyond avoiding surgery.

Why it's so much harder to eat right today.

It is ironic that we have such an abundance of food in our country today, yet it has never been harder to eat the healthy way. That's because over the last fifty years or so, we have begun to substitute highly processed foods for those in their whole, natural state. As a result, the typical American diet is one of the main contributing factors in the development of degenerative diseases.

For example, there is substantial evidence that a diet high in fiber can reduce the risk of colon and rectal cancers. Based on this evidence, the National Cancer Institute recommends a diet that contains between 25 and 35 grams of fiber each day as part of an overall program to reduce the risk of these cancers. Yet the average American consumes less than half the recommended amount, or between 10 to 15 grams of dietary fiber each day. One reason for the lack of fiber in our food supply is the result of overprocessing of natural ingredients. For instance, when whole wheat flour is processed into white flour, the fiber-rich bran layers are removed. As a result, there is less than 20% of the fiber left in white flour. So 3½ ounces of white bread contains only 2.7 grams of dietary fiber, while the same amount of whole wheat bread contains 11.3 grams. And 3½ ounces of a sugar cookie made from white flour contains just 1.1 grams of dietary fiber, while the same amount of Health Valley Fruit Jumbos® cookies made from 100% whole wheat flour contains 6.6 grams of dietary fiber, or 600% more than in sugar cookies.

There is also an established relationship between an increased risk of high blood pressure and a diet that is high in sodium. And yet salt is still one of the two most widely used additives in the processing of foods of all types, (white sugar is the other) even those that don't seem to be "salty." For instance, although you probably don't think of breakfast cereal as salty, an ounce of corn flakes contains 268 milligrams of sodium, while an ounce of potato chips contains between 180 to 260 milligrams of sodium. So there is actually more sodium in corn flakes than in potato chips!

And one of the most serious problems with the typical American diet is that it contains too much fat, particularly saturated fat. More and more clinical studies confirm that a diet high in saturated fat raises the level of blood cholesterol even more than a diet that is high in cholesterol itself. So it isn't enough to avoid foods that contain cholesterol, you should also avoid foods that are cholesterol-free but high in saturated fat. Important examples of two such food ingredients are coconut oil and palm kernel oil. Both of these oils are frequently used by food companies in baked goods, snack items, and as the oil for frying packaged foods. Although these two oils are cholesterol-free and are "vegetable" oils, they are actually higher in saturated fat than beef or beef fat. Lard or beef tallow is 50% saturated fat. But palm oil is 81% saturated fat, while coconut oil is 86% saturated fat! In fact, the reason both coconut and palm kernel oils are so popular, besides the fact that they are much less expensive than other oils, is the fact that their high saturated fat ratio gives them a longer shelf life.

Another form of oil that we have been warning people about for many years is vegetable oil that has been "hydrogenated." Essentially, hydrogenation is the process that turns vegetable oils, such as corn oil and safflower oil, which are very low in saturated fat and therefore liquid at room temperature, into fats which are solid at room temperature, such as margarine. Although hydrogenated oils are technically "cholesterol free" and are made from polyunsaturated vegetable oils, they have been made into artificially saturated fats.

Today, the government recognizes the dangers of consuming too much hydrogenated fat and coconut and palm oil. In the "Dietary Guidelines for Americans" issued by the U.S.D.A., you are advised to "limit your intake of fats and oils, especially those high in saturated fat, such as butter, cream, lard, heavily **hydrogenated fats** (some margarines), shortenings, and **foods containing palm and coconut oils.**"

At Health Valley we have never used coconut oil, palm oil or hydrogenated fats in any of our foods. Even before it became widely known that these ingredients do not promote good health, we recognized that you offer us your trust when you purchase our products. So we have always believed we have an obligation to be the guardian of your good health. As such, we are careful to avoid using any ingredients that are even questionable when it comes to the safety of your health.

The net result of all that we have described is an American diet that is drastically different from the one humans have thrived on for many centuries.

Today, the typical American diet is higher in calories because we eat so much food that is high in fat, especially saturated fat. Too much of our food has been stripped of fiber, and contains too much added salt and refined sugar, which are the two most widely used additives in all food processing. And instead of "complex" carbohydrates from fresh fruits and vegetables, whole grains, and legumes, such as beans, we tend to consume "simple" carbohydrates in the form of sugars.

The one benefit we receive from all this overprocessing is food that is quick and convenient to use. And in today's fast-paced world, most of us need convenience.

The purpose of this Guide & Cookbook is to show you how to eat the healthier way while you still enjoy the convenience you need.

One of the ways this **Healthier Eating Guide & Cookbook** is able to achieve convenience without sacrificing nutritional integrity is by allowing you to use prepared foods that have been made the healthy way. Many of these prepared foods are available from Health Valley, the leader in preparing healthier foods.

How Health Valley Foods can make healthier eating more convenient.

If you have the time and want to prepare everything from "scratch" yourself, this book provides the recipes for virtually all the ingredients you need to eat healthier, including chicken broth, pasta sauce, and even herb seasoning blends. But if you're a busy, active person who needs the convenience of prepared foods, Health Valley offers many of the foods you're looking for. For more information about Health Valley and its products, see the special section on Health Valley Products.

20

The philosophy behind Health Valley and this book.

If you've read the previous edition of this book, you may already be familiar with the philosophy behind Health Valley and this book. But if you're not, and you want to know the story of how Health Valley was established and how the company philosophy is reflected in this book, here is the story, as told by George Mateljan, the founder and president of the company:

"One morning in the spring of 1970, after a typical breakfast that included coffee, a bowl of corn flakes and some bacon, I realized that it was just the start of the day, but I already felt tired and listless. I decided to take a walk to get my circulation going, but after less than a block, I was fatigued and short of breath. Without even realizing it, years of eating a "typical American diet" had put 50 extra pounds on my body. All the thick steaks, butter-drenched baked potatoes, ice cream and other rich desserts in my diet made it impossible for me to maintain my ideal weight. It seemed as if I was always hungry, and that everything I ate turned to fat.

Of course, statistics show that I was not alone. The average American consumes 300 cans of soda, 200 sticks of gum, 100 pounds of refined sugar, 55 pounds of fats and oils, 50 pounds of cakes and cookies, 20 gallons of ice cream, and 18 pounds of candy a year.

Largely as a result of my poor eating habits, I not only gained weight, but I was suffering from tooth decay, hypoglycemia, swollen ankles and puffiness around my eyes from water retention, and I seemed to have a perpetual runny nose from one cold after another. I learned later that poor eating habits are a life-threatening problem that contribute to the fact that the average American stands a fifty-fifty chance of dying of a stroke or heart disease.

It dawned on me as I trudged back from my brief walk that I had to do something about my weight, and my health in general."

Learning About Nutrition by Reading.

"The first thing I did was to read and study everything I could find on the subject of health. Although there wasn't much information about the specific subject of the role of nutrition and health, there was just enough for me to make the connection between the two. So I decided to expand my reading to include the ingredients listed on the labels of the foods I bought.

First of all, I was alarmed by the tremendous amounts of salt, fat, sugar and chemicals hidden in food products. Sugar, I found, was in peanut butter, bread, hot dogs and even salad dressings—and breakfast cereals contain as much as 5 tablespoons of sugar per 1-ounce serving!

I discovered large amounts of salt in candy bars, bread, pancake mix, cookies, cheese, frozen dinners of all kinds and even ice cream.

Fats constitute 42% of the calories most people eat in their diet. The American diet is actually 60% to 70% fat and sugar.

Bleached white flour, which is nutritionally depleted in processing, created problems too. Laboratory studies with rats showed that enriched white bread stunts growth, and two-thirds of the rats died of malnutrition in 90 days.

Another culprit is chemicals. Over 1400 additives are approved for use in the United States, and the average American eats 3 to 5 pounds of chemicals a year!

I was also surprised by the lack of information many labels offered. My research uncovered the fact that the government had established "standards of identity" for many common foods and condiments. In order to meet these government standards hot dogs *must* contain the potent chemicals sodium nitrate and sodium nitrite. Catsup *must* contain sugar. (A tablespoon of catsup contains a teaspoon of sugar!) Other standardized products such as peanut butter are allowed to contain lard or hydrogenated fats without listing it on the label, and cheese may contain artificial coloring and preservatives without disclosing them.

Further research revealed other potential health hazards in foods, such as high levels of lead from the solder used to seal cans.

I even discovered that my breakfast corn flakes that I considered to be so healthy actually contained more salt, ounce for ounce, than potato chips. Leading brands of potato chips contain 180-260 mg sodium and corn flakes has 268 mg. That was the last straw. I knew there was absolutely no need to add salt, especially not in such huge quantities, to breakfast cereal. The grains themselves contained a natural balance of sodium that was perfectly sufficient for dietary needs.

Out of frustration, I decided to make my own foods that I could be sure were healthy, and so I could be certain what went into each product."

The Health Valley Commitment to Quality.

"At first, I prepared my healthy recipes just for myself and my family. Then I shared them with friends. And because everyone liked them so much, I began providing them to health-minded neighborhood stores. Almost before I knew it, I was in the food business. And because I vowed that I would *only* sell healthy foods, I decided to call my little venture "Health Valley."

Even though food had become a way to make a living for me, I promised never to forget that it was also a way of life for me. That meant I would make product decisions based on what was most beneficial to human nutrition and health, rather than on what was best for bottom line profits. I established a company commitment to quality that has never changed, and will never change as long as I'm alive to run Health Valley. Essentially, that commitment is this:

- **Health Valley products will never contain any ingredients harmful or even questionable in terms of human health. That means:**

- No refined white sugar
- No bleached white flour
- No hydrogenated fats
- Little or no added salt and definitely not in breakfast cereals, cookies or any baked goods
- No Monosodium Glutamate (M.S.G.)
- No artificial ingredients, not even synthetic vitamins or nutrients
- No chemical preservatives
- No lead solder in our cans for soups, chili and baked beans
- No gimmicks
- No compromises

- **At the same time, our Health Valley philosophy means doing positive things, including:**
- Using only ingredients that meet the highest standards of quality and flavor
- Clearly listing and declaring all ingredients on every package, and being the very first to do so
- Clearly listing sodium content on salted products, again being the first company to do so
- Offering the best value consistent with our quality standards
- Respecting our customers by providing them with honest, accurate product information
- Making only products I would proudly serve my family and eat myself
- Guaranteeing the quality and flavor of every product we make with a full money-back guarantee
- Keeping the company small enough to maintain all the standards listed above

This was the commitment Health Valley was founded on. And while many things have changed since 1970, this philosophy and commitment are exactly the same."

Part One

The 3 Golden Rules of Healthier Eating

Introduction to "3 Golden Rules of Healthier Eating."

Your choice of the foods you eat probably has a more direct effect on your health and well-being than any other single lifestyle factor. There is now conclusive scientific evidence that eating foods with the right nutrients, prepared in a healthy way can make a positive contribution to your good health, provide you with more energy, and substantially reduce your risk of developing degenerative diseases such as cancer, heart disease and diabetes.

In fact, the evidence is so strong and so widely accepted that specific dietary guidelines have been published by such leading health promoting agencies as the National Cancer Institute, American Heart Association and American Institute for Cancer Research, as well as the National Academy of Sciences. By following these guidelines, all Americans can enjoy the potential health benefits of this knowledge.

But in addition to knowing the rules of healthier eating, you also need to know simple, practical ways to follow them that are compatible with the way you live today. These rules must be made to fit into your busy schedule whether you're involved in a career, or you're a busy parent who doesn't have unlimited time to shop and cook, or you're an active retired person. You must be willing to make an effort to eat healthier, but you shouldn't have to sacrifice the pleasures of life to do it.

This Healthier Eating Guide & Cookbook has been created to bridge the gap between knowledge and application. It provides you with the information you need to eat healthier so that you can look your best, feel your best and have the greatest resistance to degenerative diseases. At the same time, it is an easy to understand, easy to follow, practical guide to preparing meals that are convenient, flavorful and satisfying along with providing the high levels of nutrition you need.

As the first step on the road to healthier eating, we have distilled the dietary guidelines of the leading health promoting organizations and the latest scientific data into "3 Golden Rules of Healthier Eating."

1

Golden Rule Number One

"Eat a variety of whole, natural foods that are rich in Fiber, Calcium, Vitamin A, Vitamin C, and Complex Carbohydrates"

Eat a variety of whole, natural foods

There is no one "perfect" food that provides all the nutrients you need in the amounts you require for optimum health. Even the most nutritious foods are lacking in some nutrient, or are not as rich a source as you need.

For example, carrots are an abundant source of beta carotene, but they lack vitamin D, which is necessary for strong teeth and bones, and they don't provide all the iron you need for the formation of healthy red blood cells. And peas are a good source of vitamin C and thiamine, but they are a poor source of calcium. Similary, bananas are a rich source of potassium, but they also lack calcium, which you need to maintain strong, healthy bones.

So the key to getting all the nutrients you need in the proper amounts is to eat a variety of foods.

Equally important, you should eat foods in their whole, natural form, rather than from highly processed foods made with ingredients that have been refined or altered substantially.

Many of us are in the habit of eating just a few foods that we like. But healthier eating requires that along with the "old stand-bys," we eat a variety of other foods as well. For example, whole grain cereals and breads are highly nutritious and should be eaten daily. But rather than just eating your favorite wheat or corn cereal every day, you should include cereals made with other nutritious grains such as whole oats, rice, barley, rye, millet and Amaranth. The same is true of bread and crackers.

By doing this, you'll achieve more balanced nutrition and you'll avoid the possibility of developing allergies that sometimes result from the over-consumption of a single food like wheat. You'll also enjoy a variety of flavors and textures, so try rotating cereals, bread, crackers and whole grain side dishes throughout the week.

In this book, you'll find Health Valley's Week of Healthier Eating, a full week of delicious, convenient menus and recipes that make it easy to follow this first Golden Rule. This week-long plan provides 100% or more of the U.S. RDA or generally recommended level of intake for every key nutrient – while reducing your intake of fats, cholesterol and sodium to well within the generally recommended safe levels.

Eat foods that are rich in fiber.

From epidemiological research, we know that many societies around the world that regularly consume high fiber, low-fat diets have almost negligible incidences of coronary artery disease, colo-rectal cancer, diverticulosis, varicose veins, gall bladder disease and constipation.

For this reason, the National Cancer Institute recommends eating a high fiber diet that includes 25 to 35 grams of dietary fiber each day. The typical American diet includes only about 10 to 12 grams of dietary fiber a day, or less than half the recommended amount.

The richest sources of dietary fiber are fresh vegetables and fruit, whole grains, and legumes, such as beans. But when these foods are heavily processed, which is customary in commercial foods, they become "manufactured" foods that often have much of their beneficial fiber removed.

The most obvious example of this is white flour. In the commercial milling process, much of the fiber-rich bran is milled away and then the flour is bleached to make it lighter and whiter.

The problem has been compounded by the mistaken impression that whole grain products like pasta and bread, and legumes like beans and peas are fattening. So we have curtailed our consumption of these types of foods. It's not hard to see why most of our diets are lacking in fiber.

The recipes in this book all use ingredients that are fresh or minimally processed, so you can be sure that the valuable dietary fiber is retained. And by following the *Week of Healthier Eating,* you get an average of 35 grams of dietary fiber per day. This is the exact level recommended by the National Cancer Institute as part of an overall dietary plan to reduce the risk of certain forms of cancer.

The two varieties of fiber, and why you need them both.

Dietary fiber is that component of food that cannot be digested by the human digestive system. So it reaches the large intestine in essentially the same form found in food.

Most of the information you read about fiber has focused primarily on only one type of fiber, which is water insoluble fiber as found in wheat bran. But there are actually two basic types of fiber and both of them are important components of a healthy diet.

Water Insoluble Fiber is found in greatest abundance in the bran layers of wheat, but it is also found in varying amounts in all other foods that supply fiber. That is because water insoluble fiber is primarily cellulose, hemicellulose, and lignin, substances that make up the cell walls of plants. This type of fiber provides added bulk to the diet, allowing material to move swiftly through the digestive tract, preventing constipation and reducing the amount of time carcinogens and toxins in the digestive tract are in contact with the sensitive intestinal walls. There is enough evidence that a diet high in water insoluble fiber may reduce the risk of cancer of the colon and rectum that the National Cancer Institute has included the specific recommendation to eat more foods rich in fiber in its published dietary guidelines.

Some especially good sources of water insoluble fiber are Health Valley cereals, such as Health Valley Bran Cereal with Raisins, and Health Valley Fiber 7™ Flakes, which are a light, delicious and convenient cereal that contains the fiber of seven different whole grains.

Water Soluble Fiber is found in greatest abundance in such fruits as apples and berries, in legumes, and in whole grains, especially oats and oat bran. And a series of carefully devised clinical studies in leading research centers in the United States have demonstrated that diets rich in water soluble fiber as found in oats and oat bran can help reduce the amount of cholesterol in your blood.

In the most recent study, people with so-called normal cholesterol levels averaging 210 mg/dl were able to lower their cholesterol levels to about 190 mg/dl. While this decrease may not seem numerically large, it makes the difference between a slightly elevated risk of coronary artery disease at a cholesterol level above 200 and a minimal risk of coronary artery disease at a cholesterol level of 190. And while the participants in this study at Northwestern University followed a fat modified diet, a major portion of the decrease in their cholesterol level was attributed directly to the 2 ounces of oats or oat bran they included in their daily diets.

Some especially good sources of water soluble fiber include Health Valley Oat Bran Flakes cereal, Health Valley Oat Bran Cookies and Hot Oat Bran Cereal.

Both kinds of fiber can also be beneficial in weight control programs because they add bulk to the diet, helping to fill your stomach and provide hunger satisfaction, but adding no calories.

	NORMAL		
SEVERE RISK	MODERATE RISK	MINIMUM RISK	SAFE

| 260mg | 250mg | 240mg | 230mg | 220mg | 210mg | 200mg | 190mg | 180mg | 170mg | 160mg | 150mg | 140mg |

Reducing blood cholesterol levels from 210 to 190 means going from a level of moderate risk down to a level of minimum risk of heart disease.

Obviously, it is important to include foods rich in both types of fiber in your diet. This was a specific goal when designing the **Week of Healthier Eating.** In this plan, there are superior sources of both water soluble and water insoluble fiber to provide maximum benefit for both your digestive system and your circulatory system.

RICHEST SOURCES OF WATER INSOLUBLE FIBER

FOOD	AMOUNT OF FIBER	% INSOLUBLE
ALMONDS	14.3gm/100gm	87%
APPLE	2.0gm/100gm	70%
ARTICHOKE	4.0gm/100gm	87%
BEETS	3.2gm/100gm	72%
BLACKBERRIES	6.2gm/100gm	85%
BROWN RICE	7.2gm/100gm	90%
FIGS	18.5gm/100gm	77%
GRAPES	1.6gm/100gm	81%
GREEN BEANS	3.0gm/100gm	77%
LIMA BEANS	12.9gm/100gm	74%
ONION	3.1gm/100gm	68%
PEANUTS	9.3gm/100gm	99%
PEAR	3.0gm/100gm	80%
PECANS	7.2gm/100gm	87%
PRUNES	16.1gm/100gm	71%
RADISHES	2.2gm/100gm	77%
RAISINS	6.8gm/100gm	75%
RASPBERRIES	7.4gm/100gm	95%
SPINACH	2.4gm/100gm	75%
WALNUTS	5.2gm/100gm	85%
WHEAT BRAN	42.0gm/100gm	81%
WHITE BEANS	16.2gm/100gm	71%
WHOLE WHEAT FLOUR	9.6gm/100gm	84%
YOUNG PEAS	5.7gm/100gm	75%

RICHEST SOURCES OF WATER-SOLUBLE FIBER

FOOD	AMOUNT OF FIBER	% SOLUBLE
APRICOTS	2.1gm/100gm	48%
BEANS, RED KIDNEY	19.9gm/100gm	43%
BLACKEYE PEAS, COOKED	9.9gm/100gm	45%
BROCCOLI	3.2gm/100gm	48%
BRUSSELS SPROUTS	5.8gm/100gm	40%
CABBAGE, RED	3.4gm/100gm	50%
CABBAGE, CHINESE	6.0gm/100gm	50%
CABBAGE, WHITE	2.1gm/100gm	57%
CARROTS	3.3gm/100gm	42%
CAULIFLOWER	3.3gm/100gm	76%
CHICK PEAS, RAW	15.0gm/100gm	51%
CORN	4.7gm/100gm	45%
CORNMEAL	15.3gm/100gm	59%
EGGPLANT	2.5gm/100gm	40%
KALE	6.6gm/100gm	41%
LEEKS	3.1gm/100gm	45%
LENTILS, COOKED	3.9gm/100gm	44%
LETTUCE	2.1gm/100gm	43%
OAT BRAN	14.9gm/100gm	48%
OATS, ROLLED	9.9gm/100gm	51%
POTATO, BAKED	2.4gm/100gm	50%
PUFFED WHEAT	7.2gm/100gm	47%
TURNIPS	2.5gm/100gm	42%
ZUCCHINI	3.0gm/100gm	47%

Source: _Plant Fiber in Foods_, James W. Anderson, M.D., HCF Diabetes Research Foundation, Inc., Lexington, Ky, 1986

Questions & Answers on Fiber

Q. How much dietary fiber do I need each day?

A. The typical American diet provides only about 10 grams of dietary fiber per day. And while the amount each individual requires for optimal health may vary, the National Cancer Institute recommends a daily intake of 25 to 35 grams from food. Their recommendation is based on the fact that populations that consume a diet providing this level of fiber have a lower incidence of cancer of the colon and rectum.

But when you decide to increase your fiber intake, do so gradually because too much fiber can sometimes cause problems too. For example, too much water insoluble fiber from bran can cause painful gas, bloating, or diarrhea. This is especially true when you attempt to add a lot of fiber to your diet all at once.

The best way to guard against the problems associated with too much fiber is to gradually increase the amount of fiber-rich foods in your diet from a variety of sources. You should eat whole grain breads, cereals, and pasta, brown rice and other whole grains, legumes, and plenty of fresh fruits and vegetables. The **Week of Healthier Eating** is an ideal way to get the proper level of dietary fiber in your diet in a delicious, convenient way. That's because the plan supplies about 35 grams of dietary fiber per day from a wide variety of whole foods.

Q. Should I take fiber suplements?

A. You should avoid fiber supplements unless they are specifically prescribed by your doctor. Research has shown that the beneficial effects of increased dietary fiber come from high fiber foods, not fiber supplements. Especially avoid high fiber breads and baked goods that have added cellulose from wood pulp. This is not the same type of fiber found in whole grains, fruits and vegetables, and is not part of any food which human beings are used to consuming. So check the label, and if this type of fiber is listed on the ingredient panel, don't buy the product. And make sure to get the most out of high fiber foods by eating unpeeled fruits and vegetables and eating the skin of your baked potato.

Q. Will a high fiber diet help me lose weight?

A. Consuming high fiber foods as part of a nutritious, well balanced, low fat diet will certainly help you to reach your weight loss goal. Fiber adds bulk to the diet and so provides satisfaction without a lot of calories. And high fiber diets also result in a slower release of energy from food and so can help maintain a steady energy level and a well controlled appetite. Clinical studies conducted at St. Luke's Roosevelt Hospital's obesity research center in New York showed that subjects who were given a diet of high-fiber foods consumed less food than when given a low-fiber diet. A perfect example of a healthy weight reduction plan is provided in the 1200-calorie level of the **Week of Healthier Eating** in this book. You'll most likely find that you can steadily lose weight, while feeling healthy and energetic, and without feeling deprived in any way. After all, you can eat three pounds of fresh fruit for the same number of calories you get in only one 5-ounce chocolate bar.

Eat foods rich in calcium.

Calcium is an essential mineral that your body needs to build and maintain strong bones and teeth, and to regulate heart beat, muscle action, and nerve function, and it is essential for normal blood clotting. Recent research suggests that young females should be especially careful to eat calcium-rich foods during their growing years because this may be one important way of reducing the risk of post-menopausal osteoporosis. There is also research that indicates calcium may play a role in maintaining normal blood pressure.

A recent study in the prestigious *New England Journal of Medicine* showed that calcium may also be effective in lowering the risk of some forms of cancer by preventing pre-cancerous cells from becoming cancerous.

Unfortunately, many Americans do not get sufficient amounts of calcium in their diets. This is particularly true of women. The average adult woman gets only about 70% of the recommended level of 1,000 milligrams of calcium a day in her diet. This widespread deficiency is believed to be one of the major contributing reasons why osteoporosis, which is a weakening of the bone structure, affects older women more than it does older men.

Questions & Answers on Calcium

Q. How much calcium do I need in my diet?

A. The U.S. RDA for calcium for adults and children over 4 years of age is 1,000 milligrams per day. For women who are pregnant or lactating, the U.S. RDA is increased to 1,300 milligrams of calcium per day. Most Americans do not fulfill their daily need for calcium. The average calcium intake in America is only slightly above 700 milligrams per day.

SUPERIOR SOURCES OF CALCIUM

FOOD	AMOUNT	CALCIUM mg
VEGETABLE SOURCES		
COLLARDS, COOKED	1 CUP	357
TURNIP GREENS, COOKED	1 CUP	267
KALE, COOKED	1 CUP	206
MUSTARD GREENS, COOKED	1 CUP	193
DAIRY SOURCES		
NONFAT MILK	1 CUP	296
NONFAT YOGURT	1 CUP	452
NONFAT COTTAGE CHEESE	2 OZ.	52
CHEDDAR CHEESE	1 OZ.	204
SWISS CHEESE	1 OZ.	272
CANNED SALMON	3 OZ.	167
CANNED SARDINES	7½ OZ.	500

Q. Can I get all the calcium I need from food?

A. To get 1,000 milligrams of calcium per day, you would have to eat 16 ounces of plain nonfat yogurt, or 5 ounces of cheddar cheese, or 3⅓ cups of low fat milk, or 5½ cups of broccoli, or 4 cups of spinach, or 18 ounces of canned salmon. Or you can follow our **Week of Healthier Eating** and get an average of 1489 milligrams of calcium per day, a level which fulfills the U.S. RDA for everyone.

Q. What foods are the best sources of calcium without being high in saturated fat?

A. The best low fat sources of calcium include low fat and nonfat dairy products, such as nonfat milk and yogurt; fish, such as salmon and sardines. Many people are not aware that there are some excellent plant sources of calcium, including vegetables, such as broccoli, watercress and spinach; and fruits, such as oranges, tangerines and blackberries. Very rich sources of calcium that are not commonly consumed, but which can be excellent, either steamed or in salads are vegetables such as kale, collard greens, mustard greens, and turnip greens.

Q. Is there a risk of getting too much calcium?

A. Normally, there is very little risk of getting too much calcium from food. However research has shown that too much calcium from supplements may lead to kidney stones in susceptible people. This susceptibility may be further aggravated by a shortage of vitamin B6 and magnesium. And since the body normally uses nutrients together, it is best to get them from foods, where nutrients are invariably found in proper combinations with each other.

Q. When should women begin doing something to prevent osteoporosis?

A. Although osteoporosis usually affects women after menopause, the most effective time to begin preventing its effects is during the preteen and teenage years. After menopause, it is natural for women to lose calcium from their bones. So it is important to consume a high calcium diet before the age of 35 when bones are still building their mass to prevent the likelihood of osteoporosis later in life.

In addition to eating plenty of calcium-rich foods, young women should get regular exercise, especially the outdoor activities, such as walking. That's because exercise further contributes to building strong bones, and the ultraviolet rays activate vitamin D in our bodies. Vitamin D is necessary in adequate quantities for the body to use calcium effectively.

Q. Are there any factors that can cause my body to deplete excessive amounts of calcium?

A. There are several things that can deplete calcium excessively. The most significant include cigarette smoking, excessive alcohol consumption, a high salt diet, lack of exercise, and excessive consumption of red meat. Interestingly, highly trained female athletes in whom the normal menstrual cycle has stopped are also very susceptible to excessive calcium depletion.

Q. Should I take calcium supplements?

A. There is still a great deal of controversy about whether or not calcium supplements are an effective way to prevent calcium deficiencies and osteoporosis. A study published in the New England Journal of Medicine in January, 1987 has suggested that calcium supplements did not have a significant effect in preventing postmenopausal bone loss. But the debate continues and calcium supplements and calcium supplemented foods are being sold at an astonishing rate. Most of these calcium supplements are in the form of calcium carbonate, the same form of calcium found in chalk. The body's ability to absorb and utilize this form of calcium is highly variable and whether or not all this supplemental calcium is of any real benefit is still open to discussion. And there is a real question as to the safety of consuming calcium carbonate. At levels of as low as 4000 milligrams per day a syndrome called the Milk-Alkali Syndrome has been identified. This disorder can have a serious detrimental effect on kidney function. And bear in mind too that calcium works in conjunction with other minerals and nutrients in fulfilling its functions in the human body. So taking large amounts of calcium in an isolated form may create an imbalance of other nutrients.

It is so easy to get an adequate level of calcium in a healthy diet, so why take chances? It is probably wisest to get all the calcium you need from nature's best source...whole foods.

Eat foods rich in vitamin A.

Vitamin A is essential for the maintenance and health of your digestive tract, respiratory tract, eyes, skin, and reproductive system. It is necessary for proper night vision. It aids in the detoxification of poisons, and is necessary for the normal growth and repair of cell membranes. Vitamin A is also essential in your body's ability to resist infections, allergies, and the effects of air pollution.

There are actually two things that nutritionists call vitamin A. There is the pre-formed variety that comes from animal sources, called retinol. And there is the variety found in plants called beta carotene, which your body converts into active vitamin A as it is needed.

Since consuming too much pre-formed vitamin A can be toxic, consuming beta carotene is often considered preferable. Beta carotene is only converted into vitamin A as needed, so there is a much lower risk of toxicity from consuming too much.

Beta carotene has recently been associated with other possible health benefits. For example, *The New England Journal of Medicine* recently published a study done at Johns Hopkins University which showed a significantly lower incidence of lung cancer in a group of people who had high levels of serum beta carotene, versus another control group that had lower levels. The mechanism by which beta carotene works to inhibit the development of lung cancer is not certain. It is believed that it "deactivates" free radicals, which are unstable molecules that can harm cell structures and predispose them to becoming cancerous.

The National Cancer Institute and the American Cancer Society both recommend including foods rich in beta carotene in your diet as part of a program of cancer prevention.

Here is a chart indicating how much of some vitamin A-rich foods you have to consume to fulfill your daily requirement.

As you can see, this list includes some of your favorite fruits and vegetables, and you don't have to eat huge quantities to meet the RDA's.

FOOD	AMOUNT PROVIDING 5000 I.U.
CARROTS	¼ CARROT
BEEF LIVER	½ OUNCE
ASPARAGUS	4 CUPS
BEET GREENS	⅔ CUP
GREEN PEAS	5 CUPS
SPINACH (RAW)	1½ CUPS
APRICOTS	6 APRICOTS
AVOCADO	5 AVOCADOS
NECTARINES	5 NECTARINES
SWEET POTATOES	½ LARGE POTATO
CANTALOUPE	¼ LARGE MELON
WATERMELON	⅛ MEDIUM MELON
TOMATOES	3 TOMATOES
BROCCOLI	1 MEDIUM STALK

Questions & Answers on vitamin A

Q. How much vitamin A do I need each day?

A. The U.S. RDA for vitamin A is 5,000 International Units (IU's) per day for adults.

Q. What are the best food sources of vitamin A?

A. Vitamin A is found in both animal and plant sources, but generally, plant sources are preferred, because they contain vitamin A in the form of beta carotene, which does not pose a toxicity problem. You can readily tell which vegetables and fruits are rich in vitamin A, because they are generally very dark green, orange or yellow. Red is often a very healthy color too.

Q. Should I take vitamin A or beta carotene supplements?

A. You should be aware that there is a potential toxicity problem with taking too much pre-formed vitamin A, and that the disease-preventive benefits achieved with beta carotene have all come from food sources, rather than from supplemental forms. We think it is preferable to get your vitamin A and beta carotene from your daily diet. By following the **Week of Healthier Eating,** you will get more than 52,000 I.U. of vitamin A on an average day, but since only 717 I.U. is in the form of retinol, and the balance is in the form of beta carotene, there is no risk of vitamin A toxicity.

Eat foods rich in vitamin C.

Vitamin C or ascorbic acid is an essential nutrient that your body needs to form bones, teeth and connective tissue. It acts as an anti-oxidant and helps maintain the strength of your blood vessels. Vitamin C promotes a healthy immune system and helps the body cope with stress. Eating foods with vitamin C at the same time you consume foods rich in iron can increase your body's ability to absorb the iron.

The National Cancer Institute recommends consuming a diet that includes foods rich in vitamin C as a possible means of reducing the risk of certain types of cancers.

There are many good sources of vitamin C, especially citrus fruit. Here is a list of some foods and the amounts of each you need to consume to get your daily requirement:

FOOD	AMOUNT SUPPLYING 60 MG OF VITAMIN C
ORANGE JUICE	½ CUP
BAKED POTATO	2 POTATOES
RED PEPPER	⅔ PEPPER
TOMATO	3 MEDIUM TOMATOES
BANANAS	6 BANANAS
CANTALOUPE	⅓ MELON
BROCCOLI	⅓ STALK
STRAWBERRIES	⅔ CUP
BRUSSELS SPROUTS	3-4 SPROUTS

Questions & Answers on vitamin C

Q. How much vitamin C do I need each day?

A. The U.S. RDA for vitamin C is 60 milligrams a day. While most Americans get 80 milligrams of the vitamin in their diets, experts agree that eating more vitamin C-rich foods is well advised.

Q. Is there a relationship between vitamin C and iron?

A. Yes. Vitamin C and iron work together in your body. When you consume vitamin C-rich foods along with iron-rich vegetables or meats, you'll dramatically boost the amount of iron your body absorbs. For example, drinking a glass of orange juice with your whole wheat cereal will boost the amount of absorbable iron.

Eat foods that are rich in complex carbohydrates,

as found in fresh vegetables and fruits, whole grains, and legumes, such as beans and peas.

Most foods that are rich sources of fiber, such as vegetables, fruits, whole grains, and legumes, are also rich in complex carbohydrates. These types of carbohydrates are your body's best source of sustained energy. They are broken down gradually by your digestive system, providing a steady flow of energy. Unlike simple sugars, which can be broken down quickly and can raise the level of your blood sugar rapidly, complex carbohydrates are less likely to trigger an insulin response. For this reason, complex carbohydrates are considered to be beneficial for people who wish to maintain a steady healthy level of blood sugar.

Questions & Answers on Carbohydrates

Q. What's the difference between simple carbohydrates and complex carbohydrates?

A. Essentially, simple carbohydrates are sugars, such as sucrose, glucose and fructose, while complex carbohydrates are starches, like those found in whole grains, beans, fruits and vegetables. Most whole natural foods that contain complex carbohydrates also contain some simple sugars. The sugars found in this context are generally accompanied by other nutrients, such as chromium and B vitamins, which are necessary for the body to convert the sugars into usable energy. So both simple sugars and complex carbohydrates from whole foods are essential nutrients. In fact, normally, glucose is the only source of fuel your brain uses. And the brain needs between 500 to 600 calories from glucose a day to function.

The reason we stress complex carbohydrates instead of simple sugars is to distinguish between the carbohydrate found in whole natural foods, and the simple sugars that have been highly refined, like white sugar, which is pure sucrose. Refined sugars supply nothing but pure calories, because they have been stripped of all other elements, including other nutrients. So when you consume refined sugars, your body must use its own stores of chromium, B vitamins and other nutrients to convert these simple sugars into energy. However, when you consume foods rich in complex carbohydrates, you get the balance of carbohydrates and other nutrients you need to use the energy effectively.

Q. Since complex carbohydrates are basically starches, won't eating foods rich in them cause me to gain weight?

A. This a common misconception about complex carbohydrates. In fact, the opposite is true. Whole natural foods rich in complex carbohydrates are usually rich in fiber as well. The fiber in these foods helps satisfy your appetite, but fiber adds no calories. Also, complex carbohydrates themselves help you control your weight for two reasons. First, since they are broken down gradually, they provide a steady source of energy, so you're less likely to get hungry quickly. Second, carbohydrates contain fewer than half the calories of fats (only 4 calories per gram versus 9 calories per gram for fats), so you can actually eat a much greater volume of complex carbohydrates than fats for the same number of calories.

Q. What is wrong with "fortified" or "enriched" foods?

A. Many food companies claim that their products are nutritious, when many of the naturally-occurring nutrients have been removed by over-processing, and replaced by synthetic vitamins and minerals that are often in a form that is not well assimilated by our bodies. Some of the synthetic vitamins used to "fortify" foods are derived from coal tar, a distillate of bituminous coal. Artificial colors made from it have been shown to cause cancer in laboratory animals. You should also know that synthetic vitamin C is derived from sugar. And some of the minerals are in forms that are poorly utilized by the body. For example, inorganic sources of calcium and magnesium used for fortification are similar to chalk.

Equally troublesome, not all the nutrients that are removed through processing are replaced through enriching.

For example, there are 25 known nutrients in whole wheat. Most of these are either partially or totally removed when whole wheat is processed into white flour. Yet by law, only 4 have to be replaced through enrichment.

In spite of all this, companies that fortify or enrich their foods tell you that their foods are nutritious and that your body cannot distinguish the difference between synthetic and natural vitamins, and that enriched and fortified cereals, crackers, cookies and other baked goods are as nutritious as those made with whole grains.

This lack of knowledge and concern has so often shaped the makeup of our food supply, and resulted in a typical American diet that is too high in fat, calories, salt, refined sugar and cholesterol, and too often deficient in fiber, and many other essential vitamins and minerals.

How the Week of Healthier Eating helps you fulfill the first Golden Rule for Healthier Eating.

The **Week of Healthier Eating** presented in this book is the ideal way to fulfill the first Golden Rule of Healthier Eating. The meal plan provides you with easy-to-prepare, tasty and satisfying recipes that include many of your favorite foods. And by following the meal plan, you will automatically be fulfilling the first Golden Rule. You'll be eating a variety of whole natural foods that provide an average of 35 grams of dietary fiber a day from foods rich in complex carbohydrates. By using the **Week of Healthier Eating,** you'll eat a diet that provides high levels of calcium, vitamin A and vitamin C. The meal plan provides over 1,400 milligrams of calcium on an average day, which is more than 140% of the U.S. RDA in the form your body can use best...food. The plan also provides more than 52,000 IU of vitamin A on an average day. But since only 717 IU are from pre-formed vitamin A, and the rest is in the form of beta carotene, you are not at risk of getting too much. That's because your body converts beta carotene into vitamin A only as needed. And finally, the plan provides 455 milligrams of vitamin C on an average day. This level of vitamin C is completely safe, because vitamin C is water soluble, so your body can simply excrete any excess. And there is a growing belief in the scientific community that a level of daily vitamin C intake in excess of the U.S. RDA may be beneficial to maintaining good health.

2

Golden Rule Number Two

Avoid foods that contain too much salt, refined sugar, and cholesterol.

Avoid foods that contain too much salt.

Ordinary table salt is made up of two minerals, sodium and chloride. The sodium in salt is one of the important electrolytes that help regulate the fluid levels in your body. The problem is that the more sodium you consume, the more water your body retains. So when you consume too much sodium, your body retains excess water, which is carried by your tissues in the spaces between the blood capillaries. This can cut down the transfer of oxygen from your blood to your cells, and create extra pressure against the walls of your blood vessels, which results in hypertension or high blood pressure. High blood pressure can result in burst blood vessels. When this occurs in your brain, the result is a stroke.

Recent clinical studies indicate that everyone can benefit from moderating the amount of sodium they consume. And if high blood pressure is present, or if there is a family history of high blood pressure, then a low sodium diet may be of critical importance. There is now indisputable evidence that excess salt is a major contributing factor in the development of hypertension or high blood pressure.

In general, cultures where there is high consumption of salt have a much greater incidence of high blood pressure than cultures where little salt is consumed. For example, the northern Japanese, who eat three times as much salt as most Americans, have about a 40% rate of hypertension. But societies such as the Greenland Eskimos, and aboriginal societies in China, Panama and Australia who consume very little salt have very low rates of high blood pressure.

One reason so many Americans consume too much salt is that it is the most widely used additive in the processing of foods. It is added in surprising quantities to many foods that we do not normally think of as "salty." Processed foods such as breakfast cereal, cottage cheese, chocolate cake mix and canned cream corn all contain around 400 milligrams of sodium per serving. So about 80% of the salt in the average diet comes from these "hidden" sources, where salt has been added before it reaches us. This is a dangerous situation because even if you do not add salt to your foods at the table or in cooking, you're still likely to consume too much sodium if you consume a lot of processed foods or "fast" foods. The taste for salt can be addictive, causing people to use more and more of it. And at least one-third of the people with high blood pressure are sensitive to sodium, and their condition is either caused by or aggravated by too much salt in their diets.

There is actually no need for you to add any salt to your food to get the sodium you need in your diet, because many foods naturally contain sodium already. To give you an idea of how much, here is a chart with some examples:

FOOD	QUANTITY	AMOUNT OF SODIUM
BEEF	1 LB.	295 mg.
CHICKEN	1 BREAST & DRUMSTICK	185 mg.
CELERY	6 OZ.	216 mg.
EGG	1	59 mg.
LIVER, BEEF	4 OZ.	209 mg.
LOBSTER	4 OZ.	230 mg.
MILK	2 CUPS	244 mg.
SCALLOPS	3 OZ.	219 mg.
YOGURT	2 CUPS	230 mg.

Questions & Answers on Salt

Q. Since sodium is an essential nutrient, how much do I actually need each day?

A. The actual amount of sodium you need each day is quite small. The American Heart Association states in their "Dietary Guidelines for Healthy Adult Americans" that the body is able to function quite well with sodium intakes of less than 200 milligrams per day. Since one teaspoon of salt contains about 2,300 milligrams of sodium, the amount of sodium you need each day can be obtained from 1/10 of a teaspoon of salt. On the average, the American diet includes 20 to 30 times that much, or around 8,000 milligrams, which is close to 4 teaspoons a day. The American Heart Association recommends that we consume no more than 1,000 milligrams of sodium per 1,000 calories, and no more than 3,000 milligrams per day.

Q. Is it true that there is more salt in some breakfast cereals than there is in potato chips?

A. Unfortunately, it is true. One ounce of regular salted potato chips contains between 180 and 260 milligrams of sodium. One ounce of typical commercial corn flakes contains 268 milligrams of sodium. One ounce of the most popular wheat flakes contains 370 milligrams of sodium. One ounce of the most popular oat cereal contains 330 milligrams of sodium. And one ounce of the most popular vitamin fortified cereal contains 360 milligrams of sodium. In contrast, the highest level of sodium in any Health Valley cereal is 15 milligrams per one ounce serving! And all the sodium in Health Valley cereals is the naturally-occurring sodium found in the grains themselves. There is no salt added to *any* Health Valley cereal.

Q. If there is so much sodium "hidden" in packaged foods, how can I protect myself against purchasing high sodium foods?

A. The best way to protect yourself against purchasing foods with large amounts of added salt is to read the labels carefully. Manufacturers are required by law to list ingredients in order of their prevalence, so the most prevalent ingredient is listed first and the least prevalent one is last. It is a good general rule to avoid products where salt is listed among the first five ingredients, whenever there are more than five ingredients used. For those products, such as breakfast cereal, where the actual sodium content is listed, it is a good rule not to purchase any products that contain more than 25 milligrams per serving. Also keep in mind that sodium can be listed in more than one form. There are ingredients such as MSG (mono-**sodium** glutamate), baking soda (**sodium** bicarbonate), saccharin, and preservatives, such as **sodium** benzoate that all contain sodium. It is best to avoid products that contain more than one form of sodium.

Q. When I try to cut down on salt, foods taste bland. Is there any way to avoid this?

A. If you're accustomed to a high salt diet, cutting down all at once can result in foods tasting bland. The way to avoid this problem is to cut down gradually. It usually takes 4 to 6 weeks to lose your taste for salt. So unless you are under a doctor's orders to cut down immediately, try reducing the amount of salt you use by 40%, while you gradually lose your taste for it.

Health Valley can help you get started without depriving you of the flavors you enjoy. Health Valley regular salted products contain 30%-40% less salt than comparable commercial products. But Health Valley products taste so good, you won't even notice the missing salt. In fact, most people actually prefer our foods to those with more salt.

As you gradually lose your taste for salt, you can begin switching to Health Valley's No Salt Added version of many of the same products.

Q. Do some people use more salt because they have a harder time tasting it?

A. A recent clinical study indicated that patients with high blood pressure could not taste salt as well as those with normal blood pressure. Scientists believe that this may be one reason why hypertensive people often add so much salt to their food.

Another study by British researchers indicated that as you get older, you lose your sensitivity to the taste of salt. For example, 25 year olds are ten times more sensitive to the taste of salt than 95 year olds. This may explain why as people get older, they tend to use more salt.

Q. Can cutting down on sodium help me to lose weight?

A. Reducing the amount of sodium in your diet can definitely help you to lose weight. Too much sodium causes your body to retain excess water, which results in excess weight. Dr. Garfield Duncan, an expert on the treatment of obesity, has stated that salty foods can raise your weight by as much as two to three pounds in only one day. Dr. Duncan noted that some of his severely obese patients who weighed in excess of 300 pounds, lost as much as 10 pounds in a single day simply by omitting salt. And in addition to contributing to excess weight by causing the retention of excess water, there is new evidence that adding salt may also accelerate the digestion of sugars and starches. This would lead to the availability of more calories from highly salted foods than from unsalted foods. More calories, as we know, leads to more excess pounds. So you can see that there are two very good reasons to cut down on your intake of salt if you are trying to lose weight. **The Week of Healthier Eating** in this book provides you with a practical way to put this recommendation into practice. If you follow the suggestions to prepare the recipes with no added salt, you'll be taking a big step toward reaching your weight loss goal because there are about 1170 milligrams of sodium in an average day. And remember that for every ¾ teaspoon (1,650 mg.) of extra salt you consume, your body retains about a pound of water to dilute it. So by consuming less sodium, you'll also retain less water.

Avoid foods with too much refined sugar.

If you eat a typical American diet, 25% of all the calories you consume come from a substance that contains no vitamins, no minerals and no fiber. That substance is refined sugar. The average man, woman and child in the United States consumes over 100 pounds of white sugar every year! In addition to the sugar you add to your coffee and cereal, or use in baked goods, there is sugar added to just about every kind of processed food imaginable. In fact, after salt, sugar is the most widely used additive in the processing of food. And unfortunately, white sugar adds nothing to your diet except calories. Of even more concern is the fact that excess sugar in our diets has been associated with high blood pressure, diabetes, heart disease, hyperactivity, hypoglycemia, elevated blood cholesterol, and tooth decay.

One of the serious problems with eating refined sugar is that it does not supply your body with anything except calories. And to assimilate and convert sugar into energy, your body requires the presence of vitamins and minerals, which would normally accompany the sugar if it were from a food such as a piece of fruit. So the only way your body can metabolize refined sugar is to use its stores of vitamins and minerals. Not only does the refining of sugar rob you of the nutrients that usually accompany sugar in natural foods, it also causes you to deplete the stores of these nutrients such as calcium and chromium already in your body in order to use the sugar for energy. This depletion of nutrients can lead to the degeneration of body organs which can lead to degenerative diseases.

Questions & Answers on Sugar

Q. Does refined sugar add anything to my diet except calories?

A. No, and because it supplies no nutrients other than pure carbohydrates, it requires your body to use its own nutrient stores to metabolize the sugar. Diets that are high in sugar tend to satisfy your appetite without satisfying your body's need for nutrients. Sugar keeps you from eating more nutritious foods that have a positive health benefit.

Q. Can sugar affect my health in other ways?

A. Too much refined white sugar can affect your health in many ways. First, it can lead to an increase in dental caries, or cavities as they are more commonly known. And while it has not been accepted universally, there is strong research evidence that suggests that refined white sugar can contribute to elevated serum cholesterol levels with the associated increased risk of heart disease. There is also persuasive evidence suggesting a connection between excessive sugar intake and the development of diabetes in adults.

Q. What should I eat if I need an energy boost, or just want to satisfy my craving for something sweet?

A. The best source for both energy and satisfaction of a craving for sweets is fresh fruit. Fruits contain enough naturally occurring sugar to give you an energy boost, and they also come complete with the nutrients your body needs to process them. The sugars in fruit are far less concentrated than those in something like a candy bar, so they do not trigger the excessive insulin response that can cause your blood sugar to drop drastically.

Another excellent choice of quick energy sweet foods are fruit juice sweetened products such as Health Valley cereals and snacks. These foods contain a good balance of nutrients and the sugar is in the form that your body is accustomed to using.

Q. Should I use sugar substitutes, such as saccharin and aspartame (Nutrasweet™)?

A. Although the government has allowed these sugar substitutes to be sold because they feel there is no conclusive evidence that they are harmful, there are many respected scientists who recommend a more cautious approach.

Saccharin has been banned in other countries because laboratory experiments have indicated that it can be carcinogenic in high dosages, and at the very least it is a sodium product that can aggravate the problems of those who need to lower their sodium intake. Every saccharin package contains the following warning: "Warning, saccharin has been found to cause cancer in laboratory animals."

Aspartame actually contains the same number of calories per gram as regular sucrose, but since it is 200 times sweeter, you can use less and still get the same effect. There is serious concern about using a substance that is so much more concentrated than regular sugar, which is already a much more concentrated form of sweetener than found in nature, and which the human body is unaccustomed to dealing with.

Avoid foods with too much cholesterol.

Cholesterol is a waxy substance that is an important constituent of every cell in the human body. It is an important component that the body requires to make many vital hormones. The body gets the cholesterol it needs from one of two sources. It either gets it from cholesterol supplied directly from the diet, or it makes the cholesterol it needs from raw materials provided in the diet. When you do get cholesterol from food, your body adjusts its cholesterol production, making more when there is little in the diet and making less when there is a high level in the diet. That's why eating cholesterol in the diet does not always result in elevated cholesterol in the blood. About 30% of the population is, however, sensitive to cholesterol and in these cases eating cholesterol in the diet has a marked effect on the cholesterol level in the blood.

Too much cholesterol in the diet is invariably related to too much saturated fat in the diet. And while the jury is still out as to whether dietary cholesterol leads directly to higher levels of cholesterol in the blood, the American Heart Association specifically recommends that we restrict our intake of high cholesterol foods so that we consume no more than 100 milligrams of cholesterol per 1,000 calories. And in no case, they say, should we consume a diet that supplies more than 300 milligrams of cholesterol per day.

To give you an idea of just how much cholesterol is contained in some foods, a large egg contains 251 mg., while 4 ounces of fried beef or calf liver contains 497 mg. Four ounces of roasted chicken without the skin contains a manageable 100 mg., and four ounces of lean fish like halibut has only about 60 mg. A tablespoon of butter contains 35 mg. cholesterol, but vegetable oils have none. Vegetables, fruit and grains contain no cholesterol whatsoever. Zero. That's why this book avoids liver and egg yolks (the whites contain no cholesterol), and concentrates on foods that can play a positive role in healthier eating. By using the **Week of Healthier Eating** from Health Valley, you will consume well below that amount because the meals on this plan provide a safe 97 milligrams of cholesterol on an average day.

Here is a list of some of the foods that are the highest in cholesterol:

The portion size in each case is 100 grams, or about 3½ ounces, except where otherwise indicated.

FOOD ITEM	MILLIGRAMS OF CHOLESTEROL
BEEF KIDNEY	804
CHICKEN LIVER (SIMMERED)	746
LADYFINGER COOKIES	356
CAVIAR (STURGEON)	300
BUTTER (1 STICK)	284
EGG (LARGE)	251
SPONGE CAKE	246
LOBSTER NEWBURG	182
WHIPPING CREAM (HEAVY)	133
SARDINES (CANNED IN OIL)	120
CREAM CHEESE	111
MILK (WHOLE)	109
MACKEREL (ATLANTIC, BROILED)	101
SWISS CHEESE	100
CHEDDAR CHEESE	99

Questions & Answers on Cholesterol

Q. How much cholesterol can I eat each day and still be eating healthy?

A. Since your body can manufacture all the cholesterol you need, you really don't need to consume any. The American Heart Association recommends that you restrict your intake of cholesterol so that you consume no more than 100 milligrams for every 1,000 calories you take in, and no more than 300 milligrams per day in total.

Q. Is all cholesterol bad for my health?

A. No. All cholesterol does not have the same effect on the body. That's because cholesterol is carried through the circulatory system attached to two basic types of protein. Low-density lipoproteins or LDLs are the so-called "bad" component because they seem to encourage cholesterol to form plaque in the arteries, which restricts the flow of blood and can lead to heart attack or stroke. On the other hand, high-density lipoproteins or HDLs are the "good" component because they appear to help rid the bloodstream of buildup. We have both LDLs, the "bad" cholesterol and HDLs, the "good" kind in our bloodstreams. But it is the proportion of the two that is important. A high proportion of LDL is a definite risk factor for coronary artery disease, while a high proportion of HDL and a low proportion of LDL seems to offer protection against the disease.

A total cholesterol count for all components, including LDL and HDL combined that is below 200 reduces your risk.

A diet high in monounsaturated fats, such as the type found in olive oil, and in certain polyunsaturated fats, called omega-3 fatty acids (found in fish) appears to increase your proportion of HDLs the "good" cholesterol, and lower the amount of LDLs, the "bad" cholesterol.

How the Week of Healthier Eating helps you fulfill the second Golden Rule for Healthier Eating.

The **Week of Healthier Eating** from Health Valley is the ideal way to fulfill the second Golden Rule of Healthier Eating. It has been created to let you enjoy the benefits of foods and recipes prepared with no added salt, refined sugar, or high-cholesterol butter or cream. Yet the meals you eat while following this plan are zesty, flavorful, and highly nutritious. They are also convenient, because the recipes are easy to prepare. Many of the breakfasts and lunches use Health Valley products. All Health Valley foods are free from refined white sugar and excess salt.

3

Golden Rule
Number Three

Keep the amount of fat in your diet to no more than 30% of total calories.

Although we have listed this Golden Rule last, this is probably the most important one. There is probably no single dietary change you can make that will do more for your health than cutting down on the total amount of fat you eat. The typical American diet is literally killing us with too much fat. Excess fat in our diets has been clearly linked to an increased risk of developing heart disease, diabetes and obesity. And excess fat has also been discovered to be one of the leading contributing factors to the development of some forms of cancer.

Dr. David Heber, chief of Clinical Nutrition at U.C.L.A. School of Medicine, said at a symposium on fat and disease that, "Obesity, cancer and heart disease are all interrelated, with total fat intake being the common risk factor." Dr. Heber, a leading cancer researcher, went on to say that "High fat intake usually raises blood cholesterol levels, total calorie intake, and weight, increasing the risk for heart disease and cancer of the colon, breast, uterus and prostate." He then reaffirmed the recommendations of the leading health-promoting organizations, including the American Heart Association and the American Cancer Society, to keep total fat intake below 30% of total calories. He went on to recommend balancing fat intake evenly among **saturated, monounsaturated and polyunsaturated fats.**

To understand why excess fat is such a serious health risk, it is important to understand what fat is, and how it functions within the body.

In simplest terms, fats are one of the three main components of all foods, along with protein and carbohydrates.

Fats are made up of components called fatty acids. There are about 26 different kinds of these fatty acids commonly found in foods. Although fatty acids are essential for good health, our actual physiological need for them is much less than the amounts we consume in the typical American diet.

For example, barely 3 teaspoons of safflower oil contain all the essential fatty acid called linoleic acid we need each day. Yet on the average, American adults consume between 18 and 24 teaspoons of fat a day.

To understand where all this fat comes from, consider the fact that just one fast food cheeseburger contains 35 grams of fat, or about 7 teaspoons of fat. Add a serving of French fries from the same popular fast food source, and you add about 2 teaspoons more fat.

Too much fat can overload the body's coping mechanisms, resulting in an elevated level of fats called "lipoproteins" in the blood. Elevated levels of lipoproteins are believed to be directly linked to the development of plaque deposits on the walls of the arteries that surround the heart and the brain. This condition is called atherosclerosis, and is the major cause of heart attacks and strokes. The connection between blood cholesterol and heart disease is clear. One major study showed that for every 1 percent reduction in the level of cholesterol in the blood, there is a 2 percent reduction in the risk of heart disease and eating foods high in saturated fat can increase blood cholesterol levels even more than eating foods high in cholesterol.

High-fat diets are also linked to three of the most common varieties of cancer in this country: cancers of the breast, colon and prostate. According to one leading theory, colon cancer may result from the fact that in order to digest fat, the liver produces a substance called bile. The more fat you eat, the more bile your liver produces. It is believed that when excess bile comes in contact with certain fecal bacteria in the colon, it is converted into cancer-promoting compounds. This may also explain why high-fiber diets seem to prevent colon cancer. First of all, high-fiber diets tend to be lower in fat. But fiber also increases the size of the stool and speeds its transit through the colon, keeping the concentration of bile in the colon low.

Whatever the precise mechanism, there is nonetheless, convincing evidence that a low-fat, high-fiber diet can significantly reduce your risk of developing serious degenerative diseases.

How to read the label so you know how much fat is really in the product.

Product labels show the amount of fat present in two different ways, by indicating how many grams of fat are present in each serving or by showing the percentage of fat by weight.

Often, this information can be confusing and lead to incorrect food choices when you are trying to keep the percentage of calories from fat in your diet below 30%.

When fat is shown in grams it is as part of the nutrition information panel. A typical panel looks like this...

Serving Size . . . . 1 ounce	Protein 4g
Servings Per Package 16	Carbohydrate 20g
Calories 114	Fat 2g

To calculate the percentage of calories from fat, multiply the number of grams of fat (2) times 9 (the number of calories in a gram of fat) and divide that number by the number of calories (114). For example: $2 \times 9 = 18$, $18 \div 114 = .158$. The percentage of calories from fat is 15.8%.

Some product labels contain statements such as 98% fat-free. This statement means that only 2% of the *weight* of the product is fat.

Products labeled in this way (with the exception of meat and poultry) must also contain a nutrition statement like the one above. When you see such a statement, simply use the formula to figure out the percentage of calories from fat in the product based on the number of grams of fat per serving and the number of calories per serving. Low-fat milk is often labeled in this way. And while only 2% of the weight of this milk is fat, when you calculate the percentage of calories from fat you find that 30% of the calories are derived from fat.

Meat and poultry products like ground beef are only labeled with the percentage of fat by weight. Regular ground beef is usually 30% fat by weight. *But this doesn't mean 30% of the calories are from fat.* In fact, over 70% of the calories are derived from fat. This is because a large percentage of the weight of beef is water, and water has no calories. You can use the chart found later in this section to compare the percentage of fat by weight in meats with the percentage of calories from fat.

So read food labels carefully remembering this information. In that way you'll know how much fat really is in the foods you select.

The Different Kinds of Fat, and How They Can Affect Your Health.

All fats contain the same number of calories, which is 9 calories per gram, or about 120 calories per tablespoon, which is about 2 pats of butter. This makes fat the most concentrated form of energy of all food components. Both protein and carbohydrates contain only 4 calories per gram, or less than half the calories found in fat. That's one reason why a high-fat diet tends to promote obesity.

But all fats are not the same in their chemical makeup, and they can have very different effects within your body.

There are three types of fat: polyunsaturated, monounsaturated and saturated fats. They get their names from the number of hydrogen molecules that are attached to the fatty acid molecule.

If a fatty acid contains as many hydrogen molecules as it can hold, it is **saturated** with hydrogen. If the structure of the molecule is such that there is still space for one hydrogen molecule to attach itself, it is called **monounsaturated.** And if the fatty acid has space for two or more hydrogen molecules before it would be fully saturated, it is **polyunsaturated.**

All fats and oils contain a combination of saturated, polyunsaturated and mono-unsaturated fatty acids. But vegetable oils tend to be mostly polyunsaturated (with the exception of coconut oil and palm kernel oil, which are mostly saturated). And most saturated fat comes from animal sources, particularly red meat, such as beef.

A healthy diet requires a balance of all three types of fatty acids, but in the typical American diet, we tend to consume far too much saturated fat. This creates problems for our cardiovascular systems because saturated fatty acids raise cholesterol levels in the blood, while polyunsaturated and monounsaturated fatty acids lower blood cholesterol. As we have pointed out earlier, high levels of cholesterol in the blood can be a major contributing factor in the development of atherosclerosis.

To give you a better idea of how much fat is in the typical American diet, how much of it comes from saturated, monounsaturated and polyunsaturated fats, as well as how much of each kind of fat you should be consuming, here is a brief overview:

	TOTAL FAT (% of total calories)	SATURATED FAT	MONO-UNSATURATED FAT	POLY-UNSATURATED FAT
TYPICAL AMERICAN DIET*	42%	16%	19%	7%
RECOMMENDED DIET*	no more than 30%	10%	10%	10%
WEEK OF HEALTHIER EATING	17%	5%	6%	6%

*These figures from the Senate Select Committee on Nutrition & Human Needs, 1976

Why Lowering Your Fat Intake From 40% to 30% of Calories Is So Critical.

There is now overwhelming evidence that too much fat in our diets increases our risk of heart disease and cancer.

Societies throughout the world that consume diets high in saturated fat have high rates of heart disease and cancer. Conversely, cultures that consume low-fat diets show significantly lower incidences of these diseases.

There are a number of examples to illustrate this, but in the interests of simplicity, we will cite only one. When Japanese immigrate from their homeland and give up their traditional low fat diets in favor of high-fat American diets, their incidence of heart disease and certain cancers rises dramatically. In Japan, heart disease and cancers of the breast, colon and prostate have all been rare. But once immigrants begin eating a high-fat, typical American diet, their incidences of these diseases soon reaches the same level as the rest of the American population.

The precise reason why excess fat seems to contribute to some forms of cancer isn't known, but researchers are looking into the possibility that high fat diets may contribute to hormonal changes that may trigger the problem.

The National Cancer Institute estimates that a reduction in daily fat intake from 40% of calories to 25% of calories could reduce breast cancer mortality among women by 25%. Today, some 36,000 American women die from breast cancer each year, so this dietary change alone could save as many as 9,000 lives a year!

Reducing fat intake from 40% of calories to 30% or less is critical. To understand just how much more fat Americans consume than other societies, consider that the traditional Japanese diet contained only about 10% fat, although the introduction of Western "fast" food since the end of the Second World War has raised that figure to about 15%.

That's why the nation's leading health-promoting organizations, including the National Academy of Sciences, the American Heart Association and the National Cancer Institute all recommend that you reduce your fat intake to no more than 30% of total calories. And some experts suggest that a cutback to 25% or 20% would be even better. But as Dr. David Heber of U.C.L.A. said, "Going below 30% fat in the diet is a difficult level to maintain, and may compromise other important nutrients. Even a 30% level requires conscious food selections."

Questions & Answers on Fat

Q. What is the correct balance of fats in the diet?

A. No more than 30% of the calories in your diet should come from fat, and ideally, the closer to 20% you get, the better off you'll be. The Week of Healthier Eating in this book provides only 17% of calories from fat and provides a perfect guide for eating a healthier, lower fat diet.

About one-third of your fat should come from saturated fats, about one-third from monounsaturated fats, and about one-third from polyunsaturated fats. This is almost the precise balance provided by the Health Valley Week of Healthier Eating.

Q. What are the main sources of saturated, monounsaturated, and polyunsaturated fats?

A. Foods which contain high levels of saturated fats include whole milk, cream, butter and cheese, red meat, coconut and palm kernel oils, and cocoa butter.

Foods which contain high levels of monounsaturated fats include olive oil, avocado and peanut oils, and poultry.

Foods which contain high levels of polyunsaturated fats include corn, safflower, soybean and sunflower oils, walnuts, and deep-sea cold-water fish.

Q. I notice that you did not include any recipes for red meat, what is the reason for that?

A. Red meat, such as beef is a nutritious food, but we have not included it in this book because it is generally much higher in saturated fat than fish, and chicken cooked without the skin. Since both fish and chicken provide comparable nutritional value and can be just as flavorful and satisfying as meat, we decided to concentrate on recipes for these foods instead. If you like beef, it is certainly fine to enjoy it occasionally. Here is a comparison of the amount of fat in different meats to help you select the healthiest ones:

Finding the fat in meat

	% of Fat by Weight	% of Calories from Fat		% of Fat by Weight	% of Calories from Fat		% of Fat by Weight	% of Calories from Fat
BEEF, RAW			**VEAL, RAW**			**COLD CUTS, COOKED**		
ROUND	12%	56%	CHUCK	13%	52%	BOLOGNA	28%	81%
CHUCK	20%	69%	LOIN	11%	46%	FRANKFURTERS	27%	80%
SIRLOIN	27%	77%	ROUND	9%	39%	SALAMI	26%	76%
RIB ROAST	43%	87%	**PORK, RAW**			**CHICKEN, SKINNED**		
PORTERHOUSE	36%	84%	LOIN	28%	78%	BREAST	4%	21%
HAMBURGER,			HAM	29%	80%	THIGH	11%	49%
REG.	20%-30%	50%-70%	SPARERIBS	33%	85%			
LAMB, RAW			SAUSAGE	51%	92%	(From U.S. Department of Agriculture: Handbook No. 8.)		
LEG	21%	68%	BACON	55%-70%	78%-94%			
LOIN CHOPS	32%	82%						

Q. Which foods in the typical American Diet supply the most fat?

A. Beef supplies 20% of the *total* fat in the American diet, margarine supplies 4%, salad and cooking oils supply 2.6%, and butter supplies 2.4%.

Hamburger supplies the largest single source of *saturated* fat at 9%. Butter and margarine also supply a large amount of saturated fat, with butter accounting for 3.7% and margarine for 2.6% of the saturated fat.

Q. Is it true that there is enough fat in one fast food cheeseburger so that it is the equivalent of three healthy meals?

A. Unfortunately, that's true. There is over 31 grams of fat, or more than an ounce of pure fat in the most popular fast food cheeseburger. So you could actually eat three complete healthy meals, including all the foods listed below for the same amount of fat intake:

Entrees

½-pound broiled chicken (skin removed)
1 halibut fillet
6 scallops

Grain or Legumes Side Dish

1 cup brown rice
1 cup cooked spaghetti
1 cup cooked kidney beans

Dessert or Snack

1 cup raisins
1 orange
1 cup popcorn

Vegetables

1 onion
1 pound green beans
1 sweet potato
1 ear corn
2 red beets
4 asparagus spears
½-pound green peas in their pods
1 head Bibb lettuce

Bread

2 slices whole wheat bread

Q. How is saturated fat related to cholesterol?

A. A high level of saturated fat in the diet causes an elevated level of total serum cholesterol as well as an elevated level of low density lipoprotein (LDL). Low density lipoprotein retains cholesterol in the blood as opposed to high density lipoprotein (HDL) which helps remove excess cholesterol from the blood. The American Heart Association suggests that we limit the level of cholesterol in our diet to 100 milligrams of cholesterol per 1,000 calories with a maximum daily intake of 300 milligrams. And they further recommend reducing the amount of saturated fat in the diet to less than 10% of total calories. This requires a 30% to 50% reduction in the average American's intake of saturated fat.

The **Week of Healthier Eating** from Health Valley provides only about 5% of the calories as saturated fat, and only 97 milligrams of cholesterol on an average day. So you can use this **Week of Healthier Eating** as an effective way to keep your circulatory system healthy.

Q. Is it true that eating certain kinds of fat can help me think better, while other kinds of fats may slow down my mental processes?

A. There is some evidence that polyunsaturated fatty acids may actually benefit your brain, while too much saturated fat may slow down your mental processes. Professor Carol Leprohon-Greenwood at the University of Toronto has discovered that laboratory animals fed diets high in polyunsaturated soybean oil learn mental performance tasks 20% faster and have longer memories than animals fed a high-lard diet, or a mixed low-fat diet. She speculates that the membranes of nerves that send and receive messages in the brain become hardened with saturated-fat diets, just like the walls of arteries do, but that polyunsaturates keep the nerves soft and pliable so they send and receive better. There is also evidence that eating a light, low-fat lunch that contains plenty of complex carbohydrates can keep you more alert, with more energy than a typical high-fat, high-protein lunch which can make you feel tired. According to Judith Wurtman, Ph.D., research scientist at MIT, eating the right balance of foods can help you "think more quickly, react more rapidly to stimuli, and feel more motivated and mentally energetic."

Q. Since fat is an essential nutrient, shouldn't I be concerned about not getting enough in my diet if I cut out red meat and full fat dairy products?

A. It is not common for fat deficiencies to occur, especially in diets which include whole foods. In fact, even if you eliminated red meat, full fat dairy products and all nuts, seeds, and oils, it would be unlikely that you would develop a fat deficiency. Your body can manufacture two of the three so-called essential fatty acids, linolenic and arachidonic acids, if it has an adequate level of the third, linoleic acid. Linoleic acid is commonly found in whole grains and vegetables and as little as one ounce of oatmeal can provide all the linoleic acid you need each day.

Q. I seem to crave high-fat foods, such as ice cream. Is it actually possible to become "addicted" to fat?

A. According to Dr. John Yacenda, many people do develop a psychometabolic addiction to fats. According to Dr. Yacenda, high fat foods provide a great feeling of satiety, perhaps linked to the fact that as infants, we eat foods such as milk that are high in fat. So fatty foods may subconsciously recall childhood feelings of calm, pleasure and security associated with feeding. As a result, whenever some people need something to provide a sedative effect, they are drawn to high-fat foods, such as ice cream, hamburgers, French fries, and cheese. People can actually become so hooked on fat foods that even the sight of these foods triggers an outpouring of insulin, much like a Pavlovian salivary response in dogs. Psychometabolically induced insulin production alters biochemistry, possibly creating even more demand and craving for the desired foods as blood sugar levels drop in response to the increased supply of insulin.

According to Dr. Yacenda, it is possible to become "addicted" to fats, but it is also possible to break such addictions by re-examining your diet. You should avoid habitual consumption of fatty foods at breakfast and dinner, and at times of stress. By following the **Week of Healthier Eating,** you will be consuming precisely the kind of diet Dr. Yacenda recommends.

Q. *Are all fats harmful or are some beneficial to my health?*

A. While too much fat in the diet can raise the risk of a variety of serious diseases, there are certain fats that seem to have great promise for reducing the risk of some of these same diseases.

For example, recent research indicates that diets that are rich in monounsaturated fats such as found in olive oil may have a specific positive effect on blood chemistry. In several preliminary studies, diets with a high percentage of the fat in the form of monounsaturated fats resulted in lower total cholesterol and LDL cholesterol, and stable HDL cholesterol. Remember that LDL cholesterol is the bad kind because it helps keep cholesterol in the blood stream, while HDL cholesterol is the good kind since it helps remove excess cholesterol from the blood stream. In certain Mediterranean societies of southern Europe, including Italy, Greece, Turkey, Lebanon and Yugoslavia where their diets are rich in monounsatured fats and very low in saturated fat, the premature death from heart disease is greatly diminished from the level we see in America.

There has also been a great deal of interest in a group of polyunsaturated fats found in the body oils of deep-sea cold-water fish. These are known as omega-3 fatty acids. They originally became of interest when it was discovered that Greenland Eskimos who ate very high-fat diets, which included high levels of these omega-3 fats, had a very low incidence of heart disease. Further research seems to indicate that this type of fat can be very effective in keeping the blood from clotting as well as exerting a lowering effect on blood cholesterol levels. As a result of this research, many people are hurrying to buy and consume fish oil supplements. We believe that it is better to consume more deep-sea cold water fish rather than to begin taking large levels of fish oil concentrates.

By following the **Week of Healthier Eating,** you'll get plenty of omega-3 fats because the meal plan includes salmon prepared three different ways during the week, and salmon is one of the best sources of omega-3 fats.

Q. *Is it true that eating a high-fat diet makes it easier to get fat?*

A. It certainly is true. A study at the University of Massachusetts Medical School showed that when you eat fat, your body is able to store it as fat more efficiently than when you eat carbohydrates or protein. According to the study, about 23% of the calories in carbohydrates were burned in the process of being converted into body fat, leaving a net gain of only 77 calories for every 100 calories consumed. But it takes just 3 calories to turn 100 calories of fat from food into body fat, leaving a full 97 calories of fat.

Since fat contains more than twice as many calories as protein or carbohydrates per gram to begin with, the net result is that if you consume a gram of fat, there are 8.73 calories available to be put into storage as body fat. But when you consume a gram of protein or carbohydrate, only 3.12 calories are available for storage as fat. That means that eating the same amount of fat ends up supplying almost *three* times the calories as eating protein or carbohydrates.

Q. Can I be sure of cutting down on the amount of saturated fat in my diet by selecting products that say they are made with "100% vegetable short-ening" or "pure vegetable oil"?

A. Unfortunately, no. Cutting down on saturated fat is not as easy as selecting food products made with vegetable oils. Although it's true that many vegetable oils consist primarily of polyunsaturated and monounsaturated fats, there are two vegetable oils used widely in making commercial crackers, cookies, cake mixes, granola bars and other products that contain more saturated fat than beef fat! These two oils, palm kernel and coconut oil are very popular among commercial food processors because they are so highly saturated, so they are less likely to become rancid over long periods of time. While fat from beef is 50% saturated fat, palm kernel oil and coconut oil are more than 80% saturated fat. Below is a chart comparing the amount of saturated fat in various oils:

PERCENTAGE OF FATS IN OILS

TYPE OF OIL	SATURATED	MONOUNSATURATED	POLYUNSATURATED
COCONUT	86%	6%	2%
PALM KERNEL	81	11	2
BEEF FAT	50	42	4
COTTONSEED	26	19	51
MARGARINE	23	43	30
PEANUT	19	46	30
SESAME	15	40	40
SOYBEAN	15	23	58
OLIVE	14	72	9
CORN	13	24	59
SAFFLOWER	9	12	74
CANOLA (LOW ERUCIC|ACID RAPESEED)	7	55	33

The total percentage of the three types of fats in oil and shortenings does not add up to 100 because these items also contain small amounts of other substances.

Q. In order to reduce the amount of saturated fat in my diet, should I sub-stitute margarine made from polyunsaturated vegetable oils for butter?

A. It is true that vegetable oils are richer in polyunsaturated fats than butter. But in order to transform vegetable oils (which are liquid at room temperature) into margarine, which is solid at room temperature, a chemical process called "hydro-genation" is used. Essentially, hydrogenation turns the unsaturated fats in vegetable oils into saturated fats like those found in butter. So margarine is not necessarily a good choice to reduce saturated fat in your diet because margarine itself is a significant source of saturated fat. And like saturated fats of all kinds, the saturated fat in margarine can contribute to elevated cholesterol levels in the blood, raising the risk of heart disease. We don't believe that butter or margarine are necessary components of a healthier eating plan and the **Week of Healthier Eating** uses neither, without any compromise in flavor or nutritional value.

Q. Can I get beneficial omega-3 fatty acids from all fish?

A. There can be a substantial difference in the amount of beneficial omega-3 fatty acids among different varieties of fish. The richest sources of these fats are deep-sea, cold-water fish, such as mackerel and salmon. To give you an idea of how much the levels of omega-3 fats can vary in fish, here is a chart listing some different fish, together with the amount of total fat and the amount of omega-3 fat in a 4-ounce serving:

4 OZ., RAW	TOTAL FAT (mg.)	OMEGA-3 (mg.)	CHOLESTEROL (mg.)
ATLANTIC MACKEREL	13,900	2,600	80
LAKE TROUT	9,700	2,000	48
ATLANTIC HERRING	9,000	1,700	60
ALBACORE TUNA	4,900	1,500	54
ATLANTIC SALMON	5,400	1,400	—
SOCKEYE SALMON	8,600	1,300	40
ATLANTIC COD	700	500	43
RED SNAPPER	1,200	200	—

As a general rule, oily fish from cold ocean waters, such as salmon, mackerel and herring are good sources of omega-3 oil, while mild-tasting white fish, such as halibut, swordfish and cod are poor sources.

Q. Can too much fat cut down on my energy and make me feel tired?

A. It's obvious that eating too much fat can cause you to become overweight. And carrying around extra pounds puts a physical strain on your body that can be very fatiguing. But even if you're not overweight, a high fat diet can still rob you of energy and leave you feeling tired.

When you eat too much fat, it begins to interfere with your body's use and transportation of energy and oxygen. Even at the low level of 15% of calories, fat in the diet enters the bloodstream and coats the red blood cells, causing them to "stick together." According to Julian Whitaker, M.D., this action impedes the normal flow of blood, especially through the smaller capillaries. Since red blood cells carry oxygen and other nutrients throughout the body, the reduced flow of blood can result in your body being denied as much as 30% of its oxygen supply.

Oxygen is the most vital nutrient of all. The result of oxygen deprivation can be not only fatigue and loss of energy, but more serious degeneration as well.

Q. How can I be sure of getting a balance of all the nutrients I need to be healthy?

A. The key is to eat a variety of foods in the right proportion each day. To make it easier for you to see exactly how easy, tasty and convenient it can be for you to do this, we have created the **Health Valley Week of Healthier Eating.** This meal plan has been carefully calculated to provide 100% of all the essential nutrients recommended for good health, with only 17% of your total calories from fat. The **Week of Healthier Eating** is low in sodium, and cholesterol as well. We suggest that you follow this plan closely for a week or two, until you get a feeling for the way foods and recipes should be balanced. Once you get a feel for it, you can begin substituting other recipes from this book at dinner. No matter what recipe you choose, you can be sure of keeping your fat intake below 30%, because no recipe in this book contains more than 30% fat. If you want to know exactly how much fat is in any recipe, or if you're interested in the amount of any specific nutrient in any recipe so you can balance your levels, consult the easy-to-use chart in the back of the book.

Q. Besides following the "3 Golden Rules," is there anything else I should do to stay healthy?

A. If you follow the "3 Golden Rules of Healthier Eating," you should be able to achieve and maintain your ideal weight, which is a basic recommendation of virtually all the health-promoting organizations.

In addition to that, you should limit or avoid foods that have been smoked or barbequed, because there is evidence that these cooking methods promote the development of carcinogens.

You should also limit or avoid commercial wieners, sausages and luncheon meats because they all contain nitrates and nitrites, which have been described as the most dangerous elements in our food supply.

And of course, you should try to get regular aerobic exercise, avoid smoking, and if you use alcohol, do so in moderation.

How The Week of Healthier Eating helps you fulfill the third Golden Rule of Healthier Eating.

The **Health Valley Week of Healthier Eating** in this book can be valuable in helping you fulfill the third Golden Rule of Healthier Eating. It is a tasty, practical and convenient plan that has been carefully calculated to provide an average of only 17% of your daily calories from fat, and still provides 100% of all the essential nutrients you need for good health.

The 3 Golden Rules of Healthier Eating from Health Valley

1. Eat a variety of whole, natural foods that are rich in fiber, calcium, vitamins A and C, and complex carbohydrates.

2. Avoid foods that contain too much salt, refined sugar, and cholesterol.

3. Keep the amount of fat in your diet to no more than 30% of your total calories.

Part Two

The Week of Healthier Eating from Health Valley

*Garden Veggies Casserole
(Vegetarian Recipes)*

*Easy Skillet Chicken
(Chicken Recipes)*

Rosemary Peas with Pine Nuts
(Vegetable Recipes)

California Chicken
(Chicken Recipes)

Glazed Curried Carrots and Raisins
(Vegetable Recipes)

Spinach-Cheese Turkey Loaf
(Turkey Recipes)

Raspberry Filled Melons (Dessert Recipes)

Health Valley
Jumbo Lemon Delight
(Dessert Recipes)

Introduction to The Week of Healthier Eating

This is the first comprehensive meal plan that allows you to enjoy convenient, easy-to-prepare meals that provide all the flavor and satisfaction you want, and still get 100% of the recommended amounts of fiber, calcium, vitamins A and C, and all the other nutrients you need, and an average of only 17% of your calories from fat each day.

So you can use this **Week of Healthier Eating** from Health Valley to achieve virtually any healthy dietary goal you might have.

You can use it to follow the dietary guidelines issued by the leading health-promoting organizations such as the National Academy of Sciences, the American Cancer Society, the American Heart Association, and the National Cancer Institute to reduce your risk of heart disease, cancer and other degenerative diseases, because this plan fulfills all the guidelines issued by these organizations.

You can use this **Week of Healthier Eating** for weight control or weight maintenance, because the plan offers you the option of selecting daily meal plans that average 1,900 calories or 1,200 calories a day. Equally important, the calories come from an ideal balance of nutrients, including a high percentage of complex carbohydrates and very little fat.

You can use this plan as a low sodium eating plan, because none of the recipes call for the addition of salt. Your average daily consumption of sodium on the 1,900 calorie plan is just 1,169 milligrams a day.

And of course, you can use this plan simply as an overall healthier way of eating, as its name implies.

The most effective way to use this plan is to read it over in its entirety so that you understand the overall concept behind it before you begin. Then try to follow the meal plan as closely as possible for an entire week. This will make it easier for you to master the basic techniques and to understand the way healthier meals should be created. To show you just how to balance your foods and give you an idea of the portion sizes you should be eating, we've created a full **Week of Healthier Eating** and calculated the amount of calories, fat, vitamins and minerals, fiber and other nutrients so the balance you get when you follow it is ideal.

After a week or two on this plan, you should start to feel comfortable enough to be able to create your own plans by substituting recipes at dinner, and rotating the foods you eat at breakfast and lunch. That way, you can use this plan as your regular way of eating, or you have the option of using it as a general guide to adjusting your current diet so it is healthier.

The benefits of using the Week of Healthier Eating.

When you use the **Week of Healthier Eating** from Health Valley, you will be consuming the ideal balance of foods as recommended by the nation's leading health-promoting organizations. And you'll be getting 100% of your daily requirements for all essential nutrients. For example, you'll be consuming an average of 35 grams of dietary fiber a day, which is the upper level of what is recommended by the National Cancer Institute as part of their overall guidelines for preventing colon and rectal cancer. You'll be consuming an average of 1,489 milligrams of calcium a day, which is more than the the the U.S. RDA for this essential mineral. This plan also provides an average of 717 I.U. of pre-formed vitamin A, as well as over 52,000 I.U. of beta carotene, which your body can convert to vitamin A as it is needed, making it a safer form of vitamin A to consume in large quantities. You'll get an average of 455 milligrams of vitamin C a day, well above the U.S. RDA. Keep in mind that vitamin C is a water-soluble vitamin that can easily and safely be excreted if there is an excess amount. In fact, because your body does not store water soluble vitamins to any great extent, it is important to include them as a regular part of your diet. There is also some evidence that consuming more vitamin C than the levels specified by the U.S. RDA may be beneficial. The National Cancer Institute specifically recommends eating a balanced diet that includes foods rich in vitamin C as a possible way of reducing the risk of certain types of cancers.

Equally important to the high level of nutrients provided by the **Week of Healthier Eating** is the fact that the meals you will enjoy will be truly tasty and satisfying, so you'll be able to eat the healthier way without ever feeling deprived of the flavors and foods you enjoy.

In summary, by using the **Week of Healthier Eating** from Health Valley, you will be able to:

• Look better

• Feel better

• Have more energy and endurance

• Achieve and maintain your normal weight

• Reduce your risk of developing degenerative diseases including
  a) high blood pressure
  b) diabetes
  c) cardiovascular heart disease
  d) some forms of cancer

Keep in mind that this **Week of Healthier Eating** is intended for active people who consider themselves healthy. It is *not* intended as a substitute for professional medical counseling, nor a guarantee that by following the plan you will avoid all illness. But it is based on accepted scientific research and the dietary guidelines issued by the leading health-promoting organizations, including the National Academy of Sciences, the American Heart Association, the National Cancer Institute and the American Cancer Society. By following these guidelines through this **Week of Healthier Eating,** you will be fulfilling the recommendations for maintaining maximum good health and avoiding illness.

Getting your body adjusted to a healthier way of eating.

The typical American diet is too high in fat, calories, salt and refined sugar. The one thing fat, salt and refined sugar have in common besides the fact that excess amounts of all three are very unhealthy, is the fact that they are all sources of distinct flavors. Because of this, it is easy to become accustomed to them and even to become "addicted" to their flavors. So if you are used to eating a diet that contains a lot of fat, refined sugar, salt, or any combination of the three, it may take you between 2 to 4 weeks to become accustomed to a healthier way of eating. But we urge you to be patient because by using the **Week of Healthier Eating** you will become accustomed to eating low-fat, low-salt meals without refined sugar and soon find it not only beneficial to your health, but also tasty and satisfying as well. The **Week of Healthier Eating** has been carefully created to be flavorful even to people who are accustomed to eating a high-fat, high-salt diet. Many recipes are so flavorful that you may not notice a significant difference between them and the high-fat, high-sodium versions you are now eating. But since the taste of fat and salt are so addicting, there may be some recipes in this book that you may not find completely satisfying initially. But if you find this is the case, don't give up the plan. Instead, select another recipe from the same section as a substitute. We especially recommend the recipes highlighted as "George's Favorites" because they are among the most flavorful of all.

By staying with this **Week of Healthier Eating** you will be able to re-adjust your palate to the "real" flavors of foods in their natural state, along with the fragrant aromas and zesty flavors of natural herbs and spices used as accents, rather than depending on salt and refined sugar. Equally important, you'll be able to enjoy the benefits to your health, your vitality and your appearance.

4

The Week of Healthier Eating 7-Day Meal Planner

Start your day with a burst of energy. After 8-12 hours without food, you need to replenish your body's supply of energy and nutrients. That's why we suggest you start your breakfast with a glass of juice 5 to 10 minutes *before* you start to eat. When you drink your juice first, your body can raise your blood sugar level quickly because there is nothing else to interfere with its digestion.

In addition to needing immediate energy from the juice, you also need sustained energy. The best source for long-term energy comes from complex carbohydrates. And one of the best sources of complex carbohydrates comes from whole grains. Health Valley Oat Bran Flakes are not only a rich source of complex carbohydrates, they provide an important bonus in that they are rich in oat bran. According to recent clinical studies at Northwestern University, the soluble fiber in oat bran can help you lower your blood cholesterol.

This light, but energy-packed breakfast will give you the nutrients you need to start your morning off right.

The true "power" lunch. According to Dr. Judith Wurtman, a research scientist at MIT, eating "a light low-fat lunch will prevent the slowed responses and loss of verbal facility that can result from calorie overload," and eating the right balance of foods can help you "think more quickly, react more rapidly to stimuli, and feel more motivated and mentally energetic." That's because the chemicals that enable brain cells to send messages to one another are manufactured by the brain from certain foods, including dopamine and norepinephrine, which are sometimes called the alertness chemicals. According to Dr. Wurtman, foods that are high in protein, but low in fat seem to enhance the brain's ability to produce these alertness chemicals. That's why we've created this light, low-fat, high-protein lunch that you can have anywhere, at home or at a restaurant salad bar.

Cutting down on fat without cutting down on flavor. We created this Week of Healthier Eating to show you how to cut down on fat without giving up satisfying flavor or convenience. A fine example of how you can accomplish this is found in the recipe for Vegetable Pita Pizza. Here is a recipe that captures the eating enjoyment of pizza, but does it with only 25% of the calories from fat, as compared to the 35-50% of calories from fat in a typical pizza. And because much of the flavor and texture of our pizza comes from vegetables, you also get a meal with the right balance of fiber, vitamins and minerals, too.

Snacks. You can enjoy two snacks each day, whenever you want to. Naturally, you can have fresh fruit, but you can also have healthy snacks, such as Health Valley Apple Bakes® fruit bars. An Apple Bake is real food with about the same number of calories as an apple. On the 1,900-calorie plan, you can even have two Apple Bakes.

What are healthy beverages? If you want to enjoy a healthy beverage with your meal, remember that your best choices are salt-free mineral water, herb tea, light vegetable-based soups or broth, or, if you like soft drinks, try mixing a little fruit juice with some sparkling mineral water.

MONDAY

SERVING SIZE **1900** Calories		SERVING SIZE **1200** Calories
	Breakfast:	
4 oz.	Orange juice	4 oz.
2 oz.	Health Valley Oat Bran Flakes Cereal	1 oz.
¾ cup	Nonfat milk	½ cup
½ medium	Cantaloupe	¼ medium
	Healthy beverage	
	Lunch:	
4 oz.	Tomato soup	4 oz.
2 servings	Mixed Green Salad	1 serving
¼ oz.	Health Valley Cheddar Lites™ (used as croutons)	¼ oz.
2 Tbsp.	Yogurt Honey Dressing*	2 Tbsp.
1 Tbsp.	Wheat germ	none
	Healthy beverage	
	Dinner:	
1 serving	Vegetable Cheese Pita Pizza*	½ serving
1 serving	Super Carrot Raisin Salad*	1 serving
1 serving	California Chicken*	½ serving
1 serving	Healthy Ambrosia*	½ serving
	Healthy beverage	
	SNACKS:	
¾ cup	Plain nonfat yogurt	¼ cup
2 Tbsp.	topped with wheat germ	none
1 apple	Fresh apple	1 apple

Recipes for these dishes are in the recipe sections

How to get more out of breakfast. There are many nutrients your body uses more effectively if you eat them with other nutrients. For example, your body can absorb significantly more iron if you consume foods rich in vitamin C at the same time.

This breakfast has been created to include both strawberries and Health Valley Orangeola® cereal. The strawberries are rich in vitamin C and iron, and the wheat germ contains iron. So by eating the two at the same meal, you can boost the absorbable iron.

A low-fat, high calcium lunch. Dairy foods are not the only good source of calcium. In fact, for people who want to reduce saturated fat, or who have difficulty digesting the lactose in milk, some healthy alternatives are green vegetables, such as cabbage and kale, and canned salmon because you can eat the soft bones which are rich in calcium.

This lunch features both cabbage in cole slaw and canned salmon in the sandwich, so it provides almost 20% of your daily requirement for calcium but only about 280 calories. If you were to get the same amount of calcium from whole milk, you'd be consuming almost seven times as much saturated fat, and 50% more cholesterol.

A light, elegant, nutritious dinner. This dinner menu has everything you could ask for in a meal. It's elegant and delicious, low in fat and calories, and provides balanced nutrition.

Super Light Halibut Casserole is so delicious, you can serve it at elegant dinner parties. Your guests won't suspect that it's low in fat and calories. It's also a good source of vitamin B-12, which balances perfectly with the Zesty Cauliflower recipe, which is high in all the B-vitamins. One serving of both of these elegant dishes contains under 200 calories, yet provides plenty of calcium, iron and vitamin C.

(To see how elegant this menu looks when prepared, see the color photographs.)

Special snacks. The snacks on this day's menu plan include Health Valley Amaranth Graham Crackers, which are not only tasty, they're a good source of protein and complex carbohydrates. There are no other Graham Crackers like them.

And you may be surprised to learn that the warm weather favorite, watermelon is one of the foods rich in vitamin A. (If watermelon isn't in season, substitute apricots or peaches to get the same high quality nutrients.)

TUESDAY

SERVING SIZE **1900** **Calories**		SERVING SIZE **1200** **Calories**

Breakfast:

4 oz.	Apple juice	4 oz.
3 oz.	Health Valley Orangeola® Cereal	1 oz.
1 cup	Nonfat milk	½ cup
1 cup	Plain nonfat yogurt	½ cup
3 Tbsp.	topped with wheat germ	none
2 cups	Strawberries	1 cup
	Healthy beverage	

Lunch:

1 sandwich	Salmon Salad Sandwich*	1 sandwich
½ cup	Low Fat Cole Slaw*	½ cup
1 glass	Mineral water	1 glass

Dinner:

8 oz.	Chicken broth*	4 oz.
12 crackers	Health Valley Vegetable Crackers	6 crackers
1 serving	Super Light Halibut Casserole*	1 serving
2 servings	Zesty Cauliflower*	1 serving
1 serving	Curried Carrots with Raisins*	1 serving
1 serving	Raspberry-Filled Melon*	1 serving
	Healthy beverage	

SNACKS:

2 cups	Watermelon	1 cup
10 crackers	Health Valley Amaranth Graham Crackers	4 crackers

Recipes for these dishes are in the recipe sections

Are you getting all the fiber you need? The National Cancer Institute recommends getting between 25 and 35 grams of dietary fiber in your diet every day. Most Americans only get about half that amount. Equally important, you need to get a variety of different kinds of fiber. Water soluble fiber such as oat bran helps normalize cholesterol, while water insoluble fiber such as wheat bran helps maintain a healthy digestive system.

That's why we suggest that you include Health Valley Fiber 7™ Flakes as part of your healthy breakfast. They are made from seven different whole grains so they provide both kinds of fiber you need. And the fiber is in the form of hearty, crunchy flakes, sweetened with real fruit juice.

Stay slim with a high-fiber lunch. High fiber foods can help you stay slim because fiber adds no calories, yet can help satisfy your hunger. And certain fibers also help reduce the number of calories that you absorb by hurrying high-calorie foods through the digestive system.

This lunch features two high-fiber foods, a spinach salad, which is particularly rich in insoluble fiber, and lentil soup which is rich in soluble fiber. For extra convenience, use Health Valley Lentil Soup. A serving contains only 90 calories, but you get all the flavor of homemade.

A moist and rich-tasting dinner that's low in fat. Just because you're cutting down on fat and calories doesn't mean you have to cut down on flavor. This recipe for Spinach-Cheese Turkey Loaf is moist and luscious because it's layered with tangy Swiss cheese and covered with zesty pasta sauce. You'd never guess that a serving contains under 280 calories. If you used ground beef to make this recipe, you'd consume about twice as many calories, and about three times as much fat.

(You can see how good this recipe looks in the color photo section.)

Plenty of snacks: Fresh fruit is a snack you can enjoy anytime because it's low in calories and fat, and rich in natural nutrients. Other good choices for a snack are Health Valley Apple Bakes® and Health Valley Jumbo Amaranth Cookies. They're rich in fiber and contain about the same number of calories as a medium apple.

WEDNESDAY

SERVING SIZE **1900** Calories		SERVING SIZE **1200** Calories
	Breakfast:	
4 oz.	Orange juice	4 oz.
2 oz.	Health Valley Fiber 7™ Flakes Cereal	1 oz.
2 Tbsp.	topped with wheat germ	none
¾ cup	Nonfat milk	½ cup
1 cup	Melon (watermelon or honeydew)	1 cup
	Healthy beverage	
	Lunch:	
4 oz.	Lentil soup	4 oz.
2 servings	Spinach salad or mixed green salad	1 serving
	Healthy beverage	
	Dinner:	
8 oz.	Garden salad	4 oz.
2 Tbsp.	with Mock Russian Dressing*	1 Tbsp.
1 serving	Spinach-Cheese Turkey Loaf*	1 serving
1 serving	Orange Glazed Carrots*	1 serving
1 serving	Jumbo Lemon Delight*	1 serving
	Healthy beverage	
	SNACKS:	
1 medium	Tangerine	1 medium
2 bars	Health Valley Apple Bakes®	none
2 cookies	Health Valley Amaranth Cookies	1 cookie
1 medium	Apple	none

Recipes for these dishes are in the recipe sections

Staying alert throughout the morning. To feel alert and perform well all morning, you need a breakfast that contains high quality protein, so your brain can produce dopamine and norepinephrine, the so-called "alertness" neurotransmitters. But many high protein breakfast foods, such as meat and eggs are also high in fat, which can slow down your mental responses.

Instead, have a bowl of Health Valley Amaranth Flakes. These crisp, convenient flakes are made with Amaranth which has the highest quality protein of any grain on earth. This cereal is also low in fat, containing four times more protein than fat, with virtually no saturated fat.

A light lunch that's rich in nutrients. Even if you're not a vegetarian, you should try to avoid meat completely at least one day a week. For one thing, by eating vegetables and grains exclusively, you'll be getting plenty of fiber, as well as some nutrients found predominantly in vegetables and grains. According to Dr. Marilyn Menkes of Harvard University, a study of people who eventually developed lung cancer showed that their blood contained an average of 14% less beta carotene and 12% less vitamin E than people who didn't develop the disease. While this doesn't mean that beta carotene and vitamin E will necessarily prevent cancer, Dr. Menkes encourages people to eat more orange and yellow vegetables such as carrots and squash, which are rich in beta carotene, and more whole grains which are rich in vitamin E.

By eating the Vegetarian Pita Pockets and soup, you'll be getting plenty of beta carotene and vitamin E.

A delicious dinner where you don't miss meat. The Garden Veggies Casserole is a dish that combines pasta sauce, luscious cheese, hearty brown rice and tender garden vegetables into a meal so flavorful and satisfying that you won't even notice the lack of meat. And although people associate vegetarian meals as being rich in vitamins and fiber, this recipe also supplies an abundance of minerals as well. One serving provides 16% of your daily requirement for calcium, 13% of your magnesium, 12% of your phosphorus, and 9% of your iron for the day.

Super snacks. If you're interested in getting more iron in your diet, look to that family favorite, raisins. They're also a good source of fiber. So when you want a satisfying, healthy snack, reach for fresh and dried fruits.

THURSDAY

SERVING SIZE **1900** Calories		SERVING SIZE **1200** Calories

Breakfast:

4 oz.	Grape juice	4 oz.
2 oz.	Health Valley Amaranth Flakes or Orangeola®	1 oz.
¾ cup	Nonfat milk	½ cup
3	Prunes or dried figs	3
¾ cup	Plain nonfat yogurt	½ cup
2 Tbsp.	topped with wheat germ	none
	Healthy beverage	

Lunch:

6 oz.	Split pea soup	4 oz.
1 sandwich	Chicken Apple Sandwich*	½ sandwich
1 sandwich	or Vegetarian Pita Pockets*	1 sandwich
½ cup	Low Fat Cole Slaw*	½ cup
	Healthy beverage	

Dinner:

½ serving	Mixed green salad	1 serving
1 Tbsp.	with Yogurt Honey Dressing*	1 Tbsp.
2 servings	Garden Veggies Casserole*	1 serving
2 servings	Zucchini with Leeks and Tomatoes*	½ serving
1 serving	Baked Apple*	1 serving
	Healthy beverage	

SNACKS:

1 medium	Orange	1 medium
¼ cup	Raisins	¼ cup

*Recipes for these dishes are in the recipe sections

Breakfast is a good time to get your fiber and vitamin C. Breakfast is the meal that provides the greatest amounts of fiber and vitamin C in many people's diets.

This breakfast features Health Valley Bran cereal, which is a better bran cereal because it's made with miller's bran, nature's richest source of fiber. It is also made with sprouted grains for enhanced nutrition, and it's sweetened with real fruit, with no added sugar.

You'll get almost 13 grams of fiber, which is more than 50% of your daily requirement from this breakfast, along with 96% of your daily requirement for vitamin C.

As an added tip for getting more fiber, remember that toasted bread actually increases the amount of fiber by turning some of the starches into a form of fiber your body can use.

Plenty of vitamin B-12 for lunch. Most of the B-vitamins are readily available from both plant and animal food sources. The exception is vitamin B-12, which is necessary to regulate the formation of red blood cells and to maintain healthy nerve-cell and tissue membranes. Vitamin B-12 is found mostly in meats, particularly organ meats, such as liver. But organ meats are very high in fat and cholesterol.

A healthy alternative source of B-12 is shellfish, such as clams. That's why we have included clam chowder as part of this healthy lunch. Clam chowder is a delicious way to get your B-12. And for extra convenience, as well as the hearty flavor of homemade soup, use Health Valley Clam Chowder. It's available with 40% less salt, or with No Salt Added.

A delicious dinner that's healthy for your heart. Substituting fish for red meat is a good way to add flavor variety to your meals, as well as helping keep your heart healthy. Many cold-water fish are rich in omega-3 fatty acids which appear to help maintain a healthy circulatory system. And all varieties of fish are much lower in saturated fat than meat.

This menu features orange roughy, a fish with a delicate lobster-like flavor and firm texture. This delicious, elegant recipe provides nearly three times as much monounsaturated fat, which is known to help lower blood cholesterol, as it does saturated fat. So it's a delicious way to help keep your heart healthy.

Snacks with plenty of minerals. By selecting the right snacks, you can not only get flavor satisfaction, but solid nutrition as well. Here are two that provide two important minerals, iron and calcium. Nonfat yogurt is just as rich in calcium as regular yogurt, but with only a fraction of the fat. And Health Valley Raisin Bakes are made with sun-dried raisins, which are a rich source of iron.

FRIDAY

SERVING SIZE **1900** **Calories**		SERVING SIZE **1200** **Calories**

Breakfast:

1900		1200
8 oz.	Tomato juice	4 oz.
2 oz.	Health Valley Bran Cereal	1 oz.
2 Tbsp.	topped with wheat germ	none
1 cup	Nonfat milk	½ cup
none	Whole wheat bread, toasted	1 slice
none	Natural fruit preserves with no added sugar	1 Tbsp.
	Healthy beverage	

Lunch:

1900		1200
6 oz.	Clam chowder	4 oz.
12 crackers	Health Valley Vegetable Crackers	6 crackers
2 servings	Mixed Green Salad	1 serving
¼ oz.	Health Valley Cheddar Lites™ (used as croutons)	½ oz.
2 Tbsp.	Mock Russian Dressing*	2 Tbsp.
	Healthy beverage	

Dinner:

1900		1200
1 serving	Tangy Apple Vegetable Salad*	1 serving
1 serving	Orange Fish Fillets*	1 serving
1 serving	Asparagus with Orange Sauce*	1 serving
1 large	Peach	1 medium
	Healthy beverage	

SNACKS:

1900		1200
¾ cup	Plain nonfat yogurt	½ cup
2 Tbsp.	topped with wheat germ	none
1 medium	Banana	1 medium
2 bars	Health Valley Raisin Bakes® or Apple Bakes®	2 bars

Recipes for these dishes are in the recipe sections

95

Start your day with the right nutritional decisions. Breakfast can either be the start of a healthier eating day, and the meal that provides the greatest percentage of your fiber and vitamin C, or it can be a meal laden with fat, sodium and cholesterol.

A breakfast of 4 pieces of bacon or sausage and 2 eggs contains as much fat and sodium as you should consume in an entire day, and more cholesterol than you should have in 2 days!

You're much better off with a satisfying, light breakfast of juice, nonfat milk, and a whole grain natural cereal, such as Health Valley Oat Bran Flakes. These hearty, crunchy flakes are a rich source of oat bran fiber, which can help lower your blood cholesterol. And with this breakfast, you get very little fat or sodium to start your day.

A lunch you can love from the heart. The good news in nutrition is that some fish contain fats that may help your heart stay healthy. These fats are known as omega-3 fatty acids, and they're most abundant in cold-water fish, such as salmon, mackerel and tuna.

Today's lunch is one you can love from the heart because it tastes so good, and it's made with salmon, which is a good source of omega-3 fats.

Along with the salmon, have a fresh fruit salad: cut up an apple, half a pear, half a banana, and sprinkle with a little fruit juice for extra sweetness and to keep the fruit from turning brown.

A delicious way to enjoy chicken without salt or the skin. In the past decade, the average American has reduced the amount of beef consumed each year by 15 pounds. In its place, we have substituted 15 pounds of chicken. Chicken contains about the same amount and the same quality of protein, but it contains less saturated fat. This is significant because according to Dr. William Connor, of the National Research Council, it is the amount of saturated fat that you eat rather than the amount of cholesterol that you consume that results in your having too much cholesterol in your blood. Even though chicken contains substantially less saturated fat than beef, you can reduce the amount of saturated fat even further if you remove the skin before cooking chicken. The recipe for Herbed Chicken shows you how to do this and still serve a dish that is both colorful and full of spicy, zesty flavor from a masterful blend of dill, garlic, onion and paprika in a tangy tomato-yogurt sauce.

(To see how appetizing this dish looks, see the color photograph section.)

SATURDAY

Breakfast:

1900		1200
4 oz.	Grapefruit juice	4 oz.
3 oz.	Health Valley Oat Bran Flakes Cereal	1 oz.
3 Tbsp.	topped with wheat germ	none
1 cup	Nonfat milk	½ cup
	Healthy beverage	

Lunch:

1900		1200
1 sandwich	Salmon Salad Sandwich*	1 sandwich
1 serving	Fresh fruit salad	½ serving
1 glass	Iced herb tea	1 glass

Dinner:

1900		1200
8 oz.	Garden Salad	4 oz.
1 Tbsp.	with Yogurt Dill Dressing*	1 Tbsp.
½ serving	Pasta Primavera*	½ serving
1 serving	Herbed Chicken*	1 serving
1 serving	Green Peas with Spicy Mushrooms*	1 serving
½ cup	Blueberries (fresh or frozen)	½ cup
	Healthy beverage	

SNACKS:

1900		1200
1 cup	Plain nonfat yogurt	½ cup
2 Tbsp.	topped with wheat germ	none
none	Strawberries	1 cup
2 bars	Health Valley Apple Bakes®	none

Recipes for these dishes are in the recipe sections

A brunch that's fun and nutritious, too. You can still enjoy your favorite foods, such as pancakes when you follow the Week of Healthier Eating. The only difference is that you should prepare your pancakes using whole grain flour and other minimally-processed or unprocessed natural ingredients, instead of using a commercial pancake mix made from enriched white flour and additives such as salt and fat. Or for greater convenience, use Health Valley Pancake & Biscuit Mix. Health Valley prepares this convenient mix using only 100% whole grain flour and other natural ingredients so you not only get light, fluffy, tender pancakes, but ones that provide good nutrition as well. Compared to pancakes made from a commercial pancake mix, the ones made from Health Valley's Pancake & Biscuit Mix have 3 times as much fiber. And pancakes made from a commercial mix contain almost 2½ times as much sodium, and 4 times as much saturated fat.

So by using Health Valley Pancake & Biscuit Mix, and serving your pancakes with pure maple syrup or Fresh Berry Topping (see recipe in Dressings and Sauces section), you can enjoy a delicious brunch that you don't have to feel guilty about.

A turkey recipe that's a Sunday best. Sunday evening has traditonally been a time when the whole family could sit down and enjoy a delicious meal together, like a hearty pot roast dinner. When you follow the Week of Healthier Eating, you can enjoy a delicious satisfying family dinner on Sunday, but instead of pot roast, we suggest our recipe for Gingered Turkey Breast. This exciting recipe shows you a different way to prepare turkey instead of the stuffed and roasted version prepared on Thanksgiving and other holidays. Turkey is becoming popular on occasions other than holidays because it is as flavorful and satisfying as beef, but contains substantially less total fat, and saturated fat.

For example, compared to Gingered Turkey Breast, pot roast has almost 7 times as much total fat! In fact, 53% of all the calories in pot roast are supplied by fat, compared with only 17% in our turkey recipe. Pot roast also contains about half again as much cholesterol, and a whopping 20 times as much saturated fat as Gingered Turkey Breast. So try this healthy recipe, and see if it doesn't establish a whole new tradition for Sunday dinner with your family.

SUNDAY

SERVING SIZE
**1900
Calories**

SERVING SIZE
**1200
Calories**

Brunch:

1900		1200
8 oz.	Tomato juice	4 oz.
2 pancakes	Pancakes	1 pancake
½ cup	topped with fresh strawberries	as desired
2 Tbsp.	Pure maple syrup or Fresh Berry Topping*	1½ Tbsp.
1 serving	Mixed Greens topped with Salmon Salad Sandwich Spread*	1 serving
	Healthy beverage	

Snack:

1900		1200
none	Fresh Fruit Salad	1 serving
1 cup	Plain nonfat yogurt	1 cup
2 Tbsp.	topped with wheat germ	none
1 slice	Whole wheat bread	none
1 Tbsp.	Health Valley Peanut Butter	none

Dinner:

1900		1200
4 oz.	Chicken Broth*	4 oz.
3 scallions	topped with chopped scallions	3 scallions
2 servings	Dilled Marinated Vegetables*	½ serving
1 serving	Gingered Turkey Breast*	1 serving
1 serving	Mexican Style Corn*	1 serving
3 small	Boiled new potatoes & parsley	3 small
1¼ cups	Wax beans	1 cup
1 serving	Fruit & Almond Crumble*	1 serving
2 Tbsp.	topped with wheat germ	1 Tbsp.
	Healthy beverage	

Recipes for these dishes are in the recipe sections

Clinical proof that the Week of Healthier Eating works.

The **Week of Healthier Eating** has been created for people who are healthy, but who want to improve the way they look and feel, and reduce their risk of developing degenerative diseases by following the dietary guidelines issued by the leading health promoting organizations. Although the **Week of Healthier Eating** has **not** been created specifically to be a therapeutic diet, we wanted to test its effectiveness under impartial, controlled conditions.

We were fortunate to enlist the cooperation of the highly regarded Innerhealth Center in Los Angeles, and of Dr. Cleaves Bennett, the renowned physician and author of "Control Your High Blood Pressure Without Drugs!"

Innerhealth, with Dr. Bennett supervising, conducted a series of 13-week studies in which individuals with clinically diagnosed high blood pressure prepared and ate all their meals following the **Week of Healthier Eating** from Health Valley. Innerhealth carefully and regularly monitored and measured each individual's weight, blood pressure, serum cholesterol, sodium excretion, and other key indices.

These clinical tests showed that by following the **Week of Healthier Eating,** those who needed to lose weight did so, and that all subjects exhibited measurably lower blood pressure and cholesterol levels. Subjectively, the participants reported that they felt better and had more energy. Equally important, they said they found the food on the plan to be enjoyable and satisfying, convenient to prepare, and that the overall program was easy to follow.

The results of the clinical trials.

After a series of 13-week studies using the **Week of Healthier Eating** from Health Valley among participants who had elevated blood pressure, and some of whom also exhibited elevated blood cholesterol and were overweight, Innerhealth concluded that the dietary plan was an effective one.

According to Matthew Nadler, M.S. in Gerontology, the Health Program Designer of this Innerhealth study, "The Health Valley eating plan, which is a low-fat, low-sodium dietary program is effective in lowering blood pressure, serum cholesterol and reducing weight among those with elevated levels of these factors. Subjects agreed that the eating plan is delicious and easy to follow."

We believe that using a balanced diet such as The **Week of Healthier Eating** to promote good health has a long tradition that began over 2,000 years ago, when Hippocrates, the Father of Medicine said, "Food is your medicine." More recently, Thomas Edison repeated this theme when he said, "The doctor of the future will give no medicine, but will interest his patient in the care of the human frame, in diet and in the cause and prevention of disease."

100

Testimonial comments from clinical participants.

After spending 13 weeks using the **Week of Healthier Eating** under clinical conditions, participants were asked to offer their candid comments about the taste, the convenience and the results they achieved. Here are some typical responses:

"The food is delicious...the meal plan was easy to prepare...and I feel much better since being on the plan because I have a lot more energy and a feeling of well-being."
— *G. Minor*

"The first 6 weeks I lost 12 pounds." — *R. Henderson*

"I feel 99% better — have lots of energy. Also, the meal plan offers great variety and as I became familiar with the recipes I was able to prepare them very quickly and easily." — *M. Martinsen*

"The program was the very <u>best</u> thing that could have happened to me, I love the food, and I am going to stay with the program because I feel great." — *E. Carroll*

"The program conveyed properly the different food values that enable me to make a fairly wide choice of foods and still significantly reduce my sodium and fat intake... All the recipes I used were very satisfying...and I find I am able to maintain my normal weight." — *D. Loeb*

"I have more energy now than when I first started the program. The menus were great." — *L. Clendenning*

"After I began using the plan, my doctor took me off one of my medicines. I feel good, and I no longer use salt." — *V. Howard*

"My lifestyle has changed very much since trying this eating plan. I found out I could eat without salt. The program is the best thing that I've tried." — *H. Smith*

Important Nutritional Data for The "Week of Healthier Eating"

Sodium

RECOMMENDED BY AMERICAN HEART ASSOCIATION . . . NO MORE THAN 1000mg/1000 CALORIES
"HEALTHIER EATING PLAN". . . . . 614.3mg/1000 CALORIES

RECOMMENDED BY AMERICAN HEART ASSOCIATION . . . NO MORE THAN 3000mg PER DAY TOTAL
"HEALTHIER EATING PLAN". . . . . 1169mg PER DAY TOTAL

Cholesterol

RECOMMENDED BY AMERICAN HEART ASSOCIATION . . . . NO MORE THAN 100mg/1000 CALORIES
"HEALTHIER EATING PLAN". . . . . 50.92mg/1000 CALORIES

RECOMMENDED BY AMERICAN HEART ASSOCIATION . . . . NO MORE THAN 300mg PER DAY TOTAL
"HEALTHIER EATING PLAN". . . . . 96.9mg PER DAY TOTAL

Cholesterol/Saturated Fat Index

Recently, a new index has been developed to evaluate the tendency of a diet to promote clogging of the arteries, or atherosclerosis. In discussing this new index in *The Lancet, May 31, 1986,* the authors suggest that an ideal diet at the 2,000 calorie per day level would have a CSI of 16. **"The Week of Healthier Eating"** has a CSI of 11.6 at the 1900 calorie per day level. By this method of evaluation, **"The Week of Healthier Eating"** is clearly a superior eating plan to reduce the risk of atherosclerosis and therefore heart attack and stroke.

THE CHOLESTEROL/SATURATED FAT INDEX IS CALCULATED AS FOLLOWS:
CSI = 1.01 X GRAMS OF SATURATED FAT + 0.05 X MILLIGRAMS OF CHOLESTEROL

Important Ratios

CALCIUM/MAGNESIUM 2.05:1
CALCIUM/PHOSPHORUS 621:1
POLYUNSATURATED FAT/SATURATED FAT. 1.31:1
POLYUNSATURATED FAT/MONOUNSATURATED FAT 1.22:1
SODIUM/POTASSIUM 169:1
POTASSIUM/SODIUM 5.90:1

Analysis of Health Valley's Week of Healthier Eating 1,900 Calories Per Day

The analysis indicates that Health Valley's Week of Healthier Eating keeps you below the recommended maximum level of intake for the following:

CHOLESTEROL   SODIUM

The analysis indicates that Health Valley's Week of Healthier Eating provides more than 100% of the U.S. RDA or generally recommended minimum level of intake for the following nutrients:

PROTEIN	IODINE	POTASSIUM	VITAMIN B6
DIETARY FIBER	IRON	SELENIUM	VITAMIN B12
VITAMIN A	MAGNESIUM	ZINC	FOLIC ACID
VITAMIN C	MANGANESE	THIAMINE (B1)	PANTOTHENIC ACID
CALCIUM	MOLYBDENUM	RIBOFLAVIN (B2)	VITAMIN E
CHROMIUM	PHOSPHORUS	NIACIN (B3)	VITAMIN K

U.S. RDA (*) or Generally Recommended Level of Intake and Nutrient Levels in the 1900 Calorie "Week of Healthier Eating"

NUTRIENT	RDA	PLAN	NUTRIENT	RDA	PLAN
CALORIES	—	1900 CALORIES	MANGANESE	2.5mg*	9.2mg
PROTEIN	65g*	108.0g	MOLYBDENUM	150µg	186µg
CARBOHYDRATE	—	305.0g	PHOSPHORUS	1000mg*	2398mg
FAT	—	37.9g	POTASSIUM	3750mg	6899mg
CHOLESTEROL	Max. 300mg	96.9mg	SELENIUM	50µg	50µg
DIETERY FIBER	25-35g	39.3g	ZINC	15mg*	16.0mg
SODIUM	Max. 3000mg	1169mg	THIAMINE	1.5mg*	2.4mg
VITAMIN A	5000 IU	52,839 IU	RIBOFLAVIN	1.7mg*	3.2mg
Pre-Formed		717 IU	NIACIN	20mg*	32.4mg
Beta Carotene		52,122 IU	VITAMIN B6	2mg*	2.9mg
VITAMIN C	60mg*	455.0mg	VITAMIN B12	6µg*	7.1µg
CALCIUM	1000mg*	1489mg	FOLIC ACID	400µg	873µg
CHROMIUM	50µg	207µg	PANTOTHENIC ACID	10mg*	11.1mg
COPPER	2mg*	2.1mg	VITAMIN E	30 IU*	41.7 IU
IODINE	150µg*	235µg	VITAMIN K	70µg	1384µg
IRON	18mg*	23.0mg	VITAMIN D	400 IU*	181 IU
MAGNESIUM	400mg*	726mg			

*Nutrients that have an established U.S. RDA. Those figures without asterisk represent generally recommended levels.
CODE: g = grams, mg = milligrams, µg = micrograms, IU = International Units

A brief explanation of the
Recommended Dietary Allowances (RDAs).

Your nutritional needs are as individual as your fingerprints. The amount of any given nutrient that you need depends upon your age, gender, genetic background, level of activity, lifestyle practices, general health, and individual biochemistry, among other things. So it isn't possible to say exactly how much of any vitamin, mineral or other nutrient you need to achieve and maintain optimum health.

However, in order to provide some guidelines on nutrition, the Food and Nutrition Board of the National Academy of Sciences has used available scientific knowledge to establish "Recommended Dietary Allowances" or RDAs for essential nutrients. The RDAs are the levels considered to be "adequate to meet the known nutritional needs of practically all healthy persons." As such, the RDAs are not "requirements," but are estimates of the levels of essential nutrients that "exceed the requirements of most individuals and thereby ensure that the needs of nearly all are met."

There are different categories of RDAs issued for different age and gender groups. These have been further summarized by the U.S. Food and Drug Administration into what are called the "U.S. RDAs."

We have used the U.S. RDAs as a frame of reference. So when we say that the **Week of Healthier Eating** from Health Valley meets or exceeds all your nutritional requirements, we are referring to the U.S. RDAs as the standard.

Naturally, your own individual needs may vary. But you can feel assured that if you are a normal, healthy adult, the **Week of Healthier Eating** should provide the balance of nutrients you need to maintain your good health.

Important information about the amount of protein in the Week of Healthier Eating.

The dietary guidelines issued by the leading health-promoting organizations generally recommend that 15% of total calories should be supplied by protein.

In the **Week of Healthier Eating** from Health Valley, 22% of calories are from protein.

Although this figure may appear to be too high, you should be aware of two important facts:

First, when the American Heart Association was contacted for further clarification about the 15% figure, they pointed out that this number was based on getting most of the protein from animal sources. Since animal protein tends to be found in the context of high levels of saturated fat, total fat, and cholesterol, the Heart Association's main concern in establishing the 15% was to limit the amount of fat and cholesterol, rather than concern about too much protein itself.

Second, the **Week of Healthier Eating** supplied 22% of calories from protein, but only 12% is from animal protein, including fish, chicken and nonfat dairy foods. There is no red meat at all, and the high-fat skin is removed from the chicken in all recipes. So the animal protein comes from the lowest fat sources available.

The 12% figure is well within the recommended amount of protein from animal foods, and the rest of the protein comes from vegetables, fruits, legumes, seeds, nuts and grains.

NOTE: The "Week of Healthier Eating" provides 181 IU of preformed Vitamin D, about 45% of the U.S. RDA. This is actually quite an accomplishment since it is considered to be virtually impossible to obtain 100% of the U.S. RDA for Vitamin D from your diet without the use of supplements or artificially fortified foods. The noted nutritionist Dr. Helen Guthrie, Ph.D., in her book <u>Introductory Nutrition</u> (<u>Mosby, 1971</u>) states: "Some foods such as eggs, milk, butter, and fishliver oils constitute the major sources of preformed vitamin D, but they are characteristically poor and unreliable sources, the amount present varying with the diet and breed of the animal. Vegetables are poor sources. Even when all potential dietary sources are included, it is possible to obtain only about 125 IU per day." Of course Vitamin D is known as the "sunshine vitamin" and our bodies can produce all the vitamin D we need if we get adequate exposure to the sun. In fact, just 15 minutes exposure to sunshine at mid-day can be enough to allow your body to produce a full day's supply of vitamin D.

How to Eat Healthier Even With a Busy Schedule

The main obstacle to healthier eating is lack of convenience. It's much easier to find quick, convenient "fast" food that is less than optimum for healthier eating, than it is to find quick, convenient healthy food. And we aren't going to tell you that it will ever be just as easy to eat healthier as it is to eat a high fat, high calorie, high sodium "fast" food diet. But we do know that you can eat healthier even if you have a busy, fast-paced schedule, if you're willing to do a little planning ahead.

Here are some tips on how to do that:

In our meal plan, we've selected recipes from the appropriate sections for all the various dinner courses. But obviously, we recognize that there will be times, particularly during the week, when it may not be practical to prepare two or three different dishes. We suggest that in that case, you take advantage of the convenience offered by many of our Health Valley foods. For example, you might heat some Health Valley Tomato Soup instead of preparing one of the soup recipes during the week. Or you might heat some delicious Health Valley Lentil Chili as your main course at lunch.

You can also save time during the week by making a double portion of soup or an entree on the weekend and freezing them for quick reheating on a hectic weekday. The same is true of baked goods. You can make extra Super Bran Muffins on Sunday, and enjoy them throughout the week as part of your breakfast or as a healthy snack.

Also, many of our recipes for marinated salads and vegetables can be put together the night before, and taste even better the next day.

Some of the casseroles can be assembled a day or two ahead for cooking when there wouldn't otherwise be time for such a dish.

The key to making this healthier way of eating work conveniently and economically is to plan ahead.

The important thing, though, is to keep in mind that this healthier way of eating can be a fun and exciting way to eat, so you should approach it in this spirit, rather than thinking of it as a "diet."

How to Follow the Plan
When Eating Away From Home.

We realize that in today's busy world, many people eat at least some of their meals away from home, usually at restaurants. So this plan has been designed to take such meals into consideration.

Breakfasts and lunches tend to be the easiest, because most restaurants, and even "coffee shops" offer the kinds of foods specified.

Dinner can require just a bit more creativity, but you don't have to give up eating healthy when you're in a restaurant.

To begin with, start your dinner by ordering soup, preferably broth or vegetable soups that aren't cream-based.

Then have a salad, and ask for the dressing on the side, so you can control the amount that goes on. Keep in mind that virtually all the fat, calories, and much of the sodium in a salad comes from the dressing.

Look for salads on the menu that are made with several vegetables instead of just lettuce; and patronize restaurants that serve relish trays containing raw carrots, celery, cauliflower, etc.

Enjoy some bread too, but again make a note of restaurants that serve whole grain bread or rolls and avoid white bread.

Then, when your main course arrives, concentrate on the vegetables first. If you get a baked potato, skip the butter and sour cream, but sprinkle on the chives which are nutritious. Be sure to eat the skin of the potato, because it's rich in vitamins, minerals and fiber. Enjoy what you estimate to be a 4-ounce serving of the poultry, fish or meat. You'll find that it's plenty, just as it is when you prepare the **Week of Healthier Eating** at home. Consider choosing ethnic restaurants, which often offer combination dishes that feature just a little fish or poultry with a lot of vegetables or grains. For example, Chinese restaurants always have a variety of stir-fry dishes (but ask them to hold the MSG!). Italian restaurants usually have light sauces such as a simple marinara available, or will toss your pasta with olive oil and garlic. Japanese, Indian, and even some Middle European and Mexican restaurants are all more likely to have dishes you can enjoy than the traditional American steak house.

Finally, feel free to enjoy a light dessert, particularly fresh fruit, which most restaurants offer, even if it's not on the dessert list.

By eating this way, you don't have to go off the **Week of Healthier Eating** when you go out to eat.

How to individualize the Week of Healthier Eating.

At first, we were a bit hesitant about specifying portions in our suggested meal plan, simply because there can be such vast variations in individual needs for calories and portions among different people. For example, a large adult man who is in serious training for triathlon events can easily burn up 4,000 to 5,000 calories a day, while a small woman with a sedentary occupation might only need 1,200 calories a day. So we offer two different calorie levels to allow you to determine for yourself how much food you need, based on your gender, age, frame size, level of activity, individual metabolism, and whether you want to lose weight, gain weight, or maintain your present weight.

If you choose the lower calorie level, you should be aware that it does not supply 100% of the recommended daily amounts of *all* nutrients, since it is virtually impossible to do so at this low calorie level. However, it should be safe for most normal individuals to use this lower calorie level as a weight reduction plan for a week or two. If you intend to use it as your regular calorie level over a long period of time, you would be wise to consult your doctor and consider adding a balanced nutrient supplement to your diet.

Of course, the two calorie levels provided are not the only ones you can use. After using the portion size indicated for a few days, you will be able to individualize them to your own goals and needs. We feel certain that you will have no trouble achieving your ideal levels of fat, calories and sodium while eating all you want with this healthier way of eating.

Special nutritional information to meet your special needs.

When we were creating this book, and the **Week of Healthier Eating from Health Valley,** we were aware that you may have special nutritional needs. For example, you may need to reduce the amount of sodium in your diet. Or you may need more calcium, particularly if you're a pre-menopausal female. Or you may want to be sure of getting sufficient vitamin B-12, if you're a vegetarian.

To meet your needs, we've created some easy-to-use and understand nutritional charts in the back of this book. You can use them to determine just how much each recipe contains of every major nutrient, including both those you may want to increase in your diet, such as calcium, iron, fiber and vitamin A and C, as well as those you may wish to cut down on, such as fat, cholesterol and sodium.

How to Use This Meal Plan If You're a Vegetarian.

If you're a vegetarian, you'll notice that there is minimal use of meat and animal products in this meal plan. You can easily substitute Health Valley Soy Moo® Soy Drink for nonfat milk, and also substitute our convenient Health Valley Lean Living Frozen Entrees instead of the entree called for. For even more delicious, healthy and convenient vegetarian recipes to use as substitutes, refer to our section of vegetarian entrees.

Discovering the foods that let you burn away fat.

There are actually delicious, satisfying foods that help your body burn away fat. These foods are those that are high in natural fiber and complex carbohydrates, and low in fats. When you eat these foods, which include grains, fruits, vegetables and legumes, you automatically consume less fat, and that in turn predisposes your body to burn more of the fat it has stored.

When you eat less fat, you invariably lose weight if you need to. That's because fat contains about 9 calories per gram, while protein and carbohydrates contain only about 4 calories per gram. And it's easier for your body to store fat than it is for your body to convert protein and carbohydrates into fat, and then to store it. So when you cut down on fats, you can eat much more of everything else. You can eat almost twice as much pasta, fruit, vegetables, bread and cereals as you can butter, cream and meat for the same calories.

40 foods you can enjoy anytime without gaining weight.

Vegetables:

Artichokes	Cabbage	Cucumber	Mushrooms	Spinach
Asparagus	Carrots	Eggplant	Mustard greens	Summer squash
Bamboo shoots	Cauliflower	Endive	Onions	Turnips
Beans (green)	Celery	Kohlrabi	Okra	Watercress
Beets & Greens	Chicory	Leeks	Peppers	
Broccoli	Chinese cabbage	Lettuce	Radishes	

Fruits:

Blackberries	Grapefruit	Peaches	Raspberries
Cantaloupe	Lemons	Pineapple	Strawberries
Gooseberries	Oranges	Pumpkin	Watermelon

You can add these foods to your meals or enjoy a serving anytime without fear of gaining weight. Of course, if you are sensitive to any of these foods you should avoid them or limit your intake.

Alternate meals you can make in just 10 minutes.

We recognize that there will be days when you want to continue with your **Week of Healthier Eating,** but your schedule is so hectic that you don't have time to prepare even the simplest recipes in the Recipe Sections.

That's when Health Valley products can help. You can use a variety of Health Valley Soups, Chilis, Amaranth Minute Meal,™ and frozen Lean Living™ entrees to prepare a dinner that takes just 10 minutes or less.

Here are some preparation suggestions:

Quick Lentil Chili & Pasta

1 15-ounce can Health Valley Lentil Chili

4 ounces uncooked whole wheat elbow pasta

1 ounce grated cheddar cheese

Heat the chili while you cook the pasta. Pour heated chili over pasta and top with grated cheese. Serve with whole wheat bread or crackers.

Fresh Tomato-Vegetable Soup

1 15-ounce can Health Valley Tomato Soup

2 carrots

½ cup broccoli flowerettes

½ cup cauliflower

½ ounce grated Jack cheese

Heat the can of soup, adding the chopped fresh vegetables as it heats. Top with grated cheese before serving.

Instant Amaranth Delight

1 15-ounce can Health Valley Amaranth Minute Meal™

½ cup broccoli

½ cup cauliflower

2 carrots

2 tablespoons grated Swiss cheese

Heat the can of Amaranth Minute Meal as you steam the cut up vegetables. Pour heated Minute Meal over a bed of steamed vegetables and top with grated cheese.

Chicken Wiener Casserole

2 cups cooked brown rice

2 chicken wieners

1 can vegetarian baked beans

2 ounces cheddar cheese, shredded

Preheat oven to 350°F. Spoon the rice into a glass casserole. Slice chicken wieners into ½-inch slices and scatter over rice. Spoon beans over all and sprinkle with cheese. Bake at 350°F for 6 minutes, or until warmed through. This recipe will yield four servings.

Zesty Fish Filet

1 cup pasta sauce

3 teaspoons honey

7 ounces fish filet (preferably halibut, seabass or albacore tuna)

leftover cooked brown rice or pasta

Broil the fish filet, while you heat the pasta sauce and honey mixture. Serve fish on a bed of leftover cooked brown rice (or cook some elbow pasta) and pour the sauce over the fish. Garnish with fresh lemon wedges.

Turkey-Chili Treat

1 15-ounce can Health Valley Spicy Vegetarian Chili

1 4-ounce ground turkey patty

1 cup cooked rice or pasta

Broil the turkey patty, while you heat the can of chili, and cook the pasta (you can use leftover rice, if you have some). Put cooked turkey patty on a bed of rice or pasta and top with chili.

All of these 10-minute meals comply with the guidelines used for the **Week of Healthier Eating** in that they provide balanced nutrition, including complete protein, plenty of complex carbohydrates, and supply fewer than 30% of the calories from fat. They are not as festive as many of the regular recipes, and naturally, they do not afford the same variety of flavors as many of the recipes in this book, but you may find them very handy on those occasions when you're simply too busy to prepare anything but a 10-minute meal for dinner.

The difference between the Week of Healthier Eating and the typical American "Coronary Diet."

Most of the time people simply do not consider what they are eating from a nutritional point of view. So it's easy to pile on calories, fat, salt and other undesirables without even being aware of how quickly they add up to a dangerous situation. To highlight just what a difference the **Week of Healthier Eating** can make in just one day, we've taken a typical day from the **Week of Healthier Eating** and compared it with what might be a hypothetical day of eating a typical American diet, which we've called the "Coronary Diet."

Now at first glance you may feel that we've stacked the deck against the "Coronary Diet," but keep in mind that the actual volume of food is nearly identical. With the "Coronary Diet," you would consume 2,617.2 grams of food in the entire day, and with the day from the **Week of Healthier Eating,** you'd actually be consuming a little more food, 2,674 grams total. Yet with the Healthier Eating day, you'd consume a total of only 1,939 calories, of which 20% is from fat. With less actual volume of food, the "Coronary Diet" supplies 3,584 calories, of which 45% are from fat. Not only would you consume 1,645 more calories from the same volume of food on the "Coronary Diet," you'd be taking in more than 4 times as much total fat (179.4 grams versus 43.3 grams), and you'd be consuming 7 times as much saturated fat (71.7 grams versus 10.6 grams)! The amount of carbohydrates on the two diets is very similar (303 grams for the Coronary Diet versus 349 grams on the Healthier Eating Plan) as is the actual amount of protein (132 grams for the Coronary Diet versus 102 grams for the Healthier Eating Plan).

The difference in your health risk from these two diets is enormous but not something that can be projected numerically. However, what can be more easily compared is the effect on your weight from these two different ways of eating. It takes about 3,500 calories to equal a pound of body weight. With an extra 1,645 calories a day, the difference in your weight can be as much as 3¼ pounds extra a week, or the equivalent of over 165 extra pounds a year! So it's easy to see why the typical American "Coronary Diet" makes it likely that you'll be overweight, while by following the **Week of Healthier Eating,** you should have no trouble achieving and maintaining your ideal weight without feeling hungry. The "Coronary Diet" also contains more fat, cholesterol and salt than are recommended for maintaining good health, so there is an increased risk of hypertension, heart disease and some forms of cancer with this diet.

COMPARISON OF ONE TYPICAL DAY EATING ACCORDING TO THE WEEK OF HEALTHIER EATING VERSUS THE "CORONARY DIET"

"Coronary Diet"	Total Fat (gm)	Cholesterol (mg)
Breakfast:		
8 oz. Orange juice	0.50	0
2 strips bacon	6.24	10.7
2 large eggs (cooked in butter)	12.82	492.0
1 cup coffee (with 2 Tsp cream)	1.94	6.6
Snack:		
1 glazed doughnut	11.0	13.0
1 cup coffee (with 2 Tsp cream)	1.94	6.6
Lunch:		
1 Salad (made with iceberg lettuce, carrots, broccoli, tomatoes & sprouts)	.274	0
3 Tbsp Italian dressing	21.3	0
¼ pound cheeseburger	31.0	96.0
2 oz. French Fries	7.94	0
1 chocolate milkshake	8.10	32.0
Snack:		
2 oz. potato chips	20.1	0
12 oz. cola	0	0
Dinner:		
1 Salad (see lunch)	.274	0
3 Tbsp Thousand Island dressing	16.8	14.7
6 oz. steak (broiled)	14.99	144.1
1 baked potato with	0.2	0
3 pats butter	12.18	33.0
½ cup vanilla ice cream	11.85	44.0

Week of Healthier Eating	Total Fat (gm)	Cholesterol (mg)
Breakfast:		
4 oz. Apple juice	0.14	0
3 oz. Health Valley Orangeola® cereal	12.0	0
8 oz. nonfat milk	0.44	4.0
1 cup nonfat yogurt with	0.41	4.0
3 Tbsp wheat germ	1.51	0
2 cups strawberries	1.1	0
1 cup herb tea (plain)	0	0
Snack:		
10 Health Valley Amaranth Graham Crackers	2.5	0
Lunch:		
1 Salmon Salad Sandwich*	4.45	15.4
½ cup Low Fat Cole Slaw*	0.29	0.36
8 oz. mineral water	0	0
Snack:		
2 cups watermelon	1.36	0
1 cup iced herb tea	0	0
Dinner:		
1 cup chicken broth	4.44	3.6
12 Health Valley 7 Grain Vegetable crackers	6.0	0
1 serv. Super Light Halibut Casserole*	5.12	45.0
1 serv. Zesty Cauliflower*	1.38	0
1 serv. Glazed Curried Carrots*	1.47	0
1 serv. Raspberry-Filled Melon*	0.71	0

Recipes found in this book

SUMMARY OF DAILY FAT, CHOLESTEROL, CALORIES AND SODIUM INTAKE

	CORONARY DIET	WEEK OF HEALTHIER EATING
CHOLESTEROL	892.7 mg	72.4 mg
SATURATED FAT	71.7 gm	10.6 gm
MONOUNSATURATED FAT	55.8 gm	12.0 gm
POLYUNSATURATED FAT	51.9 gm	20.7 gm
TOTAL FAT	179.4 gm	43.3 gm
TOTAL CALORIES	3,584	1,939
PERCENT OF CALORIES FROM FAT	45%	20%
SODIUM	3,944	1,442

Foods to Avoid

There are foods commonly found in the American diet that are especially guilty of contributing excess fat, saturated fat, cholesterol and sodium. Here is a list of some of the biggest offenders, compared to some healthier foods you can substitute:

FOODS TO AVOID
(figures are for 100 grams or about 3½ ounces)

FOOD	% Fat	% Saturated Fat	Calories	Sodium (mg)
Coconut oil	100%	85%	884	0
Whole milk	49%	62%	62	49
Commercial Italian dressing	91%	14%	467	789
Corn oil margarine	100%	15%	717	1,079

FOODS TO EAT INSTEAD

FOOD	% Fat	% Saturated Fat	Calories	Sodium (mg)
Safflower oil	100%	9%	884	0
Nonfat milk	.5%	62%	35	51
Yogurt Honey Dressing*	4%	20%	84	117
Corn oil	100%	13%	884	0

*See Recipe Section on Dressings and Sauces

5

❧❧

The Secrets to Staying Slim

Why dieting can be hazardous to your health.

Obesity is the most common nutritional problem in America today. More than half the population of this country is overweight. And the latest research on the effects of being overweight show that being 20% or more over your ideal weight is a significant contributing factor in the development of the most prevalent degenerative diseases, including cardiovascular heart disease, stroke, and some forms of cancer. That's why the leading national health-promoting organizations, including the American Heart Association and the American Cancer Society have issued dietary guidelines that have as their first recommendation to "maintain your ideal weight." So there are sound reasons beyond appearance for losing weight, if you need to.

However, it is equally important to realize that the way you lose weight can have a significant impact on your health, as well as your ability to keep excess weight off.

In fact, if you are overweight, you are actually better off staying that way than to repeatedly lose weight and put it back on. This so-called "yo-yo" dieting can be more hazardous to your health than being overweight.

That's because when you are losing weight, your digestive fluid called bile becomes thicker, and this can lead to an increased tendency toward gallstones in the gall bladder. And studies using laboratory animals have shown that "yo-yo" dieting can also have an adverse effect on the cardiovascular system. This is especially true when weight loss is accomplished using a diet that is mainly protein (including meat and protein powders) with few if any carbohydrate foods. These high protein/low carbohydrate diets tend to be "ketogenic" in that they tend to create a condition called "ketosis" which can contribute to changes in your body chemistry that can accelerate the development of atherosclerosis and the formation of blood clots.

Essentially, all this research indicates that you should not attempt to lose weight unless you also have a reasonable plan for *long-term* weight maintenance.

The secrets to keeping excess weight off.

At any given time, there are over 45 million people who are on weight reduction programs. That's equivalent to about 20% of the entire population of the United States. And there are countless "fad" diets that you can use to lose weight. (Over 3,000 by the last count!) But the problem with most of them is that once you go off the diet and return to your normal way of eating, you gain back all the weight you lost, and sometimes even more.

That's why it's important for you to understand the mechanism of weight loss, and to see why **the way you lose weight has a lot to do with how well you can maintain that loss over the long term.**

Weight lost on quick weight loss diets tends to be mostly water and muscle rather than fat. While the balance swings more toward fat after several weeks on these diets, by the time this happens most people have already abandoned the diet and gone back to their old eating habits and have started to gain back the weight they lost. And when weight loss is primarily from lean body mass rather than from fat, it is much more difficult to maintain the loss. Research indicates that the greatest percentage of fat is lost when the diet is properly balanced and provides a level of calories allowing gradual weight loss of two to three pounds per week.

Because muscle is more active metabolically than fat, it takes more calories to maintain muscle than to maintain fat. So when two people are the same height and weight but have a different proportion of lean body mass to fat, the one with the greater percentage of lean body mass will be able to consume more calories than the one with the greater percentage of fat, and still not gain weight. In simplest terms, you can lose weight rapidly using crash, starvation, and unbalanced diets such as high protein/low carbohydrate. But the weight you will lose on these diets will be mostly lean body mass, not fat. And when you gain back any weight, you gain back the fat you lost as fat and some of the lean body mass is replaced by fat. This sets you back even more because the new added fat gives you a body with a higher percentage of fat and a lower percentage of lean mass. And that means that your body will burn fewer calories to maintain your weight. So unless you continue to maintain a stringent calorie restricted diet, you will gain weight even more easily than before. The same number of calories that used to sustain you, now causes you to gain weight.

The secret to maintaining your weight loss is to retain as much lean body mass and lose as much fat as possible. That way, your higher metabolic rate will allow you to burn a greater number of calories just to maintain your weight. And that makes staying trim much easier. And that's also why increased exercise is such an important part of any effective weight loss program. Because regular exercise, such as brisk walking, can actually help you increase your lean body mass as you decrease the amount of body fat.

How the Week of Healthier Eating works to keep you slim.

The reason the **Week of Healthier Eating** from Health Valley works so effectively to help you achieve and maintain your ideal weight is that it provides the ideal balance of foods. Our method of eating results in your reducing the percentage of fats, and to a lesser extent, the percentage of protein in your diet, and replacing them with delicious vegetables, fruits, whole grain cereals, legumes and nuts. Since fats are nearly twice as high in calories per pound as either proteins or carbohydrates, you can eat the same amount of food as you have been, and still reduce total caloric intake.

But equally important is the relationship between different kinds of foods and the brain mechanism that controls hunger and the feeling of satisfaction. The appestat is the part of the brain that controls whether you "feel hungry." So it is the part of the brain that receives the signal from your stomach and lets you know that you are "full." We know that it takes from 20 to 30 minutes from the time you begin eating until the appestat reacts. So when you eat more slowly, or eat foods that require you to chew them thoroughly, you're less likely to overeat, because your appestat has sufficient time to let you know when you've had enough to eat.

Most high protein and high fat foods are from animal sources, such as meats and dairy products. These foods are digested almost entirely in the stomach and upper intestine, so they do not require much chewing, and can be consumed relatively quickly.

On the other hand, high carbohydrate foods are predominantly from plant sources, such as vegetables and grains. These foods require the enzymes in your saliva for digestion, which is one of the reasons why they require more chewing than most meat or dairy foods.

Because you tend to eat foods high in protein, fat and refined sugar so quickly, you automatically tend to consume more calories before you feel satisfied than when you eat foods high in carbohydrates.

For example, it takes much longer to eat a mixed salad of raw vegetables than it does ground beef, and it takes much longer to eat a raw apple than it does a piece of apple pie. The combination of the greater density of calories in high fat, high refined sugar foods, and the fact that you tend to eat such foods faster than high carbohydrate foods both contribute to your consuming more calories on such a diet.

It's also significant to note that our appestats were set to signal when our nutrition needs have been satisfied. Many highly processed foods have nutrients removed, so the appestat doesn't signal us to stop eating even after we have taken in too many calories.

Proof of this can be seen in the results of a recent study conducted at the University of California at Irvine.

In this study, healthy adult males were divided into two groups. Both groups contained both normal and overweight individuals. The members of both groups were told they could eat as much food as they wanted from preselected lists. One group's list consisted of the kinds of foods featured in our **Week of Healthier Eating.** The other group's list consisted primarily of processed foods. By their very nature, the processed foods were higher in fats, refined sugar and salt than the equivalent healthy foods. So, for example, while one group could have all the fresh fruits it wanted for dessert, the other could have all the apple pie, cake and other "junk" food it wanted.

After a prescribed period, the two groups switched lists, so those who had been eating healthy foods were given only processed foods, and vice versa.

The results of this study showed that the individuals in both groups consumed an average of nearly twice as many calories a day when eating a diet of processed foods, compared with a diet of healthy foods.

This was true whether the subject was normal weight or overweight.

In other words, the study seemed to indicate that the body needs to consume twice as many calories of nutritionally devalued processed foods before it feels satisfied.

This may explain one of the reasons why our modern diet that includes so many processed foods has resulted in so many people being overweight.

Normally, if you follow the dietary recommendations of our **Week of Healthier Eating** and maintain the proportions of carbohydrates, fats and protein in your diet, you will automatically be eating more vegetables and grains and fewer high fat meats, dairy products, and of course, far less "junk" food.

How to adapt the Week of Healthier Eating for maximum weight loss.

You should be able to lose 1 to 3 pounds per week on the 1200-calorie **Week of Healthier Eating** menu plan.

But if you want to lose weight even faster, you can still do so. To adapt the **Week of Healthier Eating** for maximum weight loss, simply cut the portions indicated for the 1200-calorie plan in half for 3 consecutive days. Then follow the 1200-calorie plan for the rest of the week. Repeat this cycle for 3 weeks, and then switch to the 1900-calorie level of the **Week of Healthier Eating.**

You should never consume fewer than 600 calories a day for more than 3 days at a time. It is not only potentially dangerous, but it is also not the most effective way to diet. That's because the latest research on weight loss indicates that just a few days of severe calorie restriction triggers the body's self-preservation mechanisms, which will actually lower your metabolic rate to conserve stored fat for energy. The most effective way to bypass this mechanism and maintain maximum weight loss is to limit severe calorie restrictions to cycles of 3 days, followed by 4 days of moderate restriction.

When you consume 600 calories for just 3 days, followed by 4 days of more normal eating, you actually speed up the weight loss process. And by switching to the full 1900-calorie plan for the fourth week, you protect yourself against any serious deficiencies.

Maximum Weight Loss Program for The Week of Healthier Eating

Week 1: 3 days at 600 calories/4 days at 1,200 calories

Week 2: 3 days at 600 calories/4 days at 1,200 calories

Week 3: 3 days at 600 calories/4 days at 1,200 calories

Week 4: 7 days at 1,900 calories

You should review this plan with your physician before starting. As with all weight loss programs that are extremely low in calories, it should be undertaken under careful medical supervision.

Part Three

Healthier Eating Kitchen

6

Cooking Methods for Healthier Eating

There are two absolutely vital parts to our healthier way of eating.

The first is to select the right kinds of foods for healthier eating and living.

The second is to make certain that you get the maximum nutrition, flavor and enjoyment out of these foods by preparing them correctly. That's why it is important for you to take a few minutes to read this section. It explains the optimum cooking techniques that will retain the most nutritional value and appetite appeal for various kinds of foods. That's because the cooking method you use can affect the nutritional value, the texture, the flavor and the caloric content of foods to the extent that it can actually turn "healthy" ingredients into "unhealthy" ones. You'll find that by using the methods outlined in this section and paying attention to the recipe directions, you'll be able to cook healthier, and at the same time, save time and effort in preparation, as well as achieving great results every time.

The methods outlined have been written so that new, first time cooks will be able to follow them, but there are also some great hints and refinements that even experienced cooks will find helpful.

Basic Cooking Methods.

When cooking is reduced to its fundamentals, there are two general classifications for conventional cooking, plus the relatively new technique of microwave cooking.

Dry heat methods include roasting and baking, broiling and grilling.

Moist heat methods include steaming, sautéing, poaching, boiling, blanching, braising, and stewing.

Both of these conventional cooking classifications involve applying heat from an external source to cook foods.

The Healthier Eating Way of Cooking Vegetables.

Vegetables play a pivotal role in the healthier way of eating. Vegetables are very dense in complex carbohydrates and other nutrients in proportion to their calorie and fat content. The best preparation techniques for vegetables are those that maintain the nutrient value, as well as the distinctive textures and flavors of vegetables. For this reason, we do *not* recommend the common practice of boiling vegetables. Boiling tends to leach out nutrients. For example, when you boil most vegetables for just four minutes, 20% to 45% of the mineral content goes into the water, along with varying amounts of vitamins, particularly the B-vitamins and C, and 75% of the natural sugar. So if you do boil vegetables, don't throw away the water, use it as the stock for soup, or to poach fish and poultry, or mix with vegetable juice to drink.

Steaming. We recommend steaming as an ideal method of preparing most vegetables (except large root vegetables, such as potatoes, yams and some squash), because steaming retains the valuable nutrients as well as the essential textures of vegetables when done properly. The key here is *not* to overcook them. Overcooking vegetables causes them to lose vitamins, color, flavor and texture. Bring a small amount of water to a rolling boil, place the vegetables in a steamer basket, lower the heat to a simmer, and cover the pot. Cook until the vegetables turn a vivid color, then test by poking with a fork or sharp knife to see if they are just tender, but not limp or soggy. Save the water for use in soups, stocks, or mix with vegetable juice to drink.

Blanching or Parboiling. With these methods, you plunge food into rapidly boiling water a little at a time, so that the water continues to boil. In our recipes, this is done quickly to help preserve nutrients and to firm the tissues of vegetables so they will remain crunchy in the recipe. These methods also help to retain the fresh color of vegetables.

Sautéing and Stir Frying Vegetables Without Fat, Cholesterol and Salt.

Sautéing is a moist heat technique for stove top cooking in a sauté pan or skillet using relatively small amounts of hot fat or oil to sear the food at once and seal in moisture and flavor. Foods to be sautéed should be about 70°F. and dry on the surface. Sautéing is sometimes called pan frying, but differs from frying in that food is not totally immersed in fat to cook. When done properly, sautéing retains the flavor and food value very well. The main drawback is that the use of fat contributes some extra calories, and depending on the type of fat used, extra cholesterol.

Some diet cookbooks recommend avoiding fat and cholesterol by sautéing in water. Unfortunately, this method tends to produce tasteless vegetables.

For healthier eating with flavor, we recommend that you try a new technique, and use broth as the liquid for sautéing. It has just a trace of oil, but enough to coat foods, seal in moisture, and enhance flavor, without adding any measurable calories. For vegetables, we recommend using chicken broth and Instead of Salt™ herb seasoning. Laboratory analysis shows that Health Valley chicken broth contains negligible fat and cholesterol.

The technique to use in sautéing vegetables is to cut them up into thin, even-sized pieces so they cook quickly and don't get soggy. Using a traditional Asian wok with steeply sloped sides produces good results, but you can also use a heavy skillet. First get the broth very hot, then reduce the heat to medium high so the broth won't all evaporate before the vegetables are cooked. Stir the vegetables around continually, and remove them quickly once they are just tender.

Baking.
Baking works best with vegetables with high starch content, such as potatoes and acorn squash. The key is to bake at a constant, moderate temperature to retain moisture.

The Healthier Eating Method of Cooking Fish.

Many people associate frying as the principal technique for cooking fish. Although properly done frying does not have to add a great deal of extra fat, the technique still results in additional calories and extra cholesterol. For healthier eating, we believe there are preferable methods of cooking fish.

Poaching. The technique of poaching is often associated with eggs. And, indeed, the term "poaching" comes from the French word for "pocket." This is in reference to the fact that when eggs are broken into water to be poached, the whites form a "pocket" enclosing the yolk.

But poaching is also a wonderful method of cooking fish. Although special fish poaching vessels with baskets for holding the fish are available, you can easily accomplish the same task in a skillet.

The key is to remember that poaching is a delicate method of cooking, using liquid that is heated to just under the boiling point. Small pieces of fish need only a small amount of poaching liquid. With larger pieces, you need enough liquid to cover the fish. Heat the liquid to a slow simmer. That means it should be hot enough for an occasional lazy bubble to rise to the surface and pop slowly.

The classic poaching liquid is court bouillon, a combination of water, white wine, vinegar, vegetables, herbs and seasonings. This is a very good liquid for poaching fish, but because it takes about 45 minutes to prepare, you might prefer the quicker method that works just as well and eliminates the wine.

You will find our new quick Basic Poaching Instructions in our recipe for Poached Fish with Dill Sauce in the Fish section.

Whenever you are cooking fish, it is important not to overcook it or it will be dry. As soon as the fish loses its translucence and the color becomes opaque, begin testing. When the fish is slightly flaky, it is done.

Broiling and Baking. Broiling and baking are both dry heat cooking methods. The difference between them is that in broiling, the heat source is directly above the food, while in baking, the heat source is normally below and further away. The baking dish in which the fish is placed will also transfer heat to the food.

Both broiling and baking can be used successfully in cooking fish. But since many varieties are low in fat, it is important to keep them from drying out by watching cooking times carefully. For example, a 3-pound fish can normally be cooked at 325°F in only 25 minutes.

It can also be helpful to baste broiling or baking fish with a marinade of chicken broth, lemon juice and just a teaspoon or less of safflower oil to keep the fish moist.

The New Healthier Eating Method of Cooking Poultry.

One of the delicious ways that we stress reducing fat and cholesterol is by sub-stituting poultry and fish for red meat. This is a trend that has become increasingly popular among health and fitness conscious people everywhere. In the past 25 years, the consumption of chicken and turkey has *increased* over 150%, while beef consumption has *decreased* more than 57%.

You will notice that when we refer to poultry, we mean chicken and turkey, rather than duck or goose, which are both very high in fat.

Roasting. The secret to roasting chicken successfully is to cook it long enough so it turns a luscious golden brown, but not to let it dry out. If you're using frozen poultry, make sure it is thawed out completely before cooking. The best way to do this is slowly, by placing it in the refrigerator overnight.

Rinse the chicken thoroughly inside and out with cold running water. Pat it dry inside and out with a paper towel. For perfect flavor, season the bird on the inside and the outside with herbs. If you're roasting a whole chicken, fill the cavity with diced celery stalk, some parsley sprigs, a bay leaf, some thin slices of ginger, some ground thyme, a coarsely chopped shallot or two, and a minced garlic clove. Place on a rack over an open roasting pan. Brush the skin with chicken broth, and con-tinue basting with broth every 15 minutes or so. Roast at 325°F for 20 to 25 minutes per pound for a 5 to 7 pound chicken, and from 35 to 40 minutes per pound for a smaller bird. To know when the chicken is done, pierce the meat with a fork. If the juice runs a clear yellow with no trace of pink, and the drumstick moves easily, the chicken is done.

Baking Chicken. In baking chicken, the chicken is cut into pieces which are placed in the baking dish or pan, frequently with vegetables or other ingredients. In baking, moisture is released from the chicken itself and forms a warm vapor in the oven, making it a moister method than roasting. See individual recipes for more specific instructions which can' vary from recipe to recipe.

Poaching. You can also poach chicken breasts in chicken broth flavored with some lemon juice and chicken seasoning. Follow similar instructions for poaching fish.

The New Healthier Eating Methods for Cooking Meats.

Our healthier Eating Guide & Cookbook does not include recipes for meat. Meat is high in saturated fat and cholesterol, and even when you trim it carefully, there can still be too much fat retained in the "marbling."

If you wish to eat red meat occasionally, we recommend that you eat small servings of 4 ounces or less. This means incorporating meat in combination dishes such as you find in Chinese stir-fry cooking, where a little meat goes a long way.

If you crave a steak or roast once in a while, be sure to choose the leanest cuts possible and trim away all visible fat. Roast, broil, or sauté in broth to eliminate as much fat and cholesterol as possible.

Our healthier eating plan is not meant to deprive you of the foods you love. But when it comes to meat, we believe you should eat it only occasionally. Our tempting variety of recipes for chicken, turkey, fish, pasta and legumes will introduce you to appealing new ideas and flavors which will be satisfying alternatives to red meat. We think that by following our guidelines, you will lose your taste for meat in just a matter of weeks.

The Healthier Eating Way of Cooking Grains, Beans and Legumes.

Grains, beans and legumes are very versatile foods. You can enjoy grains at every meal throughout the day, from whole grain cereal at breakfast to a hearty barley soup at lunch to a tasty brown rice casserole at dinner. Each dish has its own distinct flavor and texture, and nutritionally, grains, beans and legumes are rich in protein like meat. In fact, beans and legumes have been called the "meat that grows on vines" because they are 20% to 40% protein. Yet unlike meat, they contain no cholesterol or saturated fat. They are also fine sources of B vitamins, calcium, iron, and fiber; they are low in sodium; and they cost less than any other protein foods. For all these reasons, beans, legumes and grains were a basic part of the American diet as recently as 50 years ago. But with the advent of modern "fast" foods and the greater emphasis on a "meat and potatoes" diet, they have become the most overlooked category of food.

Part of the reason for the lack of popularity of these former staples is that they traditionally take longer to prepare than most meats and vegetables. Many beans also contain carbohydrates called oligosaccharides that can cause gastric distress.

For the most part, these shortcomings can be overcome by using the correct methods of cooking grains, beans and legumes.

Healthy Eating Tips for Cooking Grains. When cooking grains other than rice, rinse them only if they seem gritty because grains contain B vitamins which can be washed away. When cooking grains the regular way, without a pressure cooker, measure the amount of cooking liquid and bring it to a full boil, then add the grain and stir once. Remember that grains swell to 2 to 4 times their dry volume during cooking, so use a large enough pot. After adding the grain to the boiling water, allow the liquid to return to a boil, then reduce the heat, cover the pot, and cook slowly, until the grain is soft and fluffy, and all the liquid is absorbed. You can tell when grains are done because they will taste chewy, but not tough or hard.

For extra flavor and nutrition, the Healthier Eating method of cooking grains is to use chicken broth as the liquid to cook in.

Quick Cooking Under Pressure. The best way to cut the long cooking time required for cooking grains, beans and legumes is to use a stainless steel pressure cooker. It can cut cooking time dramatically. For example, it can reduce the time needed to cook barley from 1 hour to about 10 minutes. And it can cut the time needed to cook pinto beans from 2 hours to about 25 minutes. The chart shows approximate cooking time:

Approximate Cooking Time for Beans and Peas

	Soaked Regular method	Unsoaked Pressure cooker (15 pounds pressure)
Black-eyed peas	1 hour	20 to 25 minutes
Chick-peas	3 hours	45 minutes
Fava	45 to 60 minutes	not recommended
Lentil	30 minutes	10 to 15 minutes
Lima	1 to 2 hours	not recommended
Lima, baby	45 to 60 minutes	not recommended
Mung	1½ hours	8 to 10 minutes
Pinto	1½ to 2 hours	25 to 30 minutes
Red kidney	1½ to 2 hours	25 to 30 minutes
Soybean	3 hours	35 minutes
Split Pea	35 to 60 minutes	not recommended
White bean, small	1 to 2 hours	25 minutes

Approximate Cooking Time for Grains

Grain (1 cup)	Amount of liquid (cups)	Cooked volume (cups)	Regular method Cooking time	Pressure cooker (15 pounds pressure)
Amaranth	3	2½	20 to 25 minutes	not necessary
Barley	3	3	1¼ hours	10 to 15 minutes
Brown rice	2	3	45 minutes	15 to 20 minutes
Buckwheat groats	2 to 5	2½	15 minutes	not necessary
Bulgur wheat	2	2½	15 to 20 minutes	not necessary
Cornmeal	4	3	25 minutes	not necessary
Cracked wheat	2	2½	25 minutes	not necessary
Millet	3	3½	45 minutes	10 minutes
Oats	3	3½	30 to 40 minutes	not necessary
Wild rice	3	4	1 hour	15 to 20 minutes

Microwave cooking is a fundamentally different way of cooking because instead of applying heat itself, high frequency electromagnetic radiation penetrates food and causes the microscopic water molecules inside to vibrate rapidly. This vibration generates heat, which cooks the food from the inside out, rather than the reverse which occurs with conventional moist or dry heat cooking. Because the microwaves do not necessarily penetrate foods uniformly, heat is not generated uniformly. This is why microwave cooking is often not recommended for baking or for cooking foods such as turkey or pork, where uniform minimum levels of heat must be generated throughout to kill any potentially dangerous bacteria.

We do not consider the data on the long term effect of the microwave cooking of foods to be definitive. Therefore, we tend to favor limiting the use of microwave ovens pending further studies.

7

Cooking with Herbs & Spices

The Healthier Eating Way to Prepare Delicious Foods without Added Salt.

If you examine the use of salt throughout history, you'll see that in ancient times salt was the only means of preserving foods. Salt was widely used in curing meats and fish to kill dangerous bacteria. Ancient civilizations did not use salt as a seasoning. They flavored their foods with natural herbs and spices instead.

That's because fragrant, zesty herbs and spices are actually the ideal seasonings. Salt doesn't really enhance the flavors of foods. Herbs and spices are more subtle, so they add their individual aromas and flavor accents to the true flavors of foods without overpowering them. That's why in virtually every great cuisine in the world, the art of using herbs and spices is admired and revered.

As a guide to cooking with herbs and spices, we've listed most of the common varieties, together with a brief description of each and a few notes about the origins and history. We've also listed which foods tend to go best with each of the herbs and spices.

Before you start, just remember that most recipes that call for herbs and spices are usually referring to the dried versions. We believe you'll find fresh herbs and spices even more enjoyable. But when fresh herbs are not available, the dried variety are a very acceptable alternative. When working with dried herbs and spices, always keep them in tightly closed containers away from excess heat to prevent them from drying out completely and losing their flavor and nutritional value. If you have any doubts about the age and quality of dried herbs and spices, trust your eyes and your nose. First, look at the color, because as a general rule, the brighter the color, such as the amount of green in tarragon or the red in paprika, the more likely that it has retained its best flavor traits. Also, smell the herb or spice. If it is still worth using, it should retain its characteristic aroma.

The Secrets to Getting the Most Flavor From Herbs and Spices.

Nothing lends quite the character and authority to dishes as the right herbs and spices. And learning to season foods masterfully is really not that difficult. Of course, it requires some practice. But other than that, all you need to know are a few simple tips. Here are our secrets to getting the most from herbs and spices:

• Dried and fresh versions can be used interchangeably in most recipes. However, keep in mind that you'll need between 3 and 6 times more fresh herbs than dried to get the same seasoning effect. A good rule of thumb is that ⅓ to ½ teaspoon of dried herbs equals one tablespoon of fresh.

• To get the most flavor and fragrance from *fresh herbs,* mince the leaves finely. The more cut surfaces you expose, the more flavor and fragrance you release.

• To get the most flavor from *dried herbs,* soak them for about 15 minutes in a liquid that can be used in the recipe. For instance, soak them in lemon juice, stock, vinegar, or pure vegetable oil.

• In general, the flavor and fragrance of herbs and spices are released more quickly by heat, and much more slowly by cold. The exception to this rule is that when herbs are used to season a dish that is then frozen, the reheated dish often has a more intense herb flavor. For this reason, if you're making a dish to be frozen for use later, you might want to make it without adding the herbs and spices, and season with them before reheating.

When to Add Herbs and Spices During Cooking.

For vegetables, add the herbs and spices as they are being steamed or stir fried so the heat will release the flavors and aromas of the herbs.

For poultry and fish, rub the herbs directly into the meat with your hands before cooking. For poultry, it is best to rub the herbs into the flesh under the skin.

For meats, stocks, stuffings, casseroles and other dishes with short to moderate cooking times, add the herbs and spices at the beginning of cooking.

For savory sauces, soups, stews and longer cooking dishes, add the herbs during the last 30 minutes of cooking because prolonged cooking can dissipate the flavor and aroma.

For salad dressings and chilled dishes that are not cooked, add the herbs well in advance, even overnight, to release their full flavors. Serve salad dressing at room temperature for the most flavor.

Note: Keep in mind that ⅓ to ½ teaspoon of dried herbs or spices equals one tablespoon of fresh.

Another way to become more confident with herbs and spices is to use our herb seasoning recipes in the Condiment section. They are called for in many of the recipes in this book. But rather than simply measuring them out and adding them where called for, take the time to taste and smell them separately before you add them to the recipe. And finally, taste the recipe right after adding the seasonings, so you can begin to become familiar with the way blends of herbs and spices really affect the flavors and aromas of finished dishes.

You'll also begin to become more aware of which blends seem to work best with different kinds of foods.

INDEX:
Commonly Used Spices:

Allspice	Curry	Nutmeg
Cinnamon	Ginger	

Commonly Used Herbs:

Basil	Marjoram	Paprika
Bay Leaf	Mint	Parsley
Chili	Mustard	Rosemary
Dill	Onions	Tarragon
Garlic Powder	Oregano	Thyme

Less Commonly Used Herbs:

Anise	Coriander	Sage
Celery Seed	Cumin	Savory
Chervil	Fennel	Sorrel
Chives	Saffron	

Commonly Used Spices

Allspice

Characteristics: The name "allspice" comes from the fact that its flavor resembles a combination of cinnamon, nutmeg and cloves.

Origin: Allspice, usually known as pimiento outside the U.S. is the dried unripe berry of the Pimenta tree. Native to the West Indies and Latin America, it is the only major spice grown, on a commercial basis, exclusively in the Western Hemisphere.

Uses: Baking—Cakes, Cookies, Pumpkin Bread
      Meats—Beef, Ham, Meatloaf, Stews
      Soups—Fruit
      Vegetables—Winter Squash, Sweet Potatoes

133

Cinnamon

<u>Characteristics</u>: Cinnamon has a distinct, fragrant aroma. So much so, that in the Orient, it is sometimes called "sweet wood."

<u>Origin</u>: Cinnamon and cassia are two of the oldest spices known to man, and are frequently mentioned in the Bible. True cinnamon is the dried inner bark of a moderate-sized bushy evergreen tree of the laurel family.

<u>Uses</u>: Baking – Apple Pie, Biscuits, Fruit Breads, Muffins, Sweet Rolls
      Meats – Beef Stew, Middle Eastern Dishes
      Soups – Fruit
      Vegetables – Carrots, Pumpkins, Sweet Potatoes, Winter Squash

Curry

<u>Characteristics</u>: Curry is a very aromatic blend of spices with a distinct goldenrod yellow color derived from turmeric.

<u>Origin</u>: The name "curry" derives from the Hindustani word "turcarri," which has been shortened to be pronounced curry in English. Curry powder is actually a blend of, generally, 10 or more spices. Typical spices in a commercially packaged curry powder might include turmeric, cardamom, coriander, mustard, saffron and allspice.

<u>Uses</u>: Meats – Beef, Lamb, Pork
      Fish – Tuna
      Poultry – Chicken, Eggs, Stuffing
      Soups – Chicken, Consomme, Pea, Tomato, Vegetable
      Vegetables – Carrots, Eggplant, Winter Squash

Ginger

<u>Characteristics</u>: Ginger has a pungent, spicy-sweet aroma and a hot, clean taste that is often featured in Oriental cuisine.

<u>Origins</u>: Ginger was first cultivated by the ancient Chinese and Hindus, and was one of the first Oriental spices brought to Europe. It is obtained from the thick underground stems called rhizomes that join the stalks of the plant to its roots.

<u>Uses</u>: Baking – Breads, Cakes, Cookies, Puddings
      Meat – Oriental Dishes, Pot Roast
      Poultry – Chicken
      Vegetables – Carrots, Sweet Potatoes, Winter Squash
      Desserts – Cookies, Pumpkin Pie

Nutmeg

Characteristics: Nutmeg has a warm, sweet, highly spicy flavor that blends especially well with sweet foods.

Origins: Nutmeg is indigenous to the Moluccas and other East Indian Islands. It is obtained from a tree of the evergreen family that is remarkable in that it provides two separate spices, nutmeg and mace.

Uses: Baking—Applesauce Bread, Banana Bread, Pumpkin Bread
      Meats—Meatloaf, Swedish Meatballs
      Soups—Bean, Split Pea, Tomato
      Vegetables—Beans, Pumpkins, Spinach, Winter Squash
      Desserts—Applesauce, Custard, Rice Pudding

Commonly Used Herbs

Basil

Characteristics: Basil leaves are often associated with tomato and tomato-based recipes. Its taste is reminiscent of cloves in that it is warm, sweet and aromatic.

Origins: Basil is a spicy herb of the mint family said to be native to India, Africa and Asia, but now cultivated throughout the world. It is a small, bushy plant whose glossy leaves have been used since ancient times.

Uses: Baking—Herbed Biscuits, Yeast Breads
      Fish—Baked Fish
      Meats—Beef, Lamb, Meatballs, Stews
      Poultry—Omelets, Pasta Dishes, Stuffing, Sautéed Chicken
      Soups—Fish Chowder, Minestrone, Spinach, Tomato, Vegetable
      Vegetables—Artichokes, Asparagus, Eggplant, Spinach, Tomatoes, Zucchini

Bay Leaf

Characteristics: Bay leaves have a spicy, pungent, somewhat bitter flavor that is popular in French cuisine for flavoring stocks and soups, particularly bouillabaisse. Always discard bay leaves after cooking, as they can be toxic.

Origins: The bay laurel tree is an evergreen of the laurel family native to the Mediterranean region and Asia Minor. The leaves of this tree are harvested by hand, then dried in thin layers in a warm, sheltered place to maintain the essential oil that gives their flavor.

Uses: Meats—Beef, Lamb, Meatloaf, Pot Roast, Stews
      Poultry—Chicken Stew
      Soups—Bouillabaisse, Chicken-Rice, Tomato, Vegetable

Chili Powder

Characteristics: As a whole, chili peppers are the most widely produced seasoning in the world. Contrary to popular belief, chili powder is not always "hot," but it is usually spicy and full-flavored.

Origins: Chili powder as it is sold is actually a blend of herbs that include ground chilies together with ground oregano, cumin, garlic powder and other spices. The chilies themselves come from the juiceless, ripe, dried pods of plants called capsicum peppers. There are many different varieties of capsicum peppers that range from those with hot, pungent flavors to others so mild, they are sold as sweets. The plants are indigenous to Mexico and Central and South America.

Uses: Barbeque Sauce, Chili and Beans, Mexican-Style Meat Dishes, Stews
  Poultry – Chicken, Omelets
  Soups – Mexican-Style Soups
  Vegetables – Beans, Corn, Rice, Tomatoes

Dill

Characteristics: Dill has a clean, refreshing flavor that is especially good with fish. One of its uses traditionally has been as a flavoring in pickling cucumbers.

Origins: Dill is an annual of the parsley family indigenous to the Mediterranean and Southern Russia. It is related to anise, caraway, coriander, cumin and fennel, as well as parsley.

Uses: Baking – Biscuits, Dumplings
  Meats – Beef, Lamb
  Fish – All White Fish and other mild-flavored fish, Shrimp
  Poultry – Chicken, Turkey
  Vegetables – Beets, Cabbage, Cole Slaw, Cucumbers, Green Beans,
      Thin-Skinned Potatoes

Garlic

Characteristics: Garlic has a very strong and distinctive flavor that can produce a tingling sensation in the mouth. In many cuisines, including those of Southern Italy and Provence, garlic is a staple cooking ingredient. There is some evidence that garlic is effective in lowering blood pressure.

Origins: Garlic is thought to have originated in central Asia, and is one of the oldest cultivated plants. The bulb of the garlic plant is divided into many fat cloves which are the source of garlic.

Uses: Baking – Garlic Bread
  Meats – Beef, Fish, Italian Dishes, Lamb, Stews, Sauces
  Poultry – Chicken, Pasta Dishes, Stuffing
  Soups – Chicken, Tomato, Vegetable

Marjoram

Characteristics: Sweet marjoram has a delicate, pleasant, sweet flavor.

Origins: Marjoram is a low, bushy perennial which is indigenous to the Mediterranean region. Botanically, there is much similarity between it and oregano, although marjoram is not as pungent.

Uses: Baking – Herbed Biscuits, Yeast Breads
      Meats – Beef, Italian Dishes, Meatloaf, Pot Roast, Stews, Veal
      Poultry – Chicken, Omelets, Souffles, Stuffing, Turkey
      Soups – Creams, Fish Chowder, Onion, Potato, Vegetable
      Vegetables – Beans, Eggplant, Mushrooms, Onions, Peas, Potatoes,
            Summer Squash

Mint

Characteristics: Mint has a distinct fresh, sweet, tangy flavor with a cool aftertaste. It also has a penetrating aroma.

Origins: Mint is a hardy perennial herb indigenous to Europe and the Mediterranean, but now grown in temperate climates throughout the world. The two most popular varieties are peppermint and spearmint.

Uses: Beverages – Iced Tea, Iced Beverages
      Meats – Lamb, Veal
      Vegetables – Carrots, Peas, Spinach, Tabouli Salad
      Desserts – Applesauce, Candies, Jellies

Mustard

Characteristics: Unlike most other aromatic spices, powdered mustard has no aroma when dry. It must be moistened with water, vinegar, or lemon juice to develop its pungent aroma. Mustard has a distinct and familiar sharp, hot, tangy flavor.

Origins: There are several different varieties of mustard, all of which are hardy annuals grown in temperate climates throughout the world. The mustard seed is normally dried and ground up and then either sold in powdered form, or mixed with vinegar to protect its pungency. After black pepper, mustard is the most commonly used spice in this country.

Uses: Meats – Beef, Cold Cuts, Corned Beef, Lamb, Wieners
      Poultry – Chicken
      Sauces – Marinades, Sauces, Salad Dressing

Onions

Characteristics: Onions have a distinct penetrating, pungent odor and a familiar long-lasting flavor.

Origins: The common onion and chives belong to the lily family. Onions are believed to be native to southwestern Europe and Asia. Onions, along with garlic, are among the oldest cultivated plants, and were known throughout Egypt, China and India even before recorded history.

Uses: Baking – Onion Rolls and Bread
      Meats – Fish, All Meats, Stews
      Poultry – Chicken, Cheese Dishes, Omelets, Stuffing
      Soups – Chicken, Chowders, Consomme, French Onion, Pea, Tomato,
            Vegetable
      Vegetables – Virtually All Vegetables, Beans and Rice

Oregano

Characteristics: Oregano has a lusty, piquant aroma that carries over into its flavor, which is strong and pleasantly bitter. The milder European type is used in Italian dishes, especially pizza, while the more pungent variety is used in chili powder, chili con carne and Mexican dishes.

Origins: Oregano was formerly known as "wild marjoram" because botanically it is quite similar to marjoram. However, its flavor is distinctly different. There are basically two kinds of oregano, the more pungent Mexican variety and the milder European type that's of the mint family.

Uses: Meats – Beef, Lamb, Meatballs, Meatloaf, Mexican Dishes, Roasts, Stews
      Pasta – Italian Dishes, Pizza
      Soups – Bean, Minestrone, Tomato, Tripe, Vegetable
      Vegetables – Bean Salads, Bell Peppers, Cabbage, Corn, Eggplant, Lentils,
            Mushrooms, Onions, Tomatoes, Zucchini

Paprika

Characteristics: Most paprika sold in this country is mildly flavored, so its effect in cooking is as much a result of its brilliant red color as its taste. An unusual asset of paprika is that pound for pound, it is higher in vitamin C than citrus fruits.

Origins: Paprika is ground from dried pods of the chili family. Chili peppers come in many varieties from the extremely pungent "hot" types to the very mild. The peppers used in paprika are medium-sized, mild and quite fleshy.

Uses: Baking – Biscuits, Cheese Bread
      Meats – Fish, Hungarian Goulash, Stews, Steak
      Poultry – Chicken Paprikash, Garnish
      Soups – Bisques, Chowders, Creams, Pea
      Vegetables – Cauliflower, Potatoes

Parsley

Characteristics: Parsley has a mild, agreeable flavor and the ability to sweeten the breath, even after eating onions and garlic. It is familiar as an ornamental garnish as well as a condiment.

Origins: Parsley is one of the best known and most extensively used of all culinary herbs, especially in its fresh state. Although native to the Mediterranean area, it is found growing in cool, damp climates throughout the world.

Uses: Meats – Beef, Fish, Veal
    Poultry – Chicken
    Vegetables – Can Accompany Virtually All Vegetables

Rosemary

Characteristics: Rosemary has a clean, fresh, bittersweet flavor and an aromatic woodsy aroma that is sometimes used in soups and perfumes.

Origins: Rosemary is a small evergreen shrub of the mint family native to the Mediterranean region. Its small, narrow aromatic leaves resemble curved pine needles when dried.

Uses: Baking – Herbed Biscuits and Breads
    Meats – Beef, Lamb, Pork, Roasts, Stews
    Poultry – Chicken, Pies, Stews, Stuffing, Turkey
    Soups – Chicken, Potato, Tomato, Vegetable
    Vegetables – Broccoli, Lima Beans, Peas, Potatoes, Spinach

Tarragon

Characteristics: Tarragon leaves have a distinctive bittersweet flavor that is quite pungent, so it is best to use them sparingly.

Origins: Tarragon is a small herbaceous perennial plant indigenous to Southern Russia and Western Asia. It has been used as a culinary herb only relatively recently, compared to other herbs, but it has become one of the most popular.

Uses: Meat – Beef, Fish, Veal
    Poultry – Chicken, Egg Dishes
    Soups – Fish Chowder, Lentil, Mushroom, Tomato
    Vegetables – To Flavor Vinegar Used in Salad Dressings, Sauces

Thyme

Characteristics: Thyme has a distinctive warm, pleasant, pungent flavor that complements soups and sea foods well.

Origins: Thyme is a small perennial shrub of the mint family native to the Mediterranean region and Asia Minor. Besides being grown as a culinary herb, it has long been cultivated for its essential oil, which is used in medicine.

Uses: Baking – Corn Bread, Herbed Biscuits and Breads
     Meats – Beef, Lamb, Mild-Flavored White Fish, Pork, Roasts, Stews,
        Seafood, Stock
     Poultry – Chicken Pies, Stews, Stuffing, Turkey
     Soups – Bisques, Chowders, Tomato, Vegetable
     Vegetables – Carrots, Green Beans, Mushrooms, Onions, Potatoes,
        Summer Squash

Less Commonly Used Herbs

The following herbs each have their own distinctive characteristics that can contribute wonderful nuances of flavor, aroma and color to various dishes. They tend to be less commonly called for in recipes, but as you become more comfortable and experienced using herbs, you may wish to incorporate them into your cooking. We have listed the kinds of foods each one is particularly suited for.

Anise: A stong, licoricelike flavor and aroma. Use it in cakes, cookies and breads.

Celery Seed: A mild, pleasant flavor to use in fruit salads, potato salad, tomatoes, breads and eggs.

Chervil: Similar to parsley, but sweeter and more aromatic with a slightly anise-like fragrance. Use with soups, salads, sauces, egg dishes, chicken.

Chives: A member of the onion family, but with a mild flavor. Use with salads, eggs, potatoes.

Coriander: A mild and sweet, yet slightly pungent taste reminiscent of a combination of sage and lemon. Use in Mexican dishes and in sausages.

Cumin: A strongly aromatic, hot and bitter taste that is an essential ingredient in curry and chili powders. Use in beans, rice, curry dishes, enchiladas, chili con carne.

Fennel: Has an agreeable, warm, sweet aroma, somewhat like anise. Use with fish, stews, eggs, vegetables and cheese.

Saffron: Has a pleasantly spicy, pungent, bitter taste and a very tenacious odor. It is often used as much for its intense yellow-orange color as its flavor. Use in seafood, curries, rice and with chicken.

Sage: Has a highly aromatic fragrance and a pungent, slightly bitter taste that works well with fatty meats. Use with pork, and other meats, chicken, cheese dishes, stuffings.

Savory: Has a fragrant, piquant flavor, reminiscent of pepper, that blends well with beans, peas and lentils. Use with legumes, vegetables, meat dishes and chicken.

Sorrel: Has a strong, sharp taste that works well with dairy products. Use in sauces and soups.

Other Healthier Eating Secrets to Seasoning without Salt.

Besides using herbs and spices to bring out the true flavors of foods and add zest without salt, there are two other seasoning "secrets" that are part of healthier eating.

Lemons have a refreshingly tart flavor that we're all familiar with. But you may not fully appreciate the flavor-enhancing quality of both fresh lemon juice and fresh lemon peel. Most people know that a squeeze of lemon juice is the perfect accent for fish, but it also brightens the flavors of raw and cooked vegetables, dressings and marinades, as well as meats. It also has a surprisingly beneficial effect on fresh fruit. And there is probably nothing that adds quick zest and tang to a dull dish quite like lemon juice.

Fresh is by far the best, with frozen lemon juice next best. Avoid bottled juice because it usually contains chemical preservatives.

Also try using zests of lemon peel to brighten up sauces and desserts. But avoid getting any of the white bioflavonoid membrane right under the peel in foods because it will add a bitter flavor.

8

Equipping Your Kitchen for Healthier Eating

Today, there are more families in which both partners work, there are more single parent families, and there are more single working people than ever before. All of these people share a common need for good food every day, and they all have the common problem of having very little time to prepare it.

Our healthier recipes are created with the consideration of helping to meet the need for good food that can be prepared quickly and easily, and still offer mouth-watering taste and balanced nutrition.

It All Starts By Creating a Healthier Kitchen.

The first step to being able to prepare delicious, well-balanced, low fat meals on a regular basis is to get organized. Start by taking the time to turn your kitchen into an efficient "workshop."

If you're like many of us, your kitchen just sort of evolved. As you acquired new kitchenware and utensils, they got put with others, or were placed wherever space allowed. Chances are, by now, your kitchen is no longer as efficient as it might be, even if it started out efficient. It's also true that most of us were so preoccupied with moving in when we first arranged our kitchens that we didn't feel we had the time to really concentrate on making them as functional as possible. Well, now that you've had the benefit of experience working in the space, you're in a very good position to really make it work for you. That's why we advise that you'll save yourself countless hours in the long run, if you just take the time now to re-examine your kitchen and re-organize it.

Start by taking a "tour" of your kitchen area. Analyze where the immovable objects are, such as the sink, the built-in oven and range and cabinets. Then, rearrange your movable objects, such as your cookware, serving ware, utensils, food processing equipment, etc., to the areas where they permit the best work "flow" in conjunction with those that can't be moved. Here are some tips:

Food Preparation Area: Create one or more food preparation areas with cutting boards, knives, seasonings, etc. near each other and close to a sink for fast, easy clean up.

Herbs and Spices: To save time locating herbs and spices, arrange them all together alphabetically in clearly marked containers in or near food preparation area. But be sure this area is away from heat, which can rob herbs and spices of their flavors and nutritional value.

Cookware: Ideally, your cookware should all be stored together in a space between the food preparation area and the stove/oven. If you're short of cabinet space, consider hanging cookware from a device made just for this purpose that you can mount from the ceiling.

Utensils: Locate these nearest the areas where they're most often used. Again, if your cabinet or drawer space is limited, these can be hung together or placed in a holder made to contain cooking utensils.

Drawers: Try not to put things into drawers at random. Select which drawers you put things into by their proximity to the point of use and their frequency of use. For example, you can store regular knives, forks and spoons in an easy-to-reach top drawer nearest the serving area such as the kitchen table, while you might store infrequently used fondue forks toward the back of a bottom drawer that's out of the main flow area. It also helps to use drawer dividers to keep similar items together.

Counter tops: Try to keep counter tops clear as work areas, where you use your basic food equipment such as a blender, food processor, juicer, etc.

Cabinets: Organize cabinets so that staples and cookware that are used together are stored together, or near one another. For example, baking supplies and equipment can be stored together in cabinets near the oven.

Storage Containers: To preserve the freshness, flavor and food value of flours, grains, beans, seeds, nuts, etc., use airtight glass containers that allow you to instantly identify the contents. It is also helpful to label and date foodstuffs to insure that you use them while they're still at their best. For semi-perishables that you don't use as often, such as pancake mix, you can extend their useful life by storing in an airtight, moisture-resistant glass container in the refrigerator.

Product Storage: Refrigerator bins are most helpful in organizing produce and preserving freshness. If storage space is limited, you might consider using wire hanging baskets to store foods such as fruits, potatoes and onions.

Kitchen Wall Space: Don't overlook wall space as a useful place to hang pots, pans and utensils, and cooking aids, such as nutrition charts, conversion charts, and meal planners. A blackboard is useful for creating your shopping list.

How to Select the Right Equipment for Preparing Healthier Meals.

Our healthier way of eating has been created so that you are not required to purchase any elaborate or expensive equipment in order to make the recipes. However, it should be obvious that having good quality staple kitchenware and utensils is important, and there is optional specialty equipment that can make performing certain jobs faster and more convenient, if you wish to invest extra money in them. Naturally, it's up to you just how much you want to spend on kitchenware, and selecting specific brands or types of equipment depends a lot on personal preference. But as an aid to evaluating your needs in the kitchen, we've prepared a list of staple kitchenware that we have found to be important for ideal efficiency. You'll probably find you have many of them, so you won't have to spend extra money.

We begin with a brief evaluation of basic materials available.

The Best Materials for Preparing Healthier Meals.

Cookware and utensils are available in a variety of materials. Each material has different sets of properties, including advantages and disadvantages. In some instances, the choice of materials depends primarily on personal preferences or economics. In other cases, there are clear-cut advantages or dangers that you should consider.

Recommended Materials for Healthy Cooking.

Stainless steel as the name implies is an iron alloy that is impervious to most other materials, including many acids. It has the advantage of being easy to clean, and since it is non-porous, it does not react with foods. Stainless steel is ideal for mixing bowls, colanders, utensils and baking racks. Stainless steel conducts heat well, but it has a tendency to develop "hot spots," which means it doesn't always distribute heat evenly when used in pots and pans. The primary drawbacks are that it tends to be rather heavy and is quite expensive to produce and work with, so it is also expensive to purchase. You should be aware that there are different types of stainless steel.

For example, high carbon stainless steel is a stainless alloy specifically developed for use in knives and cutlery. It can be sharpened to hold a very sharp edge and is stain resistant. It is probably the best available metal for high quality knives, but it is also expensive.

Overall, stainless steel is ideal for cookware, utensils and accessories because it is safe and easy to keep clean.

Cast iron is an ideal metal for stovetop cookware such as skillets and pots. Once cast iron is "seasoned," it is excellent for cooking because it holds heat well and distributes heat evenly. The primary drawbacks to cast iron are the fact it is very heavy which can make it awkward to handle, and it can be somewhat expensive.

Glass is available in a variety of forms, including both heat-resistant and regular. It is non-porous, so it is easy to keep clean and doesn't react with foods. Glass is excellent for mixing bowls, measuring cups, and when heat-treated, for baking dishes and cups, and double boilers. The main drawback is that glass is breakable.

Materials that Can Be Used with Some Reservations:

Some materials are suitable for use in some circumstances, or if treated in certain ways. Below are our evaluations of materials that can be used if certain caveats or precautions are taken:

Copper is a metal that has long been considered the ideal material for cookware because it conducts heat so well and so evenly. However, copper itself reacts with foods, particularly acidic ones, such as tomatoes, so it must be lined with another inert metal such as tin or nickel, or sandwiched in stainless steel. The drawbacks of copper are that it is usually one of the most expensive materials, and it tarnishes easily, making it time consuming to maintain properly.

For these reasons, we do not recommend copper as an ideal cooking material, but if it is properly lined, it is acceptable as a safe cooking medium.

Porcelain and ceramic-ware are available in a variety of forms, including glazed and unglazed finishes. The danger with pottery is that some of the glazes are compounds that contain lead. Or, if the glaze is red or yellow in color, it is likely that the toxic mineral cadmium is involved. Cooking foods, especially those high in acids, for long periods of time or marinating such foods in ceramic bowls can leach out some of the lead or cadmium and contaminate food.

Obviously, not all pottery or porcelain poses this risk, which is why we suggest paying close attention to the manufacturing techniques used. When there is any doubt, we feel it is better to avoid these materials.

Wood is a semi-porous material that does not conduct heat. Therefore, it is ideal for use on the handles of pots and pans, and as a trivet. Because it is semi-porous, it can absorb oils and other chemicals, so extra care should be taken if you use a wooden cutting board or utensils.

Materials We Recommend You Do Not Use:

There are certain materials that are widely used in kitchen and cookware that we do not feel are safe to use. We therefore advise you *not* to select equipment made of these materials if they can be avoided.

Aluminum is a material that we do *not* recommend for cooking or any other use in the kitchen. There is evidence that aluminum can react with foods, particularly acidic ones, and can therefore end up in your diet in toxic amounts if you cook with it or store foods in it. Aluminum has been implicated as a contributor to Alzheimer's Disease, a brain disorder that can affect the memory, and has the symptoms of premature senility.

Recently, some hardened aluminum cookware has been developed that promises to eliminate the problem of aluminum residue in food, but because there is not enough conclusive evidence of its safety, we still recommend caution if you are considering aluminum cookware.

Plastics must be used selectively because they can begin to dissolve upon contact with oils, fats, and some fatty foods, such as cheese. Plastics are petroleum products, and therefore indigestible, and even toxic if consumed. Plastics are available in a multitude of forms from hard, non-porous to flexible porous varieties. All of them have the advantage of being lightweight. The hard, non-porous plastics are acceptable for use as measuring cups and serving utensils because they are easy to clean and do not react with foods. Care should be taken when using porous, flexible plastic or plastic bags for storing foods because they can absorb odors and react with oily foods. We would suggest that you try and restrict using plastic containers for storing dry foods, such as grains, nuts, flour and breads, and for fresh vegetables and fruits.

Plastic bottles should not be used for oils or milk, because the fat in these foods can cause a certain amount of disintegration and dissolution of plastic materials, which then end up as a harmful residue in foods.

The Kitchen Equipment You Need for Healthier Eating.

Baking Pans. We suggest one or two muffin pans, a round pizza pan and a cookie sheet. We recommend steel, glass or ceramics, and *not* aluminum for all these items.

Basting Brushes. Some natural bristle pastry brushes for basting and many other uses are very helpful. Use a large one for basting fowl, and a smaller one for pastry.

Blender. Select a blender with a strong motor and variable speeds, all the way from mix to liquefy, and make sure that the bowl is glass and not plastic.

Bulb Baster for removing fats and oil from stocks and soups.

Can Opener. Stainless steel.

Casserole Dishes. We suggest one medium and one large glass or ceramic casserole dishes. Optional are ramekins (individual casserole dishes) and souffle dishes.

Colander. A stainless steel colander is handy for cleaning and draining fresh fruits and vegetables, and for draining freshly cooked pasta. It can also be used as a steamer by placing across the top of a pot filled with boiling water.

Cookware. We suggest that you have three or more different sizes of pots with matching covers, starting with a 1 to 1½-quart size saucepan, all the way up to a stockpot large enough to make soup and beans.

You should also have two or three sizes of skillets with covers. A 6-inch and a 10 to 12-inch size can be very useful.

The materials we recommend are stainless steel or cast iron.

Cutting Board. Untreated, natural hardwood makes the best cutting board if it is cleaned properly after each use. Use mild soap and warm water, and then dry it carefully. Putting a wooden cutting board in the dishwasher or using very hot water can warp it.

Electric Mixer. Ideally, it's good to have two mixers—a heavy-duty electric mixer for big jobs, such as mixing large amounts of ingredients, and a smaller hand-held model for blending sauces.

Food Scale for weighing portions.

Food Thermometer for roasting and for making yogurt.

Grater. The most versatile grater is a four-sided stainless steel one in which each side can be used for different-sized grating.

Knives. There is a wide range of prices among kitchen knives. We suggest you purchase the very best ones you can afford, preferably ones with blades made of high carbon stainless or regular carbon steel, because they hold the best edge. A really good, well-balanced knife is not only much easier to work with, but it's also safer because a good, sharp knife will cut what you want cleanly with less pressure, rather than slipping off to one side and cutting something you don't want cut.

Pressure Cooker. We especially recommend this appliance as a way to cut the cooking time of beans and legumes. Many people overlook the superb flavor, nutrition and economy that can be provided by beans and legumes simply because they can take several hours to prepare. A pressure cooker can overcome this drawback. However, we do not recommend using it to cook most vegetables or meats because the temperature generated in a pressure cooker can destroy important nutrients in these foods.

Spatulas, Spoons and Soup Ladle. Having both regular and slotted spoons and spatulas is ideal. A soup ladle is handy for serving soups, stews, chili, beans, sauces, etc.

Steamer. A stainless steel steamer or steam basket is a very worthwhile investment. Steaming is an excellent way of preparing cooked vegetables so they retain more flavor and nutrients than vegetables boiled in water. You can also take bread or muffins that are starting to dry out, and by steaming them, not only heat them up, but also replace the moisture so they have a fresher texture.

Storage Containers. We recommend airtight glass canisters for storing foods because the glass does not react with foods or absorb odors, and it's easy to see inside and identify the contents.

Timer.

Toaster.

Trivets for hot pots and pans.

Wire Whisks for blending batters, sauces and egg whites.

Optional Equipment.

Beyond the basics we've just listed, you don't really have to invest in expensive, specialized equipment in order to prepare our healthier recipes. But many people find that cooking isn't just a daily necessity, it is a wonderfully rewarding and creative endeavor. If you're one of these people, and you spend a lot of pleasant time in the kitchen, you may wish to have some additional specialized kitchen tools and equipment to make food preparation even faster and easier, and to make your finished dishes more "professional" looking. So here is a list of things that aren't essential for successful cooking, but can be very useful, if you're willing to invest in them.

Convection Oven. This is basically a conventional oven, but it has special fans to circulate the hot air. The result is more even heat distribution for faster cooking and more even browning. We recommend this approach, as opposed to a microwave oven if you want shorter cooking time.

Double Boiler. A double boiler can be very important for cooking sauces and other temperature sensitive foods.

Egg Separator to separate yolks from whites easily and reliably.

Food Processor. This can be a fairly major investment, but well worth it, because a good food processor can significantly reduce the time it takes to prepare ingredients that need to be sliced, chopped, shredded, grated or puréed. You can also get attachments for some that will knead dough or even make fresh pasta.

Grain Grinder. If you wish to have the very freshest whole grain flours for cooking and baking, invest in a home stone grinder and make your own flour.

Juicer. This small appliance lets you enjoy delicious fresh juices that are absolutely at their peak of flavor and nutritional value. And since you can squeeze juices from most fresh fruits and vegetables when they are in season and at their lowest prices, it can be economical, too.

Kitchen Scissors

Melon Ball Scoop

Pizza Cutter

Sifter for flour

Spatula

Spin Dryer for lettuce and other leafy vegetables.

Slow Cooker. This is another valuable small appliance for making dishes such as stews, casseroles, beans and legumes that require long cooking times. The slow cooker allows you to put together all the ingredients the day or evening before and put them into the cooker. Then, simply turn the cooker on in the morning, and by evening you automatically have a delicious hot meal ready to enjoy. This can be an especially convenient appliance for families where both partners work outside the home.

Toaster Oven. This is a very handy and energy-efficient appliance for heating or toasting smaller items, such as open-faced sandwiches and for toasting bread.

Yogurt Maker. This will enable you to make economical low fat yogurt that's even more delicious than commercial brands because it's so fresh.

Zester for citrus fruit.

How to Stock Your Kitchen for Healthier Eating

Since time is such an important consideration for most of us, organization and planning in the kitchen are vital if we are to enjoy the benefits of healthier eating in a convenient manner.

After organizing your kitchen to be a more efficient work space, the next step is to plan your shopping so you can have all the necessary ingredients available without spending more time than necessary in the store each week.

Obviously, there is no such thing as a "properly" stocked kitchen. What's proper for one household won't necessarily be right for another. Individual food preferences, the size of the household, budgetary limitations, and other factors all influence what is needed in the kitchen. Also, your needs will vary from week to week and season to season, depending upon the weather, your schedule, and whether you plan to entertain at home. But there are certain items that most households tend to use more frequently, especially during a week of healthier eating. Here is a suggested list of supplies you might want to keep on hand:

Note: In cases where there is a Health Valley product or product line, we have specified that in parentheses after listing the generic item. When there is no other acceptable commercial version, or where the Health Valley product is not widely available, or where there are other acceptable commercial or generic substitutions, the Health Valley product is listed in plain type.

In the Refrigerator:

Dairy Products
Non-fat milk
Low fat Buttermilk (from churned raw milk, if available)
Soy milk (Health Valley Soy Moo®)
Raw milk cheese with No Salt or low salt
Low fat yogurt
Tofu (Health Valley Tofu-Ya® tofu)
Fresh eggs (use only the egg whites for healthier eating)

Vegetables

Asparagus	Cucumber	Peppers (green and red)
Broccoli	Eggplant	Spinach
Cabbages (green and red)	Lettuce	Squash
Carrots	Mushrooms	Tomatoes
Caulifower	Parsley	Other seasonal
Celery	Peas	fresh vegetables
Corn		

Fruits
Apples (red & golden Delicious for eating out of hand, Granny Smith & Pippin for salads, Rome Beauty for baking, etc.)
Lemons and limes (for seasoning)
Oranges and grapefruit
Seasonal fresh fruit (apricots, berries of all kinds, grapes, kiwi, melons of all kinds, nectarines, peaches, pears, pineapples, plums, tropical fruits, such as papayas, mangoes, guavas, etc.)

Beverages
Fruit juices (without added sugar)
Vegetable juices (without added salt)
Water (bottled low sodium, plain and carbonated)

Condiments
Catsup (No Salt Added with no added refined sugar) (**Health Valley Catch-Up**™)
Mustard (Health Valley Mustard with Herbs)
Pasta sauce (No Salt Added with no added oil or refined sugar)
Salsa
Vinegar (apple cider, red wine, optional fruit varieties)

In the Freezer:

Fish & Poultry
Chicken
Fish filets (Health Valley Best of Seafood Alaskan Fish Filet, Alaskan Fish Sticks, Halibut Steaks, Salmon Steaks, Boned Trout)

Frozen Vegetables & Fruits
Broccoli spears (all the frozen vegetables listed here are available from Health Valley)
Corn
Green beans
Lima beans
Mixed vegetables
Peas
Spinach
Blueberries (all these frozen fruits should be packed with no added sugar or syrup)
Blackberries
Cherries
Melon balls
Raspberries
Strawberries

In the Cupboard:

Seasonings
Health Valley Instead of Salt™ All Purpose Herb Seasoning
Natural herbs and spices

Crackers
Made the healthy way without hydrogenated fats **(Health Valley Herb Crackers, Health Valley Stoned Wheat Crackers, Health Valley Sesame Crackers,** plus other varieties)

Cereals
Hot cereals with no added salt or refined sugar
Cold cereals with no added salt or refined sugar (Health Valley makes 35 varieties, including **Real**® **Granola, Sprouts 7,**® **Orangeola,**® **Amaranth Cereal, Bran with Raisins, Oat Bran Flakes, Fiber 7**™ **Flakes,** & **Lites**®

Pasta
Whole grain pastas (Health Valley Spaghetti, Spaghetti with Spinach, Lasagna, Lasagna with Spinach, Elbow Pasta, Elbow Pasta with 4 Vegetables, Amaranth Pasta)

Canned Goods
Low in salt chili **(Health Valley Chili with Beans,** either Mild or Spicy)

Soups (low in salt, no MSG) **(Health Valley Chicken Broth, Beef Broth, Bean, Clam Chowder, Lentil, Minestrone, Mushroom, Potato, Split Pea, Tomato,** and **Vegetable** Soups)
Tomato Sauce (low sodium, no MSG) **(Health Valley Tomato Sauce)**
Tuna (no salt added, packed in water) (Health Valley Best of Seafood® Albacore with No Salt Added)
Beans (Health Valley Vegetarian Beans with Miso & Boston Baked Beans)

Staples:

Flours
Whole wheat
Whole wheat pastry (lighter in texture)
Amaranth

Grains & Legumes
Chick peas (garbanzo beans)
Beans (red, black, navy, pinto, kidney, etc.)
Lentils
Rice (brown rice & wild rice)

Oils & Fats
Cold pressed vegetable oils

Sweeteners
Unfiltered honey (Alfalfa, Clover or Orange Honey)
Unsulfured molasses

Part Four

How Health Valley Makes Healthier Eating Easy

9

Using Health Valley Products for Nutrition and Convenience

Most people who consume a poor diet would like to eat healthier, but they don't have the time to prepare complete, healthier meals from scratch every day.

Our menus and recipes for healthier eating were created specifically with this in mind. We wanted to make them as convenient as possible for you.

Most of the recipes are easy to prepare in a reasonable amount of time. You can make them on week nights, without spending the whole evening in the kitchen. Many of the recipes can be prepared on weekends for use during the following week. And with the help of Health Valley products, you have the option of spending as much or as little time as you like in the kitchen.

For example, if you want to make everything for yourself from scratch, you can do it. You'll find easy recipes for making chicken broth, pasta sauce, and even for mixing your own herb seasoning blends. But if you want to cut your preparation time to the minimum, you can get the same homemade quality and flavor from such products as Health Valley Chicken Broth and Instead of Salt® All Purpose Seasoning.

The soup recipes in this book are terrific, and you'll have fun making them on weekends when you have more time. During the week, you can open up a can of Health Valley Soup without sacrificing nutrition or flavor.

The same is true of our recipes for beans and other side dishes. Most of them are easy enough to make even on week nights but for those days when you're really rushed, our Health Valley Vegetarian Chili, Baked Beans and Amaranth Minute Meals™ come in very handy.

Our dessert recipes are very healthy, because they usually feature fresh fruit as the main ingredients. You'll find that they can be accompanied deliciously by our Fruit Jumbos® Cookies or Apple Bakes® fruit bars. All our bakery products are wholesome foods with plenty of nutrition and fiber, so they're perfect for lunchboxes.

Most people don't have time to cook up breakfast on working days, and that's when you'll enjoy the good nutrition and taste of Health Valley Cereals. They go great with the quickie blender breakfast recipes you'll find in the Breakfast section.

157

Every product in the Health Valley line was developed to fill your needs for healthier eating, and your taste for good foods you can prepare in minutes. They fit in perfectly with any healthier eating plan.

It's important to use Health Valley Foods whenever you can because when it comes to nutrition, quality, fiber and flavor, there are no other products like these.

What Makes Health Valley So Unique?

Health Valley is unique among food companies because it was founded and based on George Mateljan's personal commitment to healthier eating.

George himself had personally experienced a dramatic revitalization in his health and in his general well being simply by changing his way of eating from a typical high-fat, high-sugar and high-salt diet of mainly processed foods to a balanced diet of whole natural foods prepared the healthier way. So when George established Health Valley, he was not motivated by profit, but by his joy and ·enthusiasm for the benefits of proper nutrition as a way to achieve vibrant good health. George made a personal promise that Health Valley would offer only the kinds of foods that George wanted to eat himself, and would serve to his own family and friends.

Unlike other food companies whose goals are to grow as large and make as much profit as possible, Health Valley has deliberately remained a relatively small company. By doing this, Health Valley can prepare foods with the care and attention you want. This is the only way Health Valley can guarantee that all food products will meet the highest standards of quality, nutrition and flavor, without compromise. Health Valley pledges to sell only foods that are safe, and that are free from chemicals that can be harmful to your health.

We don't believe there is any other food company in the world that can offer you better, more nutritious, or more wholesome foods than Health Valley.

Health Valley Products Are Always Made With:

- The world's finest quality natural ingredients prepared with minimal processing to retain maximum nutrition, flavor and fiber

- 100% whole grains and whole grain flours

- The healthiest polyunsaturated and monounsaturated oils

- Fruit juices, pure honey and unsulfured molasses as sweeteners

- The finest herbs and spices from around the world

- 30% to 60% less salt than commercial brands in our salted products, plus 100 products without any added salt

Health Valley Products Never Contain:

- Any white flour
- Any hydrogenated shortening
- Any white sugar
- Any preservatives, artificial flavors or colors
- Any nitrates or nitrites
- Any sulfites or irradiation
- Any monosodium glutamate (MSG), baking powder or cornstarch
- Any synthetic vitamins or nutrients
- Any ingredient that is harmful or even questionable in terms of human health

Health Valley Packaging Provides You:

- Full nutritional labeling including sodium, cholesterol, fats, dietary fiber and calories on all packaging where space permits
- Lead-free cans for soups, chilis and baked beans
- A clearly stamped freshness code date on every product where spoilage can be a problem
- Safe packaging materials, with no aluminum, BHA or BHT ever touching any food

Health Valley Works Toward Bringing You Organic Foods:

- We believe in safe food, and we support and encourage farmers to produce foods free of pesticides, herbicides and synthetic fertilizers. The Amaranth we use in many Health Valley products is organically grown, and Health Valley foods also contain organically grown wheat, organically grown apricots, and any other organically grown foods we can find.

Only Health Valley Uses Sprouted Grains in Cereals, Pasta, and Pancake & Biscuit Mix.

We are the only company we know of that sprouts whole grains for use in cereals, pasta and pancake & biscuit mix, because we are the only company to have perfected the method of sprouting grains under just the right conditions for precisely the right amount of time to bring out just the right amounts of nutrients and flavor. Also sprouting is a costly and time-consuming process that big commercial food companies don't have the time or interest in duplicating.

Basically, sprouting is the natural process that plants use to reproduce themselves. It literally brings the dormant seed to life. Almost miraculously, the seed begins building stores of energy, vitamins, minerals and other nutrients that will be needed by the growing plant. So sprouted grains always have much greater food value than the original grain seed.

For example, after just 72 hours of being sprouted, the vitamin B complex in sprouted wheat increases many times than before sprouting, vitamin E content and vitamin C both increase significantly. At the same time, starches are broken down into maltose, which is a natural form of simple sugar that can easily be converted by the body into energy. Proteins are also broken down to be easier for the body to use. So sprouted grains not only contain more vitamins, minerals and protein than regular grains, they also contain them in more usable forms.

Surprisingly, the idea of sprouting grains is not really new. For thousands of years, sprouted foods have been used in China and the Middle East. The Essene Gospel of Peace says, "...moisten your wheat, that the angel of water may enter it...and the blessing...will soon make the germ of life to sprout."

We search the World for the Finest Ingredients.

At Health Valley, we search the world for the finest ingredients for all our products. For example, we get spices such as sweet cinnamon from far away Sri Lanka, curry from India, and ginger from China. We get herbs such as paprika from Hungary, saffron from Spain, and rosemary from Italy.

The apricots we use in many of our baking products are from the land of the Hunzas, the remote mountain tribe that lives longer than any other people on earth. These sweet, succulent apricots are organically grown in the cool mountain air of the Hunza Valley, where pesticides are unknown, and where the fruit is allowed to reach perfect ripeness on the tree.

Our peanut butter is made with a choice blend of the finest peanuts including the rare and costly Valencia peanuts. The apple juice we use to sweeten many products is from Northern Italy, because American apples are too high in acid for this purpose. And when we were searching for Amaranth grain, we journeyed as far as Africa and India before locating the quality of Amaranth we wanted in Mexico.

No effort or cost are spared in producing the finest foods we can offer. That is the reason why Health Valley products sometimes cost a few cents more, but isn't it worth a few extra pennies to get the finest, healthiest foods available? And you never have anything to lose when you try any Health Valley product, because every one of our foods and beverages carries our unique total guarantee.

No other food company backs up their products with such a comprehensive full guarantee like we do.

Health Valley's Total Guarantee

If you are not satisfied with the freshness, quality or taste of any Health Valley product, send us the boxtop with the freshness code date showing and the reason for dissatisfaction, together with your cash register receipt for a replacement or full refund.

Health Valley Is the Only Food Company that Features the "Wonder Grain" Called Amaranth.

Many Health Valley products offer you a special nutritional bonus in the form of a grain that most of the world has not had access to for 400 years. It is called "Amaranth" and its nutritional properties make it truly a "wonder grain."

Consider the fact that Amaranth contains the highest quality protein of any grain on earth. On top of that, Amaranth is a better source of calcium than cow's milk, and it is a rich source of other essential vitamins and minerals. Amaranth contains 3 to 4 times more fiber than most other grains. In fact, Amaranth is such a "life giving" food that the last civilization to cultivate it widely, the ancient Aztecs, were actually willing to risk their lives to grow it.

The special nutritional benefits Amaranth offers you.

Amaranth is a key part of the Health Valley product line because there is no other grain like it. It provides the same kind of high quality protein found in meat and dairy foods, but without the fat, cholesterol and calories.

To understand what a nutritional storehouse Amaranth is, let us compare it to wheat. To begin with, the "germ" of any seed is its nutritional essence, where most of its nutrients are packed. About 50% of the Amaranth grain is the "germ," compared to only about 2½% in wheat.

Amaranth is also an outstanding source of high quality protein. Amaranth seeds contain 16% protein, compared to 12% to 14% for wheat, and 7% to 10% for rice.

But equally important to the amount of protein found in Amaranth is the quality of that protein. That's because protein is comprised of amino acids. Eight of these amino acids are considered to be "essential" because the body cannot synthesize them and must get them from food sources. Most grains do not contain the proper balance of all eight amino acids to provide "complete" protein. Generally, grains lack adequate levels of one or more amino acids, most notably "lysine."

Amaranth is unique among grains in that it is an abundant source of lysine. In fact, its balance of amino acids is actually superior to that of milk or soybeans.

To give you an idea of the quality of protein in Amaranth, here is a comparison:

PROTEIN SCORES (100 PERFECT)

Amaranth	75	Wheat	56.9
Cow's milk	72.2	Peanuts	52
Soybeans	68	Corn	44

A protein score of 100 means that *all* of the protein in the food is usable by the body. No single food is perfect, but combining foods can lift the score to be closer to ideal. That's why Health Valley always combines Amaranth with wheat or other grains, so that the combination provides protein that is as high in quality as that found in meat, without all the fat and cholesterol.

161

Amaranth is also an outstanding source of a nutrient often lacking in our diets — calcium. In fact, Aztec mothers made a milk from Amaranth and fed it to their babies. Today, we know that 3½ ounces of Amaranth contains more calcium than a glass of milk.

What is equally important, the protein, calcium, vitamins and minerals in Amaranth are easy for your body to assimilate and utilize efficiently. And Amaranth does not produce the allergic reactions that many people have to other grains.

Finally, Amaranth is also a rich source of fiber, offering 3 to 4 times more fiber than most other grains.

Why Amaranth is considered to be the most important food discovery of the 20th century.

Health Valley is very gratified to be able to contribute to the re-discovery and propagation of Amaranth. As the very first company to ever produce foods made with Amaranth, Health Valley is especially pleased by the fact that such prominent food authorities as the National Academy of Sciences and the U.S. Department of Agriculture are actively promoting Amaranth and consider it to be the most important "new" food of the century. Because it is such an excellent source of protein, and because it is such a drought-resistant plant, Amaranth is one of the most promising foods available to help end world hunger, and also improve the nutritional quality of the diet for people worldwide.

Health Valley is pleased to acknowledge the efforts of other organizations that have also contributed to the promotion of Amaranth, including our friends at the Rodale Press, who have contributed such valuable research and promoted Amaranth through their publications.

Why the Aztecs were willing to die for Amaranth.

Since Amaranth is such a "super food," you may be wondering why you are just beginning to hear about it. The answer can be found in Amaranth's colorful history.

Amaranth was once the most widely cultivated and consumed grain in all of Mexico. The ancient Aztecs literally worshipped this tiny grain seed because they believed it was the source of prolonged life and vitality. Amaranth was so cherished that the Aztecs offered their ruler, Montezuma 200,000 bushels of Amaranth every year as tribute.

When the Spanish under the leadership of Cortez conquered Mexico, they realized that Amaranth was not only the foundation of the Aztec diet. It was also the mystical center of their culture.

In order to break the will of the Aztecs, Cortez decreed that anyone caught growing it would be put to death. The Aztecs defied his law and continued growing Amaranth in secret because of its incredible life-giving properties. Although Cortez did not succeed in eliminating Amaranth altogether, he did manage to suppress it to the point that it was virtually "lost" for 400 years.

How Health Valley became the first company ever to use Amaranth in its products.

George Mateljan, the president and founder of Health Valley, realizes that no single food contains all the nutrients the human body needs. So, he is constantly searching for new foods and new ways to improve the nutritional quality of the foods we already have.

During one of his many trips around the world, George found descendants of the ancient Aztecs growing Amaranth in the deepest, most remote regions of Mexico.Cortez had done such a thorough job of stamping out Amaranth that these were the only places in Mexico where it was still grown.

When George confirmed that Amaranth is indeed a "super grain" that contains a storehouse of vital nutrients, he made special arrangements with the descendants of the Aztecs. The farmers would hand tend Amaranth from the original seeds to ensure that the Amaranth he brought back had the same nutritional properties of Amaranth seeds that were unearthed from ancient pyramids. Amazingly, these seeds would still grow after hundreds of years.

The first product George made with Amaranth was Amaranth Cereal. Then came Amaranth Graham Crackers, Whole Wheat Pasta with Amaranth, and Amaranth Cookies. Public acceptance of these products was so enthusiastic that George has added Amaranth to many of his cereals and other grain products, including fruit bars. Nowhere is the "super food" called Amaranth so widely, nutritionally and flavorfully used as at Health Valley.

The Special Benefits of Health Valley Foods.

Are you or a member of your family on a special diet? Then, you will be pleased to know that Health Valley makes many products with you in mind. Along with our constant attention to making products that are high in nutrition and fiber, low in fat, cholesterol and sodium, there are a variety of Health Valley products that are:

- Wheat free, and gluten free
- Whey free, and lactose free
- Made without any added sugar
- Low in calories

In the product list that follows, you will find that each category includes the ingredients, sodium and calories for one or more products within that category. In this way, you can get a good idea of which of our foods fit your own particular needs.

We think you'll be pleasantly surprised by how many Health Valley foods you can use. So, please read all about the products—and enjoy them in good health.

Health Valley Makes Healthier Foods You Can Really Enjoy

Health Valley Instead of Salt®
All Purpose Herb Seasoning

Every great cuisine throughout the world uses zesty herbs and fragrant spices to add flavor, color and aroma to foods. This exciting herb blend lets you season foods like a master chef, without using any salt. I experimented with literally thousands of herb and spice blends before perfecting Instead of Salt. This is probably the most versatile herb seasoning blend you will ever find. You can use it in all kinds of cooking, and at the table too in place of the salt shaker.

Ingredients for Instead of Salt® All-Purpose: NATURAL HERBS AND SPICES. PARSLEY FLAKES, OREGANO, ONION FLAKES, SESAME SEEDS, GARLIC POWDER, MINT, LEMON CRYSTALS, CELERY, CELERY SEED, BAY LEAF, CARROT, DILL SEED, THYME, MUSTARD, BASIL, MARJORAM, TOMATO, CORIANDER, ROSEMARY, PAPAIN.

Sodium: 5 mg. per ½ teaspoon serving
Calories: 2 per ½ teaspoon serving

Health Valley Chicken Broth.

Here is all the rich flavor of real broth simmered slowly to bring out the essence of savory chicken. Serve this broth as a light soup to start a meal, and be sure to use it in cooking. You can sauté poultry and vegetables to a luscious golden brown in broth, instead of using butter or oil. Another great idea is to use broth instead of water in preparing rice, or as the liquid in stews for an added flavor dimension. Or use it to poach fish so it's at its moist, flavorful best. No MSG, and just 4 milligrams of cholesterol per serving. Available with 40% less salt or No Salt Added.

Ingredients for No Salt Chicken Broth: CHICKEN BROTH, CHICKEN FAT, HONEY, ONION POWDER, SPICE EXTRACTIVES OF TURMERIC AND OTHER NATURAL SPICES.

No Salt Chicken Broth Sodium Content: 55 mg. per 4 oz. serving
Calories: 15 per 4 oz. serving

Health Valley Soups.

A welcome way to start any meal is with a steaming bowl of soup that is thick with garden vegetables and tender chunks of meat, seafood or grains. Now you can enjoy the hearty flavors of real homestyle soups without the hours of cooking because Health Valley makes soups the healthy way. That means using fresh ingredients and simmering them slowly in smaller kettles. We don't use MSG, sugar or cornstarch, and we pack our soups in enamel lined lead free cans for your protection. Available with 40% less salt or No Salt Added.

Regular soups are Vegetable, Bean, Clam Chowder, Lentil, Minestrone, Mushroom, Split Pea, Potato, Beef Broth, and Tomato. Chunky soups are Chunky Vegetable, Chunky Minestrone, and Chunky Vegetable Chicken.

Ingredients for No Salt Vegetable Soup: WATER, CARROTS, GREEN BEANS, CABBAGE, TOMATO PASTE, POTATOES, OLIVE OIL, DRIED POTATOES, PEARL BARLEY, BABY LIMA BEANS, KIDNEY BEANS, TOMATOES, GREEN PEAS, SWISS CHARD, ONION POWDER, DRIED CELERY, PARSLEY, NATURAL SPICES & HERBS.

No Salt Vegetable Soup Sodium Content: 30 mg. per 4 oz serving.
Calories: 60 per 4 oz. serving

Ingredients for No Salt Tomato Soup: WATER, TOMATO PASTE, OLIVE OIL, HONEY, DRIED POTATOES, ONION POWDER, LEMON JUICE, GARLIC POWDER, NATURAL SPICES & HERBS.

No Salt Tomato Soup Sodium Content: 30 mg. per 4 oz. serving
Calories: 50 per 4 oz. serving

Health Valley Pastas.

Our pasta is made from durum wheat, the extra hard, high protein, northern wheat with the special crisp texture necessary to make the finest pasta. It's much better than the much advertised semolina flour, which is actually white flour made by removing the bran and wheat germ from good whole grain durum wheat. We take this exceptional wheat and add seven whole grains that have been sprouted to provide even more flavor and balanced nutrition.

Seven varieties are available: Pasta Spaghetti, Spaghetti with Spinach, Lasagna, Lasagna with Spinach, Elbow Pasta, Elbow Pasta with 4 Vegetables and Amaranth Spaghetti Pasta.

Ingredients for Whole Wheat Spinach Pasta: ORGANICALLY GROWN WHOLE WHEAT FLOUR, WHEAT GERM, SEVEN SPROUTED WHOLE GRAINS (WHEAT, BARLEY, AMARANTH, OATS, BUCKWHEAT, RYE, MILLET) DRY SPINACH.

Sodium Content: 10 mg. per 2 oz. serving
Calories: 170 per 2 oz. serving.

Health Valley Tomato Sauce.

Here is all the rich, tangy flavor of plump, red, field-ripened tomatoes captured in a thick, delicious tomato sauce. It's seasoned with just the right touch of herbs and spices and simmered slowly in small batches so none of the flavor or nutrition are lost. Unlike most commercial brands, this tomato sauce contains no added sugar, citric acid, preservatives or anything artificial. A wonderful time-saver when used in soups, casseroles and many other recipes. Available with 40% less salt or No Salt Added, and packed in electronically sealed and enamel lined cans that are lead-free.

Ingredients for No Salt Tomato Sauce: TOMATOES (WATER, TOMATO PASTE), NATURAL SPICES AND HERBS.

No Salt Tomato Sauce Sodium Content: 35 mg. per 4 oz. serving
Calories: 25 per 4 oz. serving

Health Valley Chilis.

Will Rogers called chili the "bowl of blessedness" because a hearty bowl of chili is both flavorful and satisfying, and packed with important nutrients. We make our chili with plump, tender beans and just the right blend of zesty chili powder and other spices so the flavor is lively, but not too hot. Contrary to what some people believe, beans are not fattening and when cooked properly, they do not have to cause gastric distress. We make both <u>mild</u> and <u>spicy Vegetarian Chili</u>, either salted or with No Salt Added. We also make <u>Chili Con Carne</u> and our own unique <u>Chili with Lentils</u>.

Ingredients for No Salt Spicy Vegetarian Chili: WATER, BEANS, SOY GRANULES, OLIVE OIL, TOMATO PASTE, CHILI POWDER (NATURAL SPICES AND HERBS), DRIED POTATOES, MOLASSES, ONION POWDER, GARLIC POWDER, PAPRIKA, CAYENNE.

No Salt Spicy Vegetarian Chili Sodium Content: 25 mg. per 4 oz. serving
Calories: 170 per 4 oz. serving.

Amaranth Minute Meal.™

Here's a new kind of pilaf that you simply heat and enjoy in 3 minutes. It's more than a side dish because it's made with high protein Amaranth grain combined with other nutritious grains and vegetables for a nutritionally superior vegetarian entree. And there are four exciting recipes on the label. Available with 40% less salt or with No Salt Added.

Ingredients for No Salt Amaranth Minute Meal: WATER, WHOLE GRAINS (AMARANTH, OATS, BROWN RICE, PEARL BARLEY, RYE), CARROTS, SOY GRANULES, GREEN PEAS, DRIED POTATOES, TOMATO PASTE, OLIVE OIL, BABY LIMA BEANS, DRIED ONIONS, NATURAL SPICES AND HERBS, PARSLEY, DRIED GARLIC.

No Salt Amaranth Minute Meal Sodium Content: 15 mg. per 4 oz. serving
Calories: 70 per 4 oz. serving

Amaranth Flakes Cereal.

This is the first flaked cereal made with Amaranth which is rich in calcium and fiber, and contains the highest quality protein of any grain on earth. These are light, crisp, ready-to-eat flakes that are sweetened with fruit juice for delicious flavor without any added sugar. They're salt-free and wheat-free too!

Ingredients: OATS, OAT BRAN, AMARANTH, CONCENTRATED FRUIT JUICES (APPLE, PINEAPPLE), BROWN RICE FLOUR, RYE FLOUR, CORN FLOUR, MALTED BARLEY.

Sodium Content: 10 mg. per 1 oz. serving
Calories: 110 per 1 oz. serving

166

Health Valley Amaranth Cereal.

Hundreds of years ago, the ancient Aztecs worshipped Amaranth, a tiny golden grain seed which grew on majestic crimson stalks. It was sacred food and they called it "the grain of the Gods," because they believed it contained the secret to prolonged life and vitality. When Cortez conquered Mexico, he decreed that anyone caught growing Amaranth would be put to death. And so, this grain was lost for 400 years until Health Valley re-discovered its fabulous qualities. Today, modern science recognizes that Amaranth has the best quality protein of any grain. It is high in lysine, an essential amino acid lacking in most grains. We take advantage of Amaranth's delicate nutty flavor and balanced protein, and blend it with other sprouted whole grains for a deliciously crunchy cereal sweetened with fruit and nuts, but no sugar or salt. Amaranth is available with <u>Bananas</u>, or wheat-free Amaranth Crunch™ with Raisins.

Ingredients for Amaranth with Bananas: SPROUTED WHOLE GRAINS, WHEAT, BARLEY, AMARANTH, BANANA FLAKES, ALMONDS, PINEAPPLE, PAPAYA, OATS, BUCKWHEAT, RYE, MILLET, BRAN, AND ORANGE OIL.

Sodium Content: 5 mg. per 1 oz. serving
Calories: 110 per 1 oz. serving

Fiber 7™ Flakes Cereal.

Different kinds of fiber provide different healthy benefits. Fiber 7 is the only cereal anywhere that contains not only wheat bran and oat bran but also fiber from the seven most nutritious grains in the world. Fiber 7 tastes great too because the grains are sprouted for lightness, and sweetened with real fruit juices.

Ingredients: 100% SPROUTED WHOLE WHEAT, CONCENTRATED FRUIT JUICES (APPLE, PINEAPPLE), WHEAT BRAN, OAT BRAN, SPROUTED WHOLE GRAINS: OATS, BARLEY, RYE, AMARANTH, BUCKWHEAT AND CORN.

Sodium Content: 15 mg. per 1 oz. serving
Calories: 100 per 1 oz. serving

Oat Bran Flakes Cereal.

Oats have always been known for their high nutritional content, and now medical research indicates that oat bran may reduce cholesterol too. Here's the first cereal with all the healthy benefits of oat bran packed into light, crisp, delicious flakes that are sweetened with fruit juices instead of sugar. Available <u>Plain</u>, or <u>with Raisins</u>, or <u>with Almonds & Dates</u>.

Ingredients for Oat Bran Flakes: ROLLED OATS, OAT BRAN, CONCENTRATED FRUIT JUICES (APPLE, PINEAPPLE), BROWN RICE FLOUR, RYE FLOUR, CORN FLOUR, MALTED BARLEY.

Sodium Content: 10 mg. per 1 oz. serving
Calories: 110 per 1 oz. serving

Fruit Lites™ Cereal.

Here's a cereal with only 45 calories in a serving, that can help you stay slim and look good. Each variety is made with whole grains that have been sweetened with fruit juice, so there's no shortage on flavor. You have a choice of Golden Wheat, Brown Rice, or Golden Corn.

Ingredients for Golden Wheat Fruit Lites: 100% WHOLE RED WHEAT, CONCEN-TRATED FRUIT JUICES (APPLE, PINEAPPLE, GRAPE AND PEAR).

Sodium Content: 2 mg. per ½ oz. serving
Calories: 45 per ½ oz. serving

Health Valley Bran Cereal.

There's no better way to start the day than with a bowl of this crisp, crunchy flavorful Bran. It's the most popular cereal Health Valley makes, and the best bran cereal you can buy. That's because we use miller's bran, which is the best kind, as well as the choicest parts of the wheat. So this cereal is rich in beneficial fiber and has a satisfying nutty flavor. It's available with Raisins, or Apples and Cinnamon.

Ingredients for Bran with Raisins Cereal: WHEAT BRAN WITH OTHER PARTS OF WHEAT KERNEL, SPROUTED WHEAT, SPROUTED BARLEY, RAISINS.

Sodium Content: 5 mg. per 1 oz. serving
Calories: 70 per 1 oz. serving

Health Valley Real® Cereal.

Start the day with the bright flavor of a cereal filled with the sweetness of real fruit and the crunch of nuts. Here is a cereal that really deserves to be called "Real" because it's made the way real cereal should be made. That means we use whole grains and real fruit, and no added salt, refined white sugar or saturated fats, such as coconut or palm oil. Try Real cereal with the lush flavors of real Hawaiian Fruit, Almond Crunch, or Raisin Nut.

Ingredients for Real® Cereal with Hawaiian Fruit: ROLLED OATS, OAT BRAN, PURE HONEY, WHOLE WHEAT FLAKES, AMARANTH, SOY OIL, DRIED PINE-APPLE, DRIED PAPAYA, BANANA FLAKES, UNSULFURED MOLASSES, WHEAT GERM, ALMONDS, PURE VANILLA, ORANGE OIL.

Sodium Content: 5 mg. per 1 oz. serving
Calories: 110 per 1 oz. serving

Health Valley makes 35 delicious varieties of cereal for all kinds of tastes, including whole grain flaked cereals, Healthy Crunch™ wheat-free cereals, Lites® puffed cereals, Hot Oat Bran, unique Orangeola® and Sprouts 7® multi-grain cereal. Try several, and start every day on a bright, healthy note.

Health Valley Stoned Wheat Crackers.

Bite into one of these delicious snack crackers and enjoy the crisp texture and wonderful hearty flavor of 100% whole wheat. These crackers are made a whole new way—a way that professional bakers told us couldn't be done—without white flour, sugar, or hydrogenated shortening. They're so flavorful and nutritious that you can use them in place of bread, because, after all, crackers were actually the first form of bread—and ours have very much the same nutrition as whole wheat bread. Try stoned wheat crackers and discover why there are just no others like them.

Ingredients for No Salt Stoned Wheat Crackers: 100% WHOLE WHEAT FLOUR, SAFFLOWER OIL, CRACKED WHEAT, MALT, YEAST.

No Salt Stoned Wheat Crackers Sodium Content: 15 mg. per 1 oz. serving
  (approx. 13 crackers)
Calories: 120 per 1 oz. serving

Health Valley Herb Crackers.

Here are crackers with the extra zesty flavors of real herbs. So they're delicious all by themselves, and they're also convenient to use in recipes. For example, when you crumble them up, they make a wonderful flavorful breading for fish or chicken because the herbs are already blended in.

Ingredients for No Salt Herb Crackers: 100% WHOLE WHEAT FLOUR, SAF-FLOWER OIL, MALT, CRACKED WHEAT, GARLIC, ONION, CARROT, YEAST, TOMATO, CELERY, CHILI, SWEET BASIL, PARSLEY, SAVORY, THYME, OREGANO, DILL.

No Salt Herb Crackers Sodium Content: 110 mg. per 1 oz. serving (approx. 13 crackers)
Calories: 120 per 1 oz. serving

There are six different varieties of Health Valley Crackers, including Stoned Wheat, Herb, Sesame, 7-Grain Vegetable, French Onion, and Cheese Wheels.™ They're all available with 40% less salt, and all but Cheese Wheels are available with No Salt Added. Also available are Honey Graham Crackers.

Amaranth Graham Crackers.

It's almost as if high fiber graham flour and high protein Amaranth grain were made for each other. Together, they produce the best tasting graham cracker ever—delicately nutty and delicious, and highly nutritious. The whole family loves them for snacking, dunking in milk or tea, and even crumbled in soup and on salads.

Ingredients: 100% WHOLE WHEAT FLOUR, AMARANTH FLOUR, GRAHAM FLOUR, PURE HONEY, CONCENTRATED FRUIT JUICES (PEAR, PINEAPPLE), SOYBEAN OIL, SOY LECITHIN, UNSULFURED MOLASSES, PURE VANILLA, BAKING SODA, SALT.

Sodium Content: 45 mg. per 3 cracker serving
Calories: 50 per 3 cracker serving

169

Health Valley Fruit Lovin's™ **Animal Snaps.**™ These thinner cookies taste scrumptious without any bleached white flour, sugar, salt, or hydrogenated shortening. Cinnamon or Vanilla, sweetened with fruits and fruit juice.

Cinnamon Animal Snaps Sodium Content: 5 mg. per cookie
Calories: 10 per cookie

Apple Bakes,® **Date Bakes**® **and Raisin Bakes**® are moist, chewy, nutritious snack bars baked with real fruit and nuts, and without any added salt, white sugar, hydrogenated shortening or preservatives. They're more than just a snack, they're a natural pick-me-up.

Ingredients for Apple Bakes®: 100% WHOLE WHEAT FLOUR, APPLESAUCE, HONEY, DATES, RAISINS, SOYBEAN OIL, UNSULFURED MOLASSES, OATS, ALMONDS, AMARANTH, SOY LECITHIN, WHEAT GERM, NATURAL SPICES, NATURAL FLAVORS, BAKING SODA.

Apple Bakes Sodium Content: 35 mg. per 2 bars
Calories: 170 per 2 bars

Health Valley Potato Chips. Now you can enjoy snacks again in a healthy diet. We use only the highest grade potatoes with the skins on to retain maximum flavor and nutrition. We simmer them in pure sunflower and safflower oils, highest in polyunsaturates – we never use cottonseed or palm oils or blends with chemical antioxidants added, as some others do. And, we salt them lightly with 40% less salt than others, and they're also available with No Salt Added. Choose from Natural Potato Chips, Dip Chips. new Country Chips® which are a thicker cut potato chip, and new Country Ripples® which are a rippled snacking chip.

Ingredients for No Salt Country Chips and Country Ripples: FRESH WHOLE POTATOES WITH THE SKINS LEFT ON, SAFFLOWER AND SUNFLOWER OILS.

No Salt Potato Chips Sodium Content: 1 mg. per 1 oz. serving
Calories: 160 per 1 oz. serving

Buenitos™ **Tortilla Chips with Amaranth.** There have never been tortilla chips like this before – they're the only ones made with high protein Amaranth, the "super grain" of the Aztecs. We combine Amaranth with golden corn, so they're high in nutrition, fiber and flavor. They're light, crunchy and delicious – and they're available with 40% less salt, or No Salt Added. Also available with Nacho Cheese & Chili.

Ingredients for No Salt Buenitos: STONEGROUND CORN, SAFFLOWER AND SUNFLOWER OIL, AMARANTH.

No Salt Buenitos Sodium Content: 5 mg. per 1 oz. serving
Calories: 130 per 1 oz. serving

170

Health Valley Corn Chips. We form our chips from stoneground whole corn and gently simmer them in sunflower and safflower oils, the two oils that are highest in polyunsaturates and lowest in saturated fats. Seasoned with 40% less salt or No Salt Added, they're also available with <u>Cheese</u>.

Ingredients for No Salt Corn Chips: STONEGROUND CORN, SAFFLOWER AND SUNFLOWER OILS.

No Salt Corn Chips Sodium Content: 1 mg. per 1 oz. serving
Calories: 160 per 1 oz. serving

Cheddar Lites.™ They're lighter in calories, lighter in salt than other puffed snacks—yet they're the tangiest, most scrumptious cheese puffs you've ever tasted. That's because they're made with succulent yellow corn and real aged cheddar cheese. They're baked not fried so they contain only 2 calories per puff, and we season them with 40% less salt. Also available Low Sodium.

Ingredients for Low Sodium Cheddar Lites™: YELLOW CORN MEAL, SAFFLOWER OIL, SUNFLOWER OIL, NATURALLY AGED CHEDDAR CHEESE (MILK, VEGE-TABLE ENZYMES, ANNATTO [VEGETABLE COLORING], SALT).

Low Sodium Cheddar Lites Sodium Content: 10 mg. per ¼ oz. serving
Calories: 40 per ¼ oz. serving

NEW! Cheddar Lites with Green Onions. A new zesty taste of tangy green onions plus lots of naturally aged cheddar cheese.

Carrot Lites.™
  They're light, they're crisp, they're delicious—and there are only 2 little calories in each puff! A single serving of Carrot Lites provides you with 500 IU of Vitamin A, which is important for good health and good looking skin. No salt, or anything artificial.

Ingredients: YELLOW CORN MEAL, SAFFLOWER OIL, SUNFLOWER OIL, DRIED CARROTS, CARROT OIL, CINNAMON.

Sodium Content: 10 mg. per ½ oz. serving
Calories: 60 per ½ oz. serving

Health Valley Baby Cereal.

Get your child started eating the healthy way by making baby's first solid food Health Valley Baby Cereal. They're made from whole grains so they contain the valuable germ and bran. No added salt or sugar, and no artificial ingredients of any kind. Two varieties: Brown Rice and Sprouted.

Ingredients for Brown Rice Baby Cereal: 100% WHOLE GRAIN BROWN RICE, MALTED BARLEY, DRIED BANANAS.

Sodium Content: 5 mg. per ½ ounce serving
Calories: 60 per ½ ounce serving

Fruit Jumbos® Cookies.

Fruit Jumbos are everything you've been looking for in a cookie. They're light and crisp, with the full fresh flavors of luscious fruit and natural fruit juices...and without any added sugar! There's no white flour, no butter or added salt. Three scrumptious varieties: Tropical Fruit, Raisin Nut, and Almond Date.

Ingredients for Fruit Jumbos with Tropical Fruit: 100% WHOLE WHEAT FLOUR, CONCENTRATED FRUIT JUICES (APPLE, PINEAPPLE), SOYBEAN OIL, OATS, PAPAYA CHUNKS, ALMONDS, AMARANTH, ORANGE, SOY FLOUR, NATURAL FLAVORS, SOY LECITHIN, BAKING SODA.

Fruit Jumbos Tropical Fruit Sodium Content: 35 mg. per jumbo cookie
Calories: 70 per jumbo cookie

Oat Bran Fruit Jumbos® Cookies.

Our newest Fruit Jumbos are made with oat bran, which research indicates may reduce serum cholesterol. They also have the tangy freshness of organically grown apricots for full fruit flavor, so they're delicious as well as healthy.

Ingredients for Oat Bran Fruit Jumbos: 100% WHOLE WHEAT FLOUR, OAT BRAN, CONCENTRATED FRUIT JUICES (APPLE, PINEAPPLE, PEARS, GRAPES), SOYBEAN OIL, OATS, APRICOTS, NATURAL FLAVORS, SOY LECITHIN, BAKING SODA.

Sodium Content: 35 mg. per jumbo cookie
Calories: 80 per jumbo cookie

The Great Tofu Cookie.™

Now you can enjoy a high energy cookie that makes tofu taste great! It's moist and chewy, and sweetened with real fruit juice. It's high performance food because it's made with protein-rich tofu – and without animal fats, cholesterol, wheat, added sugar or salt. But you really have to taste these cookies to realize how scrumptious they are. There are no other cookies like this.

Ingredients: BARLEY FLOUR, NATURAL FRUIT & FRUIT JUICES OF PEACHES, PINEAPPLE, APPLES AND PEARS, TOFU, OATS, SOYBEAN OIL, SOY LECITHIN, PURE VANILLA, BAKING SODA.

Sodium Content: 80 mg. per 4 cookie serving
Calories: 130 per 4 cookie serving

Health Valley Soy Moo® Non-Dairy Soy Drink.

Soy Moo is a smooth, creamy soy beverage that tastes very much like milk, so it's delicious on cereal, with cookies, or straight out of the carton. It's made from soybeans with no cholesterol, no animal fat, no lactose, and no preservatives.

Best of all, you can store it in the refrigerator for weeks, even months, before opening it and it will still be fresh.

Ingredients: SPRING WATER, DEHULLED SOYBEANS, MALTED BARLEY, FRUIT JUICES, DULSE (SEA VEGETABLE), VANILLA.

Sodium Content: 50 mg. per 8 oz. serving
Calories: 120 per 8 oz. serving

Other Health Valley Products You Should Look For.

Health Valley makes over 200 products. Each is made to the highest standards of quality, flavor and good nutrition. Some of these products are readily available, while others are usually found only in well-stocked health food stores or natural foods ranch markets, and specialty stores.

Health Valley Frozen Vegetables. Frozen vegetables are not all alike. These are very special Grade A vegetables, grown on the fertile west slope of California's San Joaquin Valley. Once the bed of an ancient lake, this valley is enriched with minerals and blessed with the West's finest topsoil. The legendary vegetables that spring from this sunny region are picked at the height of their season and frozen moments afterward to preserve their delicious flavor and important nutrients. Fresh tasting varieties include: Broccoli Spears. French Cut Green Beans, Baby Lima Beans, Mixed Vegetables, Whole Kernel Corn, Peas, and Chopped Spinach.

Broccoli Sodium Content: 20 mg. per 3½ oz. serving
Calories: 25 per 3½ oz. serving.

Lean Living™ Frozen Meals are unique because they're low in calories, and they're prepared with no added salt or refined sugar. Our secret is to make every calorie count. Each bite is rich with the flavor and goodness of natural ingredients like vegetables, cheese and whole grains so they satisfy your appetite, instead of filling you up with calories from sugar, fillers and extenders you find in so many commercial dinners. They're all under 390 calories and they come in 4 delicious varieties: Spinach Lasagna. Cheese Enchiladas, Chicken Crepes Marco Polo, and Chicken a la King.

Ingredients for Spinach Lasagna: TOMATOES, 100% WHOLE WHEAT LASAGNA NOODLES, TOMATO SAUCE, HOOP CHEESE, ONIONS, SPINACH, RICOTTA CHEESE, CHICKEN STOCK, ZUCCHINI, EGG WHITES, APPLE JUICE CONCENTRATE, MUSHROOMS, CELERY, GREEN PEPPERS, NATURAL HERBS AND SPICES, UNSALTED BUTTER, WATER, GARLIC, PAPRIKA, DRIED GARLIC.

Spinach Lasagna Sodium Content: 70 mg. per 9 oz. serving
Calories: 170 per 9 oz. serving

Best of Seafood® frozen fish from cold, unpolluted northern waters include: <u>Alaskan Fish Fillets</u>, <u>Alaskan Fish Sticks</u>, <u>Alaskan Halibut Steak</u>, <u>Alaskan Salmon Steak</u> and <u>Boned Trout</u>.

Canned Tuna. Big, solid chunks of fish in vegetable broth, not oil. Available with 40% less salt, or No Salt Added.

Ingredients for No Salt Tuna: SOLID WHITE TUNA PACKED IN WATER AND VEGETABLE BROTH.

No Salt Tuna Sodium Content: 115 mg. per 6½ oz. can
Calories: 200 per 6½ oz. can

Fruit Coolers. Coolers are sweeping the country, but these are the first that truly fit today's lighter, vital, healthier lifestyles. They're light, delicious, sparkling and refreshing with the fresh flavors of pure fruit juice and effervescent sparkling spring water – there's no alcohol, sugar, or anything artificial added. Three tempting varieties: <u>Wild Berry</u>, <u>Cranberry Apple</u>, and <u>Black Cherry</u>.

Ingredients for Black Cherry Cooler: SPARKLING SPRING WATER, BLACK CHERRY AND GRAPE JUICE CONCENTRATES, NATURAL FLAVOR.

Black Cherry Cooler Sodium Content: 15 mg. per 6 oz. serving
Calories: 67 per 6 oz. serving

Health Valley Boston Baked Style Beans. Now you can enjoy the most delicious baked beans, yet they contain no refined white sugar or meat. Sweetened with honey and molasses for a real slow-cooked baked bean flavor. Available with 40% less salt or No Added Salt, and packed in electronically sealed and enamel lined cans that are lead free. For a different kind of treat, try <u>Vegetarian Baked Beans with Miso</u>, that gets its deep, rich flavor from miso which is an intensely flavored soybean paste.

Ingredients for No Salt Boston Baked Style Beans: WATER, BEANS, UNSUL- FURED MOLASSES, DRIED POTATOES, TOMATO PASTE, HONEY, ONION POWDER, NATURAL SPICES AND HERBS.

No Salt Boston Baked Style Beans Sodium Content: 25 mg. per 4 oz. serving
Calories: 110 per 4 oz. serving

Health Valley Peanut Butter. There can be great differences in taste and quality between peanut butters. You never tasted better peanut butter than Health Valley because ours are a blend of several top quality peanuts, including the rare and costly Valencia peanut which is incomparable in flavor. No preservatives, hydro-genated oils, emulsifiers or sugar, which you find in many peanut butters. Available in <u>Creamy</u> or <u>Chunky</u>, with 40% less salt or No Salt Added.

Ingredients for No Salt Peanut Butter: UNBLANCHED, LIGHTLY ROASTED PEANUTS INCLUDING THE BENEFICIAL SKINS, BRAN AND GERM, IT IS A MOST DELICIOUS BLEND OF PEANUTS FEATURING SUN DRIED VALENCIA PEANUTS.

No Salt Peanut Butter Sodium Content: 1 mg. per tablespoon
Calories: 80 per tablespoon

Health Valley Pancake & Biscuit Mix. Most mixes are just white flour, baking powder and salt. If you want good hearty whole grain pancakes, biscuits, muffins and waffles, try this. It's made with seven different whole grains that have been sprouted for lightness, digestibility, added nutrition and flavor. And the grains feature Amaranth, the mystical high protein grain of the ancient Aztecs. Nine sensational recipes on the package.

Ingredients: 100% WHOLE WHEAT FLOUR, SPROUTED GRAINS (WHEAT, BARLEY, AMARANTH, OATS, BUCKWHEAT, MILLET, RYE), CULTURED DRY BUTTERMILK, CREAM OF TARTAR, BAKING SODA.

Sodium Content: 170 mg. per 1 oz. serving
Calories: 100 per 4 oz. serving

Tofu-Ya® Tofu is made the traditional way with organic soybeans, natural nigari and pure water. It's a superfood because it's high in protein, low in sodium, calories and saturated fats, and contains no cholesterol. Choose Firm or Soft.

Ingredients for Tofu-Ya: ORGANICALLY GROWN SOYBEANS, PURIFIED WATER, NATURAL NIGARI (BITTERNS FROM SEA WATER).

Sodium Content: 10 mg. per 4 oz. serving
Calories: 100 per 4 oz. serving

Catch-Up.™ Most catsup contains at least 20% sugar, while ours is sweetened with honey. Rich, ripe tomato flavor and NO VINEGAR! Available Salted or No Salt Added.

Ingredients for No Salt Catch-Up: RED RIPE TOMATOES, WATER, HONEY, AND NATURAL SEASONINGS.

No Salt Catch-Up Sodium Content: 70 mg. per tablespoon
Calories: 15 per tablespoon

Mustard. Made with three different kinds of mustard seeds and herbs for tangy flavor.

Ingredients for Mustard: STONE GROUND MUSTARD SEED, VINEGAR, SEA SALT, GROUND CINNAMON AND HERBS.

Sodium Content: 65 mg. per teaspoon
Calories: 5 per teaspoon

Health Valley Cookies.

Many commercial bakers said it was impossible to make a really good cookie without sugar, white flour or hydrogenated shortening, but we have perfected the "impossible" cookie. Made the way cookies were meant to be, with 100% whole wheat flour, and sweetened with pure fruit juice. Furthermore, we never use "a pinch of salt" or baking powder, yet you'll never notice it's missing. Varieties include: Peanut Butter, Raisin Oatmeal, Date Pecan and Tropical Fruit.

Ingredients for Peanut Butter Cookies: 100% WHOLE WHEAT FLOUR, CON-CENTRATED FRUIT JUICES (APPLE, PINEAPPLE), NATURAL CHUNKY PEA-NUT BUTTER, SOYBEAN OIL, ROLLED OATS, SOY FLOUR, WHEAT GERM MEAL, PURE VANILLA, BAKING SODA.

Sodium Content for Peanut Butter Cookies: 20 mg. per cookie
Calories: 40 per cookie

175

Health Valley Shopping List

SOUPS—Comes 40% less salt or no salt added
*Vegetable
*Minestrone
*Tomato
*Chicken Broth
*Lentil
*Split Pea
Mushroom
Clam Chowder
Potato
Beef Broth
Bean
Chunky Vegetable
Chunky Minestrone
Chunky Vegetable Chicken

CRACKERS—Comes 40% less salt or no salt added
*Stoned Wheat
*Sesame
*Herb
*Cheese Wheels™ (salted only)
7-Grain Vegetable
*Honey Grahams (salted only)
*Amaranth Graham (salted only)
French Onion

CONDIMENTS
Mustard
Catch-Up™
Catch-Up™ No Salt Added

COOKIES, SNAPS & BAKES—No Salt Added
*Apple Bakes® Snack Bars
*Raisin Bakes® Snack Bars
*Date Bakes® Snack Bars
Date Pecan Cookies
Raisin Oatmeal Cookies
Peanut Butter Cookies
Fruit Lovin's Cinnamon Animal Snaps™
Fruit Lovin's Vanilla Animal Snaps™
*Honey Jumbos™ Cinnamon Cookies
*Honey Jumbos™ Oatmeal Cookies
*Honey Jumbos™ Peanut Butter Cookies
*Fruit Jumbos® Cookies with Tropical Fruit
*Fruit Jumbos® Cookies Raisin Nut
*Fruit Jumbos® Cookies Almond Crunch
*Oat Bran Fruit Jumbos® Cookies
The Great Tofu Cookie™
The Great Wheat Free Cookie™
*Amaranth Cookies

CEREALS & PANCAKES—No Salt Added
*Oat Bran Flakes Cereal
*Oat Bran Flakes with Raisins
*Oat Bran Flakes with Almonds & Dates
*Amaranth Flakes Cereal
*Fiber 7™ Flakes Cereal
*Fruit Lites™ Cereal Golden Wheat
*Fruit Lites™ Cereal Brown Rice
*Fruit Lites™ Cereal Golden Corn
Swiss Breakfast® Raisin Nut
Swiss Breakfast® Tropical Fruit
Hot Oat Bran Cereal with Apples & Cinnamon
Hot Oat Bran Ceral with Raisins & Spice
*Bran with Raisins
*Bran with Apples & Cinnamon
*Sprouts 7® with Raisins
*Sprouts 7® with Bananas & Hawaiian Fruit
*Orangeola® with Almonds & Dates
*Orangeola® with Bananas & Hawaiian Fruit
*Amaranth Cereal with Bananas
Amaranth Crunch™ with Raisins
Brown Rice Lites®
Golden Wheat Lites®
Golden Corn Lites®
*Raisin Bran Flakes
Stoned Wheat Flakes
Real® Cereal Hawaiian Fruit
Real® Cereal Almond Crunch
Real® Cereal Raisin Nut
Wheat Germ & Fiber with Almonds & Dates
Wheat Germ & Fiber *
    with Bananas & Tropical Fruit
Healthy Crunch™ Almond Date
Healthy Crunch™ Apple Cinnamon
*Sprouted Baby Cereal
*Brown Rice Baby Cereal
Buttermilk Pancake & Biscuit Mix
Miller's Bran Flakes

PASTA
*Whole Wheat Spaghetti Pasta
Whole Wheat Lasagna
Spinach Spaghetti Pasta
Spinach Lasagna
*Amaranth Spaghetti
Whole Wheat Elbows
Elbows with 4 Vegetables

CANNED TUNA
Best of Seafood® Albacore Tuna
    No Salt Added
Best of Seafood® Tuna

INSTEAD OF SALT® SEASONINGS
*All Purpose

*Asterisk products are readily available in nutrition sections and low sodium centers in nutrition-conscious stores.

CHIPS — Comes 40% less salt
   or no salt added
*Corn Chips
*Potato Chips
*Dip Chips
*Cheddar Lites™ Cheese Puffs
*Cheddar Lites™ with Green Onions
Country Chips® Potato Chips
Country Ripples® Potato Chips
Corn Chips with Cheese
Buenitos™ Tortilla Chips
Carrot Lites™

CHILIS, BEANS & SAUCES — Comes
   40% less salt or no salt added
*Spicy Vegetarian Chili
*Mild Vegetarian Chili
*Lentil Chili
Vegetarian Baked Beans with Miso (salted only)
Boston Baked Beans
Tomato Sauce
Amaranth Minute Meal™
Chili Con Carne (salted only)

PEANUT BUTTER — With salt and no salt added
Chunky Peanut Butter
Creamy Peanut Butter

SODAS & COOLERS
Wild Berry Cooler
Cranberry Apple Cooler
Black Cherry Cooler

TOFU-YA® TOFU
Firm
Soft

SOY MOO® NON-DAIRY SOY DRINK
*Plain

LUNCHEON MEATS — No Nitrates
*Chicken Wieners
*Turkey Wieners
*Beef Wieners
Knockwurst
*Sliced Chicken Bologna
*Sliced Beef Bologna
Sliced Salami

BREAKFAST MEATS — No Nitrates
*Pork Bacon

CHINESE ROLLS
Egg Roll
Shrimp Roll
Nut Roll
Teriyaki Roll
Lobster Roll

FROZEN VEGETABLES
*Peas
*Mixed Vegetables
Green Beans
Broccoli Spears
Corn
Lima Beans
Chopped Spinach

LEAN LIVING™ FROZEN MEALS —
   No Salt Added Low Calorie
*Cheese Enchiladas
*Spinach Lasagna
*Chicken a la King
Chicken Crepes Marco Polo

BEST OF SEAFOOD
Alaskan Fish Sticks
Alaskan Fish Fillets

*Asterisk products are readily available in nutrition sections and low sodium centers in nutrition-conscious stores.

Health Valley Foods... Healthier Eating Benefits You Should Know

Health Valley has hundreds of products that meet or exceed the dietary guidelines issued by the leading health promoting organizations, such as the American Heart Association and the National Cancer Institute. Here are some specifics:

- **FIBER** – Over 40 products that supply *2 grams or more per serving*
- **CALCIUM** – 20 products that supply 50 milligrams or more per serving
- **VITAMIN A** – 25 products that supply 250 I.U. or more per serving
- **VITAMIN C** – 30 products that supply 3 milligrams or more per serving
- **SALT** – Every Health Valley salted product contains at least 30% less salt than similar commercial products, and over 100 Health Valley products are naturally low in sodium or contain no added salt
- **FAT** – 75 Products with 4 grams or less of fat per serving, and over 150 products with no animal fats or cholesterol

We have prepared this information to provide the facts that you want about the key nutrients in our foods. You will find it to be a handy source of valuable information.

FIBER

The National Cancer Institute recommends a daily intake of 25 to 35 grams of dietary fiber as part of an overall dietary plan to reduce the risk of some forms of cancer.

Richest Health Valley Sources of Dietary Fiber

FOUR OR MORE GRAMS PER SERVING

CEREALS

SPROUTS 7—BANANAS & HAWAIIAN FRUIT	4.70g
SPROUTS 7—RAISINS	4.70g
BRAN W/RAISINS	4.50g
BRAN W/APPLES AND CINNAMON	4.50g
AMARANTH W/BANANA	4.20g

CHILI AND BEANS

CHILI CON CARNE	10.80g
LENTIL CHILI	8.45g
VEGETARIAN BEANS W/MISO	6.53g
BOSTON BAKED BEANS	6.53g
BOSTON BAKED BEANS—NO SALT ADDED	6.53g
MILD VEGETARIAN CHILI	5.20g
MILD VEGETARIAN CHILI—NO SALT ADDED	5.20g
SPICY VEGETARIAN CHILI	5.20g
SPICY VEGETARIAN CHILI—NO SALT ADDED	5.20g

TWO TO FOUR GRAMS PER SERVING

CEREALS

RAISIN BRAN FLAKES	3.85g
STONED WHEAT FLAKES	3.85g
FIBER 7 FLAKES	3.60g

HOT OAT BRAN—APPLES AND CINNAMON	3.10g
HOT OAT BRAN—RAISINS AND SPICE	3.10g
SWISS BREAKFAST—RAISIN NUT	3.00g
SWISS BREAKFAST—TROPICAL FRUIT	3.00g
AMARANTH FLAKES	2.80g
AMARANTH W/RAISINS	2.80g
OAT BRAN FLAKES	2.80g
REAL GRANOLA—ALMOND CRUNCH	2.49g
BABY CEREAL—SPROUTED	2.10g

CRACKERS

SESAME CRACKERS—NO SALT	3.20g
SEVEN GRAIN VEGETABLE CRACKERS	3.20g
SEVEN GRAIN VEGETABLE CRACKERS—NO SALT	3.20g
HERB CRACKERS	3.10g
HERB CRACKERS—NO SALT	3.10g
FRENCH ONION CRACKERS—NO SALT	3.10g
SESAME CRACKERS	3.10g
FRENCH ONION CRACKERS	3.00g
STONED WHEAT CRACKERS	2.90g
STONED WHEAT CRACKERS—NO SALT	2.90g
CHEESE WHEELS	2.60g
HONEY GRAHAM CRACKERS	2.10g

Breakfast Cereals, Chilies and Beans—all varieties, Crackers—all varieties, Pasta—all varieties, Green Split Pea Soup, are a superior choice for fiber. These foods provide 1.25 grams or more per 100 calories.

CALCIUM

The U.S. RDA for Calcium is 1,000 milligrams per day

Richest Health Valley Sources of Calcium

FIFTY MILLIGRAMS OR MORE PER SERVING

CHILI AND BEANS

VEGETARIAN BEANS W/MISO 53.00mg

SOUPS

POTATO SOUP—REGULAR AND
    NO SALT 112.00mg
MUSHROOM SOUP—REGULAR
    AND NO SALT 53.00mg
BEAN SOUP—REGULAR AND NO SALT . .   52.00mg

Vegetarian Beans with Miso, Cinnamon Animal Snaps, Instead of Salt – all varieties, Tomato Sauce, Clam Chowder, Mushroom Soup, Potato Soup, are superior choices for calcium. These foods provide more than 50mg per 100 calories.

VITAMIN A (CAROTENE)

The U.S. RDA for vitamin A is 5,000 International Units per day.

Richest Health Valley Sources of Vitamin A

MORE THAN 250 IU PER SERVING

CEREALS

SWISS BREAKFAST — TROPICAL FRUIT . . . . 378 IU

CRACKERS

HERB CRACKERS — NO SALT . . . . 380 IU
HERB CRACKERS . . . . 373 IU

SOUPS

CHUNKY VEGETABLE CHICKEN SOUP . . . . 5107 IU
CHUNKY VEGETABLE CHICKEN SOUP —
   NO SALT . . . . 5107 IU
CHUNKY VEGETABLE SOUP — NO SALT . . . 2494 IU
CHUNKY MINESTRONE — REGULAR
   AND NO SALT . . . . 2475 IU
CHUNKY VEGETABLE SOUP . . . . 2451 IU
VEGETABLE SOUP — REGULAR
   AND NO SALT . . . . 1870 IU
MINESTRONE — REGULAR AND NO SALT . 1640 IU
TOMATO SOUP — REGULAR
   AND NO SALT . . . . 860 IU

CLAM CHOWDER — REGULAR AND
   NO SALT . . . . 692 IU
GREEN SPLIT PEA SOUP —
   REGULAR AND NO SALT . . . . 340 IU
POTATO SOUP — REGULAR
   AND NO SALT . . . . 314 IU

CHILI AND BEANS

MILD VEGETARIAN CHILI —
   REGULAR AND NO SALT . . . . 1709 IU
SPICY VEGETARIAN CHILI —
   REGULAR AND NO SALT . . . . 1709 IU
LENTIL CHILI . . . . 1250 IU
CHILI CON CARNE . . . . 534 IU
BOSTON BAKED BEANS —
   REGULAR AND NO SALT . . . . 304 IU
VEGETARIAN BEANS WITH MISO . . . . 255 IU

Chunky Vegetable Chicken Soup, Chunky Minestrone Soup, Chunky Vegetable Soup, Tomato Sauce, Vegetable Soup, Minestrone Soup, Spaghetti with Spinach, Tomato Soup, Mild and Spicy Vegetarian Chili, Chili Con Carne, Lentil Chili, Clam Chowder, Potato Soup, Herb Crackers, are superior sources of vitamin A. These foods provide 250 IU or more of vitamin A per 100 calories.

VITAMIN C

The U.S. RDA for vitamin C is 60 milligrams per day

Richest Health Valley Sources of Vitamin C

MORE THAN 3 MILLIGRAMS PER SERVING

CEREALS

ORANGEOLA W/BANANAS AND
   HAWAIIAN FRUIT 7.45mg
REAL GRANOLA—HAWAIIAN FRUIT 5.62mg
BRAN W/RAISINS.................. 4.80mg
BRAN W/APPLES AND CINNAMON 3.60mg
SPROUTS 7 W/RAISINS............. 3.60mg

SOUPS

VEGETABLE SOUP—REGULAR
   AND NO SALT.................. 7.5mg
CHUNKY VEGETABLE CHICKEN—
   REGULAR AND NO SALT 7.2mg
CHUNKY VEGETABLE—NO SALT........ 6.8mg
TOMATO SOUP—REGULAR AND NO SALT .. 6.8mg
CHUNKY VEGETABLE—REGULAR 6.7mg
CLAM CHOWDER—REGULAR
   AND NO SALT.................. 5.5mg
CHUNKY MINESTRONE—REGULAR
   AND NO SALT.................. 6.4mg

MINESTRONE SOUP—REGULAR
   AND NO SALT.................. 6.4mg
GREEN SPLIT PEA SOUP—
   REGULAR AND NO SALT 6.0mg
POTATO SOUP—REGULAR AND NO SALT... 4.7mg
MUSHROOM SOUP—REGULAR
   AND NO SALT.................. 3.5mg
BEAN SOUP—NO SALT ADDED......... 3.3mg
BEAN SOUP 3.2mg

COOKIES AND BAKES

AMARANTH JUMBOS 3.54mg

CHILI AND BEANS

CHILI CON CARNE................ 10.60mg
LENTIL CHILI 8.32mg
MILD VEGETARIAN CHILI—
   REGULAR AND NO SALT 5.30mg
SPICY VEGETARIAN CHILI—NO SALT 4.65mg
SPICY VEGETARIAN CHILI 4.64mg

Tomato Sauce, Instead of Salt – all varieties, Tomato Soup, Chunky Vegetable Soup, Vegetable Soup, Chunky Minestrone Soup, Potato Chips – all varieties, Green Split Pea Soup, Clam Chowder, Potato Soup, Chili – all varieties, Orangeola with Hawaiian Fruit, Pasta Spaghetti with Spinach, Spinach Lasagna, Amaranth Jumbo Cookies, Mushroom Soup, Bran Cereal with Hawaiian Fruit, Sprouts 7 with Raisins, Bran Cereal with Apples and Cinnamon, Bean Soup, are superior choices for vitamin C. These foods provide 3mg or more of vitamin C per 100 calories.

SODIUM

There is no U.S. RDA for sodium, but the American Heart Association recommends consuming no more than 1,000 milligrams of sodium per 1,000 calories and in no case more than 3,000 milligrams per day.

SODIUM CONTENT OF HEALTH VALLEY FOODS VERSUS COMMERCIAL BRANDS

CEREALS

HEALTH VALLEY BRAN W/RAISINS .	10mg per oz.
COMMERCIAL BRAN CEREAL	320mg per oz.
HEALTH VALLEY OAT BRAN FLAKES	10mg per oz.
COMMERCIAL OAT FLAKES	275mg per oz.
HEALTH VALLEY AMARANTH FLAKES	10mg per oz.
COMMERCIAL WHEAT FLAKES	280mg per oz.
NATURAL CORN FLAKES	310mg per oz.
HEALTH VALLEY RAISIN BRAN FLAKES	1mg per oz.
COMMERCIAL RAISIN BRAN	205mg per oz.
NATURAL RAISIN BRAN	256mg per oz.
HEALTH VALLEY SPROUTS 7 W/RAISINS	5mg per oz.
COMMERCIAL WHEAT NUGGETS . .	195mg per oz.

CHIPS

HEALTH VALLEY CHEDDAR LITES . .	140mg per oz.
COMMERCIAL CHEESE PUFFS	260mg per oz.
HEALTH VALLEY POTATO CHIPS . . .	60mg per oz.

COMMERCIAL POTATO CHIPS	260mg per oz.
HEALTH VALLEY CORN CHIPS	90mg per oz.
COMMERCIAL CORN CHIPS	235mg per oz.

SOUPS

HEALTH VALLEY CHICKEN BROTH .	250mg per 4 oz.
COMMERCIAL CHICKEN BROTH . .	401mg per 4 oz.
HEALTH VALLEY TOMATO SOUP . .	370mg per 4 oz.
COMMERCIAL TOMATO SOUP . . .	465mg per 4 oz.

COOKIES

HEALTH VALLEY HONEY GRAHAM CRACKERS	160mg per oz.
COMMERCIAL GRAHAM CRACKERS	210mg per oz.
HEALTH VALLEY APPLE BAKES	42mg per bar
COMMERCIAL GRANOLA AND FRUIT BAR—APPLE	150mg per bar
HEALTH VALLEY OATMEAL JUMBOS	70mg per oz.
COMMERCIAL OATMEAL COOKIE . .	154 mg per oz.

All No Salt Added products except Clam Chowder, Chunky Minestrone Soup, and Beef Broth. 7 Grain Vegetable Crackers, Cheddar Lites, Corn Chips with Cheese, Buenitos Tortilla Chips, Corn Chips, Potato Chips, all cookies except Date Pecan Cookies, Instead of Salt—all varieties, Breakfast Cereals—all varieties, Pasta—all varieties, are superior choices to avoid sodium. These foods supply less than 100mg of Sodium per 100 calories.

FAT

There is no U.S. RDA for fat, but it is recommended that you should keep the level of fat in your diet to 30% of total calories or less. Based on a 2,000 calorie daily diet, this would equal a maximum of 66 grams of fat per day.

Best Health Valley Sources for Avoiding Fat

FOUR GRAMS PER SERVING OR LESS

CEREALS

FRUIT LITES—CORN	TRACE
FRUIT LITES—RICE	TRACE
FRUIT LITES—WHEAT	TRACE
LITES—RICE	TRACE
LITES—WHEAT	TRACE
LITES—CORN	TRACE
RAISIN BRAN FLAKES	TRACE
STONED WHEAT FLAKES	TRACE
AMARANTH FLAKES	1.00g
BRAN W/RAISINS	1.00g
BRAN W/APPLES AND CINNAMON	1.00g
BROWN RICE BABY CEREAL	1.00g
HOT OAT BRAN— APPLES AND CINNAMON	1.00g
HOT OAT BRAN—RAISINS AND SPICE	1.00g
OAT BRAN FLAKES	1.00g
SPROUTED BABY CEREAL	1.00g

SPROUTS 7—BANANAS AND HAWAIIAN FRUIT	1.00g
SPROUTS 7—RAISIN	1.00g
AMARANTH W/BANANA	2.00g
AMARANTH W/RAISINS	2.00g
SWISS BREAKFAST—RAISIN NUT	2.00g
SWISS BREAKFAST—TROPICAL FRUIT	2.00g
HEALTHY CRUNCH—ALMONDS AND DATES	3.00g
HEALTHY CRUNCH—APPLE CINNAMON	3.00g
REAL GRANOLA—ALMOND CRUNCH	3.00g
REAL GRANOLA—APPLE CINNAMON	3.00g
REAL GRANOLA—RAISIN NUT	3.00g
ORANGEOLA W/ALMONDS AND DATES	4.00g
ORANGEOLA W/HAWAIIAN FRUIT	4.00g

CRACKERS

AMARANTH GRAHAM CRACKERS	1.00g

SOUPS

BEEF BROTH—REGULAR AND NO SALT . . . TRACE
CHUNKY MINESTRONE SOUP—
   REGULAR AND NO SALT 1.00g
GREEN SPLIT PEA SOUP—
   REGULAR AND NO SALT 1.00g
CHICKEN BROTH—REGULAR AND NO SALT . 2.00g
CHUNKY VEGETABLE SOUP—
   REGULAR AND NO SALT 2.00g
POTATO SOUP—REGULAR AND NO SALT . . 2.00g
TOMATO SOUP—REGULAR AND NO SALT . . . 2.00g
BEAN SOUP—REGULAR AND NO SALT 3.00g
CLAM CHOWDER—REGULAR AND
   NO SALT 3.00g
MUSHROOM SOUP—REGULAR
   AND NO SALT 3.00g
LENTIL SOUP—REGULAR AND NO SALT 4.00g
MINESTRONE SOUP—REGULAR
   AND NO SALT 4.00g
VEGETABLE SOUP—REGULAR
   AND NO SALT 4.00g

CHILI AND BEANS

BOSTON BAKED BEANS 1.00g
BOSTON BAKED BEANS—NO SALT 1.00g
VEGETARIAN BEANS W/MISO 1.00g

COOKIES AND BAKES

CINNAMON ANIMAL SNAPS 1.00g
VANILLA ANIMAL SNAPS 1.00g
AMARANTH JUMBOS 2.00g
CINNAMON JUMBOS 2.00g
OATMEAL JUMBOS 2.00g
PEANUT BUTTER JUMBOS 2.00g
WHEAT FREE COOKIES 2.56g
TOFU COOKIES. 2.65g
FRUIT JUMBOS—ALMOND DATE. 3.00g
FRUIT JUMBOS—RAISIN NUT. 3.00g
FRUIT JUMBOS—TROPICAL FRUIT 3.00g
APPLE BAKES 4.00g
DATE BAKES 4.00g
RAISIN BAKES 4.00g

All Health Valley Breakfast Cereals, Tomato Soup, Vegetable Soup, Potato Soup, Bean Soup, Green Split Pea Soup, Minestrone Soup, Fruit Bakes – all varieties, Amaranth Graham Crackers, Cinnamon Jumbo Cookies, Amaranth Jumbo Cookies, Oatmeal Jumbo Cookies, Baked Beans, Tomato Sauce, Pasta – all varieties, are superior choices to avoid fat. These foods provide less than 30% of calories from fat.

Part Five

Healthier Eating Recipes

Introduction

When you open up most cookbooks, you will find hundreds of recipes, sometimes even a thousand – and you soon discover that there are only three or four recipes in the entire book that you will ever try.

With this book, we think you'll find three or four recipes in each section that you will want to make part of your regular weekly menus. That's because we've included only the very best and easiest recipes for you. They're easy to learn and prepare, and they're healthy in every way. They're rich in the nutrients and fiber you need, and every recipe fulfills the latest dietary guidelines for consuming less fat, cholesterol, sodium and calories. Every recipe has less than 30% of calories from fat – even the salad dressings and sauces!

The most extraordinary thing about the recipes is that along with all these benefits, they also taste good. This is quite an achievement, when you consider that these recipes are made without any butter, egg yolks, salt, cream, refined sugar, white flour, wine, cocoa or chocolate. We use only whole grains, pure vegetable oils, low fat milk and yogurt, fruit juices and honey as sweeteners, and natural herbs and spices as seasonings.

We have included complete nutritional information about every recipe for you. In the back of the book you will find a complete breakdown for each recipe that includes calories, fat, cholesterol, sodium, fiber, and 15 key vitamins and minerals. Red type calls out the nutrients for which the recipe is a superior source.

If you have a special interest in a certain nutrient, there are additional charts to help you. You will find charts with headings according to the nutrient, such as "CALCIUM" and "IRON" and "VITAMIN C." You can tell at a glance which recipes in the book are the best sources of this nutrient. Charts also include other foods that are rich sources. So if you want more calcium, or some other nutrient, you can find out in a few seconds which recipes and foods will supply you with the most.

Finally, every recipe has been carefully tested and re-tested using the kinds of equipment and appliances found in a normal kitchen, rather than the specialized kind found in a professional kitchen. That's because we wanted to be absolutely certain that you'll be able to achieve the same spectacular results in terms of appetite appeal and balanced nutrition in your own home as we have in our Health Valley kitchen.

As much as possible, we've worked to make every recipe in this book "foolproof" even for the first time cook.

We're very excited about the recipes we finally selected from the thousands that we started with, and when you taste them, we think you'll be exicted, too.

Fish & Seafood

Fish is truly a nutritional gift from the sea. It provides the same high quality, complete protein as red meat, but contains only half the calories and a fraction of the saturated fat found in meat.

Most of the fat in fish is monounsaturated or polyunsaturated, and is considered to be beneficial in helping to maintain a healthy balance of blood lipids. Recently, it has been discovered that several varieties of fatty fish are very rich sources of omega-3 fatty acids. Studies of populations that consume diets high in these fatty acids show that cardiovascular heart disease is virtually non-existent. So nutritional authorities recommend including fish, such as salmon, sardines, tuna and mackerel, which are rich in omega-3 fatty acids in your diet to help promote a healthy circulatory system.

Fish and seafood are also a good source of vitamins and the minerals magnesium, iron, iodine, phosphorus and copper. There are so many nutritional benefits you can get only from fish, and that is why you should include more fish in your diet.

There are two keys to preparing great fish dishes: (1) freshness, and (2) proper cooking. Truly fresh fish generally turns to an opaque solid color within a matter of minutes which is your signal that the fish is done. It will not have a "fishy" odor. If you can smell it, it's overcooked!

The best ways to cook fish are usually the simplest. The whole idea is to bring out and enhance the natural delicate flavor of the fish, rather than disguising or overpowering it.

This is not to say that fish cannot be prepared in more elaborate recipes. We have included both simple recipes and party dishes in this section. In that way, it will be easy for you to make these delicious, healthy dishes a regular part of your personal plan of healthier eating.

"One of My Favorites"

George Mateljan

Health Valley Super Light Halibut Casserole

A typical souffle prepared in the classic manner includes 3 or 4 eggs, a few tablespoons of butter, milk and cheese. It tastes heavenly when carefully prepared, but it's also loaded with fat and cholesterol.

I like our version of a classic fish souffle for several reasons. First of all, it's one of our very best recipes for both flavor and appearance. Second, it's obviously much lower in fat, cholesterol and calories than a typical recipe. Third, and possibly most important, it's much easier to prepare. The usual souffle recipe requires a very deft hand and precision timing to come out right, while our "Super Light Halibut Casserole" is somewhat less "temperamental." Our only requirement is that you serve it immediately because, just like any souffle, it will fall if it is allowed to stand too long. Try this recipe on dinner guests – it's so elegant, light and delicious that they'll never realize they're eating low fat, low sodium cooking.

The **nutritional highlights** of this recipe are that it contains only 160 calories per serving and only 30% of calories from fat, while providing significant amounts of the B vitamins, 14% of the U.S. RDA for calcium and 6% of iron.

Health Valley
Super Light Halibut Casserole

Preparation Time: 20 minutes   Cooking Time: 30 minutes

1 pound halibut steaks
1 cup plain nonfat yogurt
1½ tablespoons mayonnaise
2 teaspoons fish seasoning
(recipe in Condiment section)

¼ cup grated muenster cheese
(about 1 ounce)
6 egg whites

Steps:
1. Poach halibut (see page 194 for poaching instructions). Flake and set aside.
2. Preheat oven to 350°F.
3. Combine yogurt, mayonnaise, fish seasoning, muenster cheese and halibut.
4. Beat the egg whites until stiff and fold into fish mixture.
5. Pour into 10x6x2-inch casserole dish. Bake at 350°F for 30 minutes or until firm and puffy.

Yield: 6 servings

Poached Fish with Dill Sauce

Preparation Time: 15 minutes   Cooking Time: 25 minutes

Halibut is a firm, delicious, white-flesh flatfish belonging to the flounder family. They are frequently enormous in size, with Pacific halibut weighing up to 600 pounds. Can you imagine one fish serving 1,500 people?

Try to buy fresh fish whenever possible. Steaks and fillets should look freshly cut, firm and moist, with no brown edges. If you choose frozen fish, avoid packages with a build-up of ice crystals, and dry or discolored fish—especially around the edges.

Basic Poaching Instructions

4 cups water
3 tablespoons lemon juice
1 inch lemon peel

1 tablespoon fish seasoning
(recipe in Condiment section)
4 7-ounce halibut or salmon steaks

Steps:

1. In medium saucepan, bring all ingredients except fish to a boil. Simmer over very low heat (just an occasional bubble) 10 minutes for seasonings to blend. Add fish and simmer partially covered for 4 minutes.
2. Remove fish and drain.

Yield: 4 servings

Dill Sauce

1 cup low fat milk
1 tablespoon arrowroot
2 teaspoons dill weed

½ teaspoon fish seasoning
(recipe in Condiment section)
4 teaspoons lemon juice
½ teaspoon honey

Steps:

1. In medium saucepan, slowly stir cold milk into arrowroot. Heat milk, stirring constantly until thickened.
2. Stir in remaining ingredients. Serve over fish.

Yield: 1 cup

Easy Fish Stew

Preparation Time: 15 minutes   Cooking Time: 15 minutes

1 tablespoon safflower oil
2 cups pasta sauce (recipe in Dressings and Sauces section)
½ teaspoon dried basil
pinch of saffron (optional)
½ pound fresh broccoli, or 1 10-ounce package frozen broccoli spears, thawed
1 7-ounce halibut steak
3½ ounces fillet of sole

½ teaspoon all purpose seasoning (recipe in Condiment section)
2½ teaspoons fish seasoning (recipe in Condiment section)
½ teaspoon honey
3 ounces cooked shrimp, rinsed and drained
1 6½-ounce can minced clams, drained and rinsed
chopped parsley for garnish

Steps:

1. In a medium saucepan, heat oil over medium heat. Add pasta sauce, basil and saffron, and simmer for 2 minutes.
2. Cut broccoli into chunks, about 1½ inches long. Add to pan and cook for 8 minutes.
3. Meanwhile, cut halibut and sole into pieces about 1-inch square. Add halibut, sole, seasonings and honey to ingredients in pan, and cook for 3 minutes longer. Add shrimp and clams, just to warm slightly. Sprinkle stew with chopped parsley.

Yield: 4 servings

Note: When you use canned clams, as in this recipe, or other canned foods, it is important to rinse carefully because salt is usually added in the canning process.

Shellfish are good sources of protein and many vitamins. However, all shellfish (except oysters and soft-shell clams) are relatively high in cholesterol, and lobster is high in sodium too. We don't think you have to eliminate them entirely from your diet, but use them sparingly as in this recipe. Use our chart below for reference, and remember to limit your cholesterol intake to 100 mg. per 1000 calories, not to exceed 300 mg. cholesterol per day.

4 oz. meat from:	Sodium	Fat	Cholesterol
Shrimp	159 mg.	.9 g	170 mg.
Crab	1 mg.	1.1 g	113 mg.
Lobster	238 mg.	2.2 g	96 mg.
Clams	136 mg.	1.86 g	56 mg.
Oysters	83 mg.	2.5 g	57 mg.

"One of My Favorites"

George Mateljan

Orange Fish Fillets

Orange roughy is a delicious, delicately flavored white fish that has become popular in recent years, and is now widely available. I think that orange roughy tastes a little like lobster – without the cost or cholesterol – and that's one reason why I like this recipe so much.

It is important to use orange roughy and not a substitute like sole in this recipe, or it won't have the flavor and texture that makes this dish so remarkable. It is also important to use fresh orange roughy, because frozen fish will dilute the marinade and thus the flavor. If you simply cannot find orange roughy, an acceptable substitute is sea bass.

The **nutritional highlights** of this recipe are that it contains only 24% calories from fat, and is rich in vitamins C, B_{12}, niacin, phosphorus and calcium.

Orange Fish Fillets

Preparation Time: 10 minutes
Marinating Time: 45 minutes

Cooking Time: 15 minutes

**1 pound orange roughy
(or sea bass)**

**2 tablespoons frozen orange
juice concentrate, thawed**

1 tablespoon lemon juice

½ teaspoon dried dill weed

½ teaspoon fish seasoning
(recipe in Condiment section)

**1 tablespoon finely chopped
parsley**

¼ cup water

**2 tablespoons toasted
sesame seeds**

Steps:

1. Place fish in glass casserole.
2. Combine remaining ingredients except sesame seeds and pour over fish. Cover and marinate in refrigerator 45 minutes, turning once.
3. Preheat broiler.
4. Remove fish from marinade and place on well oiled broiler pan. Broil fish 4 inches from heat till fish flakes, about 10-15 minutes. Baste often with marinade.
5. To serve, brush with heated marinade and top with toasted sesame seeds.

Yield: 4 servings

Basic Rules for Cooking Fish

One of the reasons fish isn't more popular is that it is too often overcooked, so many people associate it with food that is dry and unappetizing. Follow this basic rule for cooking fish by any method (boiling, frying, baking, simmering, poaching, steaming). A *fresh* – not frozen – piece that is 1-inch thick takes 10 minutes. For each ¼-inch above or below one inch, add or subtract 2 minutes. When fish is cooked properly, there is little if any "fishy" odor. The substances that cause the odor are released only after reaching temperatures higher than necessary for perfect cooking. So, if you begin to smell the fish – it's done. To be sure of eliminating odor, sprinkle fish with lemon juice before cooking.

"One of My Favorites"

George Mateljan

Salmon Salad Sandwich Spread

Salmon are a unique fish in that they live in the ocean, but migrate into fresh water rivers to spawn. Although we tend to think of salmon meat as pink, the color actually varies according to variety. The flesh of chinook salmon is white, Atlantic salmon is white or pink, and sockeye salmon is red. The taste of the salmon varies, depending on the variety, and upon the type of food the salmon has eaten. Canned salmon contains more calcium than fresh salmon, because you are able to eat the soft bones.

The **nutritional highlights** of this recipe are that ½ cup of the spread contains 12% of the U.S. RDA for calcium, and almost 50% of vitamin D.

Salmon Salad Sandwich Spread

Preparation Time: 20 minutes

8 ounces canned salmon, flaked   ½ cup plain nonfat yogurt
¼ cup chopped celery   1 tablespoon honey
¼ cup chopped red onion   1 teaspoon lemon juice
2 tablespoons chopped parsley   1 tablespoon prepared mustard

Steps:

1. Combine all ingredients. Spread on whole grain bread or stuff whole grain pita bread. Add lettuce, tomato, and sprouts as desired. May also be spread on crackers for snacks or appetizers.

Yield: 2¾ cups (enough to make 6 sandwiches)

Halibut Fillets in Tomato Sauce

Preparation Time: 15 minutes   Cooking Time: 40 minutes

1½ cups chopped Italian
    tomatoes
1 cup chopped zucchini
½ cup minced onion
1 teaspoon grated lemon peel
2 tablespoons lemon juice
2 pounds halibut fillets

1 teaspoon fish seasoning
(recipe in Condiment section)
2 teaspoons lemon juice
    to sprinkle on fish
3 teaspoons chopped fresh
    fennel weed

Steps:

1. Preheat oven to 350°F.
2. Combine tomatoes, zucchini, onion, lemon peel and 2 tablespoons lemon juice in a small saucepan and bring to a boil. Reduce heat and simmer mixture for 15 minutes.
3. Spoon half of the sauce into an ovenproof glass baking dish. Place fish fillets on top. Sprinkle with fish seasoning and additional 2 teaspoons lemon juice. Cover with remaining sauce.
4. Bake uncovered at 350°F. for 20 minutes.
5. Remove from oven and arrange fillets on a warmed serving platter. Spoon sauce over top and sprinkle with fennel weed.

Yield: 6 servings

Fat in Fish

Fish contain varying amounts of fat. Lean fish (less than 2% fat) are generally cooked in buttery sauces, which the recipes in our cuisine avoid. Lean fish include halibut, sole, bass, perch, cod, lobster, shrimp and red snapper. Moderately fatty fish (2-6%) fat can be broiled or baked, and lend themselves to mayonnaise-type sauces. Moderately fatty fish include buffalo, whitefish and swordfish. Fatty fish (over 6% fat) are good with citrus juices or vinegar. Fatty fish include trout, tuna, mackerel and salmon.

Halibut Steaks with Avocado Dill Sauce

Preparation Time: 10 minutes   Cooking Time: 20 minutes

It almost seems as though nature created dill as the perfect complement just for fish. This fragrant herb has a fresh, clean taste and aroma that enhances the delicate flavors of almost any kind of fish. And it is so nourishing that many athletes include it in their diets.

2 teaspoons fish seasoning
(recipe in Condiment section)

1 tablespoon lemon juice
avocado dressing

2 7-ounce halibut steaks

1 teaspoon chopped fresh dill,
or ¾ teaspoon dried dill

Steps:
1. Preheat oven to 400°F. and oil an 8-inch square pan.
2. Add fish seasoning and lemon juice to dressing. Place fish steaks in prepared pan and spread dressing evenly over fish. Sprinkle dill on top. Bake for 20 minutes.

Yield: 2 servings

Avocado Dressing

⅓ cup yogurt dill dressing (recipe in Dressings and Sauces section)

2 tablespoons avocado

Steps:
1. Combine ingredients. Mix well.

Yield: 2 servings

"One of My Favorites"

George Mateljan

Brown Rice with Curried Shrimp

Rice is the staple food in the diet of six out of 10 people in the world. It is also one of the oldest cultivated foods used by humans. There is evidence that rice was cultivated at a site in what is now Thailand as early as 3,500 B.C. Although the West tends to consider rice as a side dish or a substitute for potatoes or bread, it is the main source of nutrition in many Eastern cultures, where it is prized for its simplicity and nourishment. In fact, one of the terms for "wife" in Chinese is the same as "bowl of rice."

I have always been fond of brown rice recipes, and this is one of my favorites. Both the flavor and nutrition found in the brown rice are perfectly complemented by that of the shrimp in curry sauce.

But be sure to use brown rice, rather than white rice. Because brown rice retains the bran and germ of the rice kernel. White rice, which has had both these parts removed, is mostly starch. Even enriched white rice lacks the fiber and riboflavin of brown rice.

The **nutritional highlights** of this recipe are that it contains only 8% of calories from fat, while providing over 100% of the U.S. RDA for vitamin A, 15% iron, and good percentages of all the B vitamins.

Brown Rice with Curried Shrimp

Preparation Time: 30 minutes   Cooking Time: 25 minutes

1 teaspoon safflower oil
1 large onion, sliced
2 teaspoons minced garlic
1 tablespoon curry powder
¼ teaspoon cinnamon
1¼ cups chicken broth
(recipe in Soup section)
2 large carrots, cut into
½-inch cubes
2 large potatoes, cut into
½-inch cubes

1 large zucchini, cut into
½-inch cubes
1 16-ounce can tomatoes,
cut into chunks, plus juice
½ cup raisins
½ pound medium shrimp,
deveined and rinsed
4 cups cooked brown rice
(still hot)

Steps:

1. Heat the oil in large heavy saucepan over medium high heat and saute onion and garlic until soft. Combine curry powder, cinnamon and chicken broth and pour over onion mixture. Bring to a boil and add carrots and potatoes. Cover the pan and simmer mixture for 10 minutes.
2. Add zucchini, tomatoes with their juice, and raisins. Cover and simmer 5 minutes longer. Add the shrimp and remove from heat.
3. Arrange the hot cooked rice on a serving platter and pour the vegetable-shrimp mixture over it.

Yield: 8 servings

Brown Rice with Curried Chicken: If you'd prefer to make this
recipe with chicken instead of shrimp, use 1½ pounds chicken breast, skin removed and cut into 1-inch cubes. Add chicken in Step 1, at the same time you add the carrots and potatoes. Adjust curry powder to 1½ tablespoons, and chicken broth to 1 cup.

"One of My Favorites"

George Mateljan

Spaghetti with Garlic and Shrimp

This recipe gets some of its wonderful, satisfying flavor from garlic, which is one of the oldest and most widespread cultivated plants. It has been used since pre-Biblical times as a seasoning as well as for therapeutic purposes. At various times, garlic has been prescribed for virtually every kind of ailment. And there is sound basis for this reputation as a curative, because garlic contains allicin, which is a natural antibiotic.

Because garlic has such a persistent flavor and pungent aroma, it has always evoked strong reactions, both pro and con.

The reason I like this recipe so much is that even people who normally aren't too fond of garlic like this dish. It is one of the few pasta dishes that is full-flavored and satisfying without any added salt, and without a sauce made with a lot of fat.

The **nutritional highlights** of this recipe are that it contains only 29% of calories from fat, and a serving provides 26% of your daily requirement for calcium.

Spaghetti with Garlic and Shrimp

Preparation Time: 15 minutes   Cooking Time: 3 minutes

8 ounces whole wheat spaghetti*
4 cloves garlic, minced
1 tablespoon olive oil
¼ cup chopped parsley
¼ cup pimientos

8 ounces cooked medium shrimp, rinsed and drained
2 teaspoons dried basil
4 ounces Swiss cheese, grated

Steps:
1. Cook spaghetti according to package directions. Set aside and keep warm.
2. In medium saucepan, saute garlic in olive oil. Remove from heat.
3. Add spaghetti and remaining ingredients except cheese to saucepan and toss well. Turn onto a hot serving platter. Sprinkle with grated cheese and serve immediately.

Yield: 6 servings

This product is available from Health Valley

Tuna Pita Sandwich

Preparation Time: 15 minutes

Tuna that is packed in water instead of oil contains about 20% more protein and up to 160 less calories. There are many types of tuna including albacore, blackfin and yellowfin. Only albacore is white meat tuna, and is the best you can buy. Comparing tuna to beef steak, you find that tuna contains 3-4 times as much niacin (important in dieting, because it helps break down starches and sugars), and 25% more vitamin B_{12} (important in exercising, because it helps your blood cells carry oxygen).

1 6½-ounce can water packed
   albacore tuna, drained
½ cup chopped green pepper
½ cup chopped red onion
1 cup chopped celery
2 tablespoons mayonnaise

½ cup plain low fat yogurt
1 teaspoon all purpose seasoning
   (recipe in Condiment section)
½ 10-ounce package (3 loaves)
   whole wheat pita bread
1 cup fresh alfalfa sprouts

Steps:

1. In medium bowl, break tuna into coarse flakes with a fork. Add green pepper, onion, celery, mayonnaise, yogurt and seasoning. Mix well.
2. Cut each bread loaf in half and open halves to form pockets. Fill pockets with tuna-vegetable mixture. Top with alfalfa sprouts.

Yield: 6 sandwiches

Creamed Salmon and Broccoli

Preparation Time: 20 minutes | Cooking Time: 20 minutes

1 large bunch broccoli, trimmed
and separated into spears
(about 1½ pounds)
1 tablespoon lemon juice
3 tablespoons whole wheat flour
⅛ teaspoon cayenne
⅛ teaspoon nutmeg

1 teaspoon dry mustard
2½ cups nonfat milk
12 ounces poached, flaked salmon
(see page 194 for poaching instructions)
¼ cup grated Swiss cheese
4 teaspoons pine nuts, toasted
(sunflower seeds may be used)

Steps:

1. Preheat oven to 450°F.
2. Steam broccoli for 5 minutes until tender-crisp. Drain and put in bottom of glass casserole. Sprinkle with lemon juice and set aside.
3. Combine flour, cayenne, nutmeg and dry mustard with ½ cup nonfat milk. In saucepan, bring remaining 2 cups of milk to a simmer, stirring constantly with a wire whisk. Slowly add flour mixture and simmer for 1 minute, until thickened.
4. Add salmon to sauce and pour over broccoli. Sprinkle with grated cheese. Bake for 15 minutes. Sprinkle with pine nuts and bake for 5 minutes longer.

Yield: 8 servings

Why Broccoli Is a "Superfood"

Broccoli is incredibly rich in vitamins. Just one medium stalk (about 2 cups) of raw broccoli provides 60% of the U.S. RDA for vitamin A and 270% of vitamin C. When you combine broccoli with salmon, milk and cheese as in this recipe, with all of them being so high in protein, calcium and riboflavin, you have a "superdish."

"One of My Favorites"

George Mateljan

Quick Bouillabaisse

There are as many recipes for bouillabaisses as there are French chefs and, like most recipes, they automatically include salt for seasoning. I don't think it's necessary. Our recipe recommends using saltwater fish like snapper, cod or halibut which contain enough natural sodium to be flavorful, but not so much as to exclude them from low salt diets. Saltwater fish are high in vitamins B_1, B_6, D, niacin and pantothenic acid, and are also high in phosphorus, sulfur, selenium, and iodine.

Other **nutritional highlights** of this recipe are that it contains only 29% of calories from fat, and one serving provides 54% of your daily requirement for vitamin A.

Quick Bouillabaisse

Preparation Time: 30 minutes | Cooking Time: 30 minutes

½ teaspoon safflower oil
1 cup chopped onion
1 cup chopped celery
½ cup diced carrots
1 green pepper, seeded and chopped
¼ cup chopped parsley
1 cup chicken broth
(recipe in Soup section)
2 cups tomato sauce*
2 teaspoons lemon juice
½ teaspoon honey

2 teaspoons minced garlic
1 teaspoon all purpose seasoning
(recipe in Condiment section)
1 teaspoon fish seasoning
(recipe in Condiment section)
1 teaspoon oregano
½ teaspoon dried basil
1 pound white fish such as snapper, cod or halibut, cut into bite size pieces
3 ounces scallops
3 ounces cooked shrimp, rinsed

Steps:

1. In large saucepan, heat oil over medium heat, add onion and saute until soft. Add celery, carrots, green pepper and parsley. Cook until soft.
2. Add chicken broth, tomato sauce, lemon, honey, garlic and seasonings. Cook 15 minutes. Add fish one at a time, except shrimp, bringing soup to simmer after each addition. Cook 5-10 minutes longer. Add shrimp just before serving.

Yield: 8 servings

This product is available from Health Valley

209

11

Chicken

More and more, chicken is being chosen by health conscious people. That's because chicken is equal to red meat as an outstanding source of complete protein, and chicken is much lower in total fat, and calories. Another important advantage of choosing chicken instead of red meat is that chicken is much lower in saturated fat. The fat in chicken is predominately polyunsaturated or monounsaturated, the same type of fat found in olive oil and considered to be highly beneficial in helping to maintain a healthy balance of lipids in the blood. Chicken is also low in sodium (about 65 milligrams per 3½-ounce serving). And chicken is an excellent source of other important vitamins and minerals including niacin, B6, phosphorus, and iron.

Most of the fat in chicken is in or just under the skin, so our recipes instruct you to remove the skin and visible fat before cooking in most cases, but always before eating. Cooking chicken with the skin on results in a more moist end result, but chicken cooked with the skin on and removed before eating contains 50% more fat than chicken cooked with the skin off.

We've included a wide variety of chicken recipes because it's a delicious food that is so versatile, economical, nutritious and popular. Many of the recipes combine chicken with vegetables, grains and dairy foods that are outstanding sources of other nutrients, so that the recipe becomes almost a meal in itself. For example, Chicken Vegetable Stew contains nearly 300% of the U.S. RDA of vitamin A in the safe form of beta carotene. And California Chicken provides 40% of the U.S. RDA of vitamin C, 30% of the U.S. RDA for calcium, 40% of the U.S. RDA of magnesium, and 20% of the U.S. RDA for zinc. So it's easy to see why we are such enthusiastic supporters of chicken and these outstanding chicken recipes as a replacement for red meat.

When purchasing chicken, allow approximately one pound per serving of uncooked whole chicken because shrinking from cooking and the weight of the bones reduces the serving portion considerably. When you remove the skin and fat too, the portion will usually be at an acceptable size for our recipes.

A Healthy Alternative for Extra Convenience

For those times when your busy schedule keeps you from having time to prepare these recipes, always keep a supply of Health Valley Lean Living™ frozen entrees in the freezer, including Chicken a la King and Chicken Crepes Marco Polo. They're quick, delicious, and nutritious.

"One of My Favorites"

George Mateljan

Health Valley Sesame Chicken With Broccoli

Oriental stir-fry dishes are quick and easy to prepare, and they have a lot of flavor without a lot of fat, cholesterol and calories. But most Oriental cooking is liberally sprinkled with soy sauce and MSG (monosodium glutamate), which are both dangerously high in sodium. In fact, some people get such a bad reaction from MSG that it is sometimes called "The Chinese Headache." This recipe offers zesty Oriental flavor without any added salt, soy sauce or MSG. It tastes so good because the chicken is marinated in orange juice, ginger and other healthy seasonings. For best flavor, marinate chicken overnight.

This recipe is a favorite of mine because it provides you with so many of the key nutrients you need on very few calories.

The **nutritional highlights** of this recipe are that there are only 218 calories in a serving with only 19% of calories from fat, yet look at the nutritional benefits: 250% of the U.S. RDA for vitamin C, 56% of vitamin A, over 17% of iron, 11% of calcium, and high percentages of all the B vitamins.

Sesame Chicken is the kind of recipe that should be a cornerstone in your healthier eating menus, and it is especially valuable if you are dieting because it makes sure you are getting essential nutrients that are frequently overlooked on weight loss programs.

Health Valley Sesame Chicken With Broccoli

Preparation Time: 15 minutes

Cooking Time: 15 minutes
Plus Marinating Time: 30 minutes or longer

1 chicken breast, skinned, boned and cut into cubes
1 tablespoon chicken seasoning (recipe in Condiment section)
½ teaspoon paprika
1 teaspoon minced ginger root
2 tablespoons toasted sesame seeds
½ cup chopped onion
5 tablespoons orange juice concentrate
¼ cup water
1 pound broccoli, coarsely chopped
1 lemon

Steps:

1. Combine all ingredients except broccoli and lemon in bowl, cover and marinate for at least 30 minutes.
2. Heat wok or skillet over medium high heat. Stir-fry chicken mixture and broccoli for 15 minutes or until broccoli is just tender. Do not overcook.
3. Serve with fresh lemon wedges.

Yield: 4 servings

Lemon Chicken On Spinach Leaves

Preparation Time: 30 minutes   Cooking Time: 30 minutes

·This elegant dish is quick, easy and nutritious – perfect for company. Your guests will think you have spent all day in the kitchen when, in fact, from start to finish this recipe takes just one hour! In most dishes of this nature, the chicken is sautéed in butter or oil first. We simmer it in the sauce instead to cut down on fat and calories, not to mention saving you work and pans.

2 tablespoons whole wheat pastry flour
1 cup chicken broth
(recipe in Soup section)
2 tablespoons honey
2 teaspoons chicken seasoning
(recipe in Condiment section)
½ teaspoon oregano
½ teaspoon dried basil

⅓ cup lemon juice
2 whole chicken breasts, skinned, halved and filleted
1 bunch fresh spinach (about 1½ pounds), washed, trimmed and coarsely shredded
1 15-ounce can unsweetened apricot halves, drained

Steps:

1. In saucepan, combine flour, chicken broth and honey. Mix well. Cook over medium heat, stirring constantly, 3-5 minutes until sauce is smooth and starts to thicken.
2. Add chicken seasoning, oregano, basil and lemon juice. Stir to combine.
3. Place chicken breasts in sauce, cover. Reduce heat and simmer 20 minutes.
4. Arrange spinach on serving platter. Place chicken on spinach. Pour a little sauce over chicken, and serve the remainder on the side. Arrange apricot halves around chicken on top of spinach.

Yield: 4 servings

Lemons: The Perfect Seasoning

Lemons are one of nature's great seasoning gifts. They enhance the flavors of meats, poultry, and vegetables with as much zest as salt, but instead of contributing to health disorders as salt does, lemons contribute valuable nutrients. Lemons are high in vitamin C and bioflavonoids, as well as minerals, potassium, calcium and magnesium. To release the natural lemon oil from the inside of the peel, let the fruit come to room temperature, then roll it with the palm of your hand on a hard surface before cutting.

Orange Honey Glazed Chicken

Preparation Time: 15 minutes

Cooking Time: 50 minutes
Plus Marinating Time: 24 hours

Five different types of honey are available today: liquid, solid, comb, cut comb and chunk. Most Americans use honey only in the liquid form, but Canadians enjoy solid honey which is known in the north as creamed honey or honey spread.

½ **cup frozen orange juice concentrate, thawed**

1 **tablespoon lemon juice**

1 **teaspoon safflower oil**

1 **tablespoon honey**

1 **teaspoon chicken seasoning**
(recipe in Condiment section)

½ **teaspoon dry mustard or curry powder**

¼ **teaspoon paprika**

6 **chicken breast halves or chicken thighs, skinned and fat removed**

orange slices for garnish

Steps:
1. In a medium bowl, combine all ingredients except chicken. Mix well. Place chicken pieces in marinade and coat well. Cover and place in refrigerator for 24 hours or longer.
2. Preheat oven to 400°F.
3. Remove chicken from bowl and place in a baking dish. Bake at 400°F for 30 minutes. Baste chicken with remaining marinade, turn and baste again. Bake until juices run clear when pierced with a fork, about 20 more minutes.
4. Serve with orange slices as garnish.

Yield: 6 servings

"One of My Favorites"

George Mateljan

California Chicken

This recipe gets its name from the fact that many of the ingredients, including the avocado are found in California.

Although most of the avocados raised commercially in this country are grown in California and Florida, avocados are believed to have been cultivated first in Central and South America before the 16th century.

Avocados are usually thought of as a vegetable, but they are really a fruit. And they're one of the few fruits that is high in fat. But 80% of that fat is unsaturated, and avocados are a powerhouse of potassium, thiamine, riboflavin and niacin.

The reason this recipe is a favorite of mine is that it lets you enjoy all the rich, delicate flavor and creamy texture of avocados, yet they're used in such a way that they only add about 6 grams of fat.

The **nutritional highlights** of this recipe include the low fat, and the fact that a serving provides 30% of your daily requirement for calcium.

California Chicken

Preparation Time: 5 minutes   Cooking Time: 30 minutes

2 whole chicken breasts, skinned, halved, and filleted
1 tablespoon lemon juice
chicken seasoning (recipe in Condiment section)
½ avocado, peeled and sliced in 4 slices
½ teaspoon honey

dash of cayenne
1 cup pasta sauce (recipe in Dressings and Sauces section)
4 ounces whole wheat spaghetti,* uncooked
¾ cup shredded Swiss cheese
parsley sprigs for garnish

Steps:

1. Preheat oven to 350°F.
2. Place chicken fillets in a 9-inch square glass casserole. Sprinkle with lemon juice and chicken seasoning. Place an avocado slice on each fillet. Stir honey and cayenne into pasta sauce. Pour over chicken.
3. Bake at 350°F for 20 minutes.
4. While chicken is baking, cook spaghetti according to package instructions.
5. Remove chicken from oven. Sprinkle with cheese. Return to oven and bake an additional 10 minutes.
6. Arrange chicken on bed of spaghetti. Garnish with parsley.

Yield: 4 servings

This product is available from Health Valley

Note: It is preferable to use imported Swiss cheese in this recipe. It has a fuller, nuttier flavor than domestic Swiss cheese, and provides a tangy contrast to the chicken and avocado.

"One of My Favorites"

George Mateljan

Herbed Chicken

Once upon a time, it was believed that dill cured hiccoughs and kept away witches. Dill weed is the leaves of the plant, and dill seed is the flowers. Dill weed is most flavorful when the flowers are in bloom.

Dill is commonly used to season fish, but it is equally effective in enhancing the flavor of chicken.

This recipe is a favorite of mine because it exemplifies what our book is all about. It is low in fat, sodium and calories, but it is not lacking in flavor. The fresh, refreshing taste of dill is combined with the hot sweetness of paprika, tangy yogurt, onion powder and garlic powder into a sauce that is so good you'll sop it up with bread.

The **nutritional highlights** of this recipe are that it derives only 21% of calories from fat, while providing over 86% of the U.S. RDA for niacin, over 34% of B_6, and 10% of iron.

Herbed Chicken

Preparation Time: 15 minutes   Cooking Time: 20 minutes

1 cup chicken broth
(recipe in Soup section)
½ teaspoon dried dill weed
1 teaspoon onion powder
1 teaspoon garlic powder
¼ teaspoon curry powder

1 pound chicken breast,
skinned, boned and filleted
2 tablespoons tomato sauce*
¼ teaspoon honey
2 teaspoons paprika
3 tablespoons plain nonfat yogurt
⅓ cup shredded cheddar cheese

Steps:
1. Combine chicken broth, dill weed, onion powder, garlic powder and curry powder in heavy saucepan. Add the chicken fillet and bring to a boil. Lower heat and let simmer for 10 minutes.
2. With slotted spoon, remove chicken to a heated serving platter. Keep warm.
3. Reduce liquid in saucepan to ½ cup and stir in tomato sauce, honey and paprika. Heat to simmer. Remove from heat and slowly stir in yogurt and cheese. Spoon mixture over chicken.

Yield: 4 servings

This product is available from Health Valley.

Cheddar Chicken

Preparation Time: 15 minutes — Cooking Time: 40 minutes

4 chicken breasts, skinned and cut into halves
1 teaspoon safflower oil
¼ cup chopped onion
1 cup tomato sauce*
1 15-ounce can mushroom soup*
¾ teaspoon garlic powder

2 teaspoons chicken seasoning
(recipe in Condiment section)
1 teaspoon all purpose seasoning
(recipe in Condiment section)
8 ounces uncooked whole wheat spaghetti*
1 10-ounce package frozen peas
1 cup shredded cheddar cheese

Steps:

1. In a large skillet, brown chicken on both sides in 1 teaspoon safflower oil. Add onion and saute until tender.
2. Combine tomato sauce, mushroom soup, garlic powder and seasonings. Pour over chicken. Cover and simmer for 40 minutes or until chicken is tender.
3. Cook spaghetti according to package directions.
4. Arrange spaghetti on heat proof platter, arrange peas over spaghetti. Place chicken on peas and spaghetti. Pour sauce over all. Top with cheese and place under broiler until cheese is melted and slightly browned.

Yield: 8 servings

This product is available from Health Valley

What to Avoid When Buying Chicken:
Don't buy chicken with brownish areas – it's been in the super-market refrigerator too long or has been stored improperly. Also avoid chicken with skin that looks dry, purplish, bruised or scaly.

Easy Skillet Chicken

Preparation Time: 20 minutes   Cooking Time: 1 hour 40 minutes

Eating poultry is both better for you and more economical than eating red meats. Poultry is lower in fat and calories than red meat, but contains the same high quality protein. If you wish to avoid as much total fat, saturated fat, cholesterol and calories as possible, remove the skin before cooking. Combination dishes such as this are a good way to make sure you're eating sufficient quantities of vegetables. Along with protein, this Easy Skillet Chicken provides significant quantities of 12 essential vitamins and minerals including iron and zinc.

4 chicken breasts, skinned and cut into halves
2 medium onions, coarsely chopped
2 zucchini, sliced 1-inch thick
2 carrots, sliced
1 green pepper, diced

½ red pepper, diced
1 cup sliced mushrooms
chicken seasoning
(recipe in Condiment section)
1 cup chicken broth (optional)
(recipe in Soup section)

Steps:

1. Place chicken, onions and half of vegetables in large skillet. Sprinkle with chicken seasoning. Simmer over low heat for 45 minutes.
2. Turn chicken. Add remaining vegetables and sprinkle with more chicken seasoning. Cook for 40 minutes.
3. (Optional) Add chicken broth, cover and simmer for 15 minutes until chicken is tender.

Yield: 8 servings

Note: Without chicken broth, the onions will caramelize and vegetables will brown. With broth, this will not happen but the dish will be juicier. So enjoy it the way you prefer.

"One of My Favorites"

George Mateljan

Mustard Chicken

This recipe gets its delicious, full flavor from a marinade based on mustard. The mustard is combined with other seasonings, including coriander, lime juice and a little honey, and the flavors penetrate into the chicken and add the kind of zesty flavor you normally have to add salt to achieve. But when you try this recipe yourself, I think you'll agree that you don't even miss salt.

One of the reasons is that mustard is such a full-flavored seasoning. It is also one of the oldest seasonings known to the human race. The people of the Indus Valley in Asia used it to season wheat and barley as far back as 3,500 B.C. And the ancient Sumerians used mustard both as a seasoning and for therapeutic purposes. A key to the popularity of mustard throughout history is its widespread availability. The mustard plant grows so freely that it really didn't need to be cultivated.

The **nutritional highlights** of this recipe are that it contains only 29% calories from fat, and provides over 60% of the U.S. RDA for niacin.

Mustard Chicken

Preparation Time: 15 minutes
Plus Marinating Time: 3 hours

Cooking Time: 30 minutes

3 chicken breasts, skinned,
  boned and filleted
½ cup prepared mustard
3 tablespoons lime juice
1 tablespoon safflower oil
2½ tablespoons honey

½ cup water
1 teaspoon ground coriander
2 teaspoons grated lime peel
  lettuce leaves
  lime wedges for garnish

Steps:

1. Remove skin and all visible fat from chicken pieces and place chicken into a shallow glass pan.
2. Whisk together the mustard, lime juice, safflower oil, honey, water, coriander and lime peel. Pour over chicken and cover pan. Marinate chicken for 3 hours in the refrigerator, turning pieces once or twice.
3. Preheat oven to 350°F.
4. Place chicken pieces in ovenproof baking dish and bake at 350°F. for 30 minutes or until chicken is tender, basting once with remaining marinade after first 15 minutes of baking.
5. Serve on a bed of lettuce leaves and garnish with lime wedges.

Yield: 6 servings

Healthy Roast Chicken

Preparation Time: 30 minutes   Cooking Time: 1½ hours

1 3-pound roasting chicken
chicken seasoning
(recipe in Condiment section)
1 teaspoon tarragon leaves

⅓ cup celery leaves
6 lemon slices
6 onion slices

Steps:

1. Preheat oven to 350°F.
2. Clean chicken. Loosen skin from flesh on the breast and back by running knife tip under the skin and pulling skin away with fingers. Handle gently to avoid tearing skin.
3. Sprinkle chicken seasoning generously on meat under skin. Rub into flesh with fingers.
4. Put ½ teaspoon tarragon inside cavity and the remainder under skin. Divide celery equally between cavity and under skin of chicken.
5. Put 2 slices of lemon and 2 slices of onion in the cavity, 2 of each under breast skin and 2 of each under back skin.
6. Tie legs and wings close to body with string.
7. Place chicken on roasting rack. Roast at 350°F for 1½ hours, or until tender. Baste once or twice during cooking.
8. To serve, remove skin and slice.

Yield: 6 servings

How To Reduce Fat Intake From Chicken
Chicken that is roasted with the skin is delicious, but high in fat. A 4-ounce serving of chicken breast with skin contains 8.9 grams of fat while 4 ounces without skin contains only 4 grams. However, if you roast chicken without the skin it comes out dry and bland. The answer is to loosen the skin of the chicken and season the flesh under the skin..Then, roast with the skin on to retain moisture and allow seasoning to seep into the chicken. Remove the skin just before serving, and your chicken will be moist and flavorful with only ½ the fat.

Herb Cracker Stuffing

Preparation Time: 20 minutes   Cooking Time: 30 minutes

This Herb Stuffing may be baked in the oven as a side dish, or used to stuff a turkey or chicken. The recipe is sufficient to stuff a 12-pound turkey. You can adjust the recipe proportionately according to the size of the bird, but it's always a good idea to bake extra dressing on the side because it's so delicious everyone will want more.

1 cup coarsely chopped celery
½ cup chopped onion
1½ cups chicken broth
(recipe in Soup section)
1 medium apple, coarsely chopped
¼ cup raisins

1 6½-ounce package herb crackers,* coarsely crumbled
1 teaspoon chicken seasoning
(recipe in Condiment section)
¼ teaspoon sage
¼ teaspoon oregano
¼ teaspoon marjoram

Steps:
1. Preheat oven to 350°F.
2. In medium skillet, simmer celery and onions in ¼ cup chicken broth until tender.
3. Add remaining ingredients and mix well. Place in covered casserole and bake at 350°F. for 30 minutes.

Yield: 6 servings

This product is available from Health Valley.

Note: If you use dressing to stuff chicken or turkey, adjust chicken broth to 1 cup.

"One of My Favorites"

George Mateljan

Bombay Chicken

Chicken is part of almost every cuisine in the world. It is featured in such national favorites as Hungarian chicken paprika, Indian tandoori, Arabian couscous, Malayan satay, Florentine pollo alla diavola, Russian kunik and West Indian creole chicken. One thing that all of these international recipes have in common is that they combine chicken with interesting vegetables and spices, which is very helpful when you are trying to cook without salt.

In the Far East, they have cooked with curry, garlic and fruit for thousands of years. These ingredients bring wonderful flavors to chicken, and they are very healthy too.

I believe that you should cultivate your taste for herbs, spices and citrus, and use them freely to replace salt in cooking. This recipe for Bombay Chicken is a great delicacy that is worthy of being served to dinner guests, and I think you'll find that they won't even miss the salt.

The **nutritional highlights** of this recipe are that it is rich in vitamin C, thiamine, niacin and iron. Only 30% of the calories are from fat, while a typical curry chicken recipe made with butter can be as high as 50%.

Bombay Chicken

Preparation Time: 40 minutes   Cooking Time: 1¼ hours

1 tablespoon whole wheat
  pastry flour
1 tablespoon chicken seasoning
  (recipe in Condiment section)
½ teaspoon paprika
1½ teaspoons safflower oil
6 small chicken thighs,
  (about 1½ pounds) skinned
1 cup chopped onion
2 cups cored and diced
  pippin apples

2 teaspoons curry powder
1 clove garlic, minced
¾ cup raw brown rice, rinsed
2 cups chicken broth
  (recipe in Soup section)
½ cup blanched, slivered almonds
1 cup raisins
1 11-ounce can unsweetened
  mandarin oranges, with juice
1 tablespoon lemon juice

Steps:

1. In heavy plastic bag combine flour, chicken seasoning and paprika. Place chicken thighs in bag and toss to coat evenly with flour mixture.
2. In medium saucepan, heat oil and brown chicken on both sides over medium high heat. Remove to plate. Set aside.
3. Preheat oven to 350°F.
4. Add onions to saucepan and cook until soft, stirring often. Add apples, curry powder, garlic, rice and chicken broth. Bring to boil. Reduce heat and simmer 10 minutes.
5. Remove from heat. Add almonds, raisins, mandarin oranges and lemon juice. Mix well. Turn into glass casserole. Place chicken on top of rice mixture. Cover.
6. Bake at 350°F for 1 hour. Remove cover and bake 15 minutes longer.

Yield: 6 servings

Chicken Vegetable Stew

Preparation Time: 30 minutes   Cooking Time: 45 minutes

The French word "hochepot" means "pot on a hook" and is the origin of "hodgepodge." Hochepots were used for stewing. The medieval French royal courts consumed 14,900 chickens in one week! (They knew how to entertain in those days!)

1 3-pound chicken, skinned,
cut into serving pieces

2 cups chicken broth
(recipe in Soup section)

1 tablespoon chicken seasoning
(recipe in Condiment section)

2 teaspoons vegetable seasoning
(recipe in Condiment section)

5 medium carrots, cut into
1-inch pieces

2 small onions, cut into wedges

6 small celery ribs, cut into pieces

6 small potatoes, quartered

1 tablespoon lemon juice
chopped parsley for garnish

Steps:

1. Place chicken, broth and seasonings in large saucepan. Cover and bring to boil, reduce heat and simmer 10 minutes
2. Add vegetables and cook until chicken and vegetables are done, 45 minutes. Add lemon juice.
3. Serve in bowls. Garnish with chopped parsley.

Yield: 8 servings

Chicken Apple Sandwich

Preparation Time: 10 minutes

King Henry IV claimed that he brought such prosperity to France that every house had a "poulet au pot" (chicken in its pot). About 400 years later, Herbert Hoover made this his slogan when he ran for president, but he lost.

½ cup cooked, chopped
   chicken breast
¼ cup chopped apple
¼ cup chopped celery
 1 tablespoon chopped walnuts
 1 teaspoon lemon juice

1½ teaspoons mayonnaise
1½ tablespoons plain nonfat
   yogurt
¼ teaspoon curry powder
   whole wheat bread

Steps:
1. In a medium bowl, combine chicken, apple, celery, and walnuts. Sprinkle with lemon juice.
2. In a separate bowl, mix mayonnaise, yogurt and curry. Toss well with chicken mixture. Spread on whole wheat bread.

Yield: 2 sandwiches

12

Turkey

Many of us eat turkey only on traditionally festive occasions such as Thanksgiving and Christmas. But with the increased concern over lowering the amount of fat in our diets to reduce the risk of degenerative disease such as heart disease and cancer, turkey has experienced a new popularity as a food to include in our everyday meal planning.

Turkey breast with the skin removed is even lower in fat than chicken or fish, and they're all much lower than beef in calories, total fat, saturated fat and cholesterol. You can see at a glance why it's so much healthier to eat poultry and fish.

FOOD (per 3½ oz.)	CALORIES	TOTAL FAT	SATURATED FAT	MONOUN-SATURATED FAT	POLYUN-SATURATED FAT	CHOLESTEROL
Turkey Breast – no skin	135	0.74 gm	0.24 gm	0.13 gm	0.20 gm	83.3 mg
Chicken Breast – no skin	165	3.57 gm	1.01 gm	1.24 gm	0.77 gm	84.9 mg
Halibut	100	2.71 gm	0.46 gm	0.89 gm	1.35 gm	50.0 mg
Hamburger – 21% Fat	287	20.71 gm	8.54 gm	10.37 gm	0.85 gm	96.3 mg
Sirloin Steak	388	31.76 gm	14.29 gm	16.19 gm	1.27 gm	92.9 mg

Turkey, like chicken, provides the same high quality protein as meat and is rich in magnesium, iron, zinc, phosphorus and the B-complex vitamins. And, also like chicken, most of the fat is located in and just under the skin. This is why our recipes have you remove the skin before cooking or serving.

But while most of us now see the wisdom of including more turkey in our personal healthier eating plan, few of us know how to do much more than stuff and roast a turkey. That's why we know you'll be pleased with the delicious, easy-to-prepare turkey recipes in this section. There is the wonderfully simple and delicious Ginger Turkey Breast, the interestingly tangy Turkey Meatballs in Yogurt Cilantro Sauce, and the unusual Turkey Vegetable Patties with Red Beet Sauce. These recipes combine the nutritional benefits of turkey with flavorful and nutritious garden fresh vegetables and natural herbs. For example, our recipe for Spinach Cheese Turkey Loaf contains twice the U.S. RDA for vitamin A (as beta carotene), 70% of the U.S. RDA for vitamin C, and 42% of the U.S. RDA for calcium in a serving that supplies only 288 calories.

So be sure to make turkey part of your meal planning and enjoy the nutrition and flavor benefits of this extraordinary food and these extraordinary recipes.

"One of My Favorites"

George Mateljan

Spinach-Cheese Turkey Loaf

I'm sure you've noticed that there are no meat recipes in this book. One of the problems with meat is that even when you trim off all visible fat and roast or broil the meat to eliminate more fat, it is still high in saturated fats.

I know that hamburgers and meatloaf are staple dishes in many American homes but the fact is this: even when you buy lean ground beef and broil it instead of frying it, your hamburgers will still contain 62% calories from fat.

This recipe is a special favorite of mine because it is a very elegant looking and flavorful "meat" loaf without all the saturated fat.

The **nutritional highlights** of this recipe are that only 23% of calories are from fat, while a single serving provides 42% of the U.S. RDA for iron, 25% of zinc, 40% of niacin, 233% of vitamin A and 71% of vitamin C, all in only 288 calories.

Spinach-Cheese Turkey Loaf

Preparation Time: 20 minutes   Cooking Time: 30 minutes

1 pound ground turkey breast

3½ tablespoons chicken seasoning
(recipe in Condiment section)

2 egg whites

½ cup crumbs made from Health Valley Oat Bran Flakes Cereal

2 tablespoons wheat germ

½ cup pasta sauce (recipe in Dressings and Sauces section)

1 10-ounce package frozen chopped spinach, thawed and drained

1 cup grated Swiss cheese

1 bunch fresh spinach, cleaned mushrooms

cherry tomatoes

Steps:

1. Preheat oven to 350°F.
2. In a large bowl, combine turkey, chicken seasoning, egg whites, Oat Bran Flakes crumbs, wheat germ and pasta sauce. Mix well.
3. Lay out a large sheet of wax paper. Spread turkey mixture evenly to ¼-inch thickness on paper.
4. Press excess moisture out of thawed spinach. Place on turkey evenly, leaving 1-inch border. Sprinkle cheese on top of spinach. Roll up jelly roll fashion.
5. Place in glass loaf pan. Bake at 350°F. for 30 minutes. Remove from pan gently. Place on platter lined with a bed of fresh spinach leaves. Garnish platter with sliced raw mushrooms and cherry tomatoes. Let sit a few minutes before slicing. Top with additional heated pasta sauce, if desired.

Yield: 6 servings

Note: This meatloaf tastes delicious cold, so you can refrigerate any leftovers.

Turkey Vegetable Loaf

Preparation Time: 20 minutes   Cooking Time: 1 hour

Ground turkey meat is much leaner than ground beef and makes a much healthier meat loaf. Turkey can also be dry and fall apart, which is why we combine it with moist vegetables, egg whites and cracker crumbs to make a flavorful, and more nutritionally balanced entree.

1 teaspoon safflower oil
2 large cloves garlic, minced
   (about 2 teaspoons)
1 cup finely chopped celery
½ cup chopped onion
1½ cups diced red pepper
2½ cups sliced mushrooms
1 pound ground turkey meat

2 egg whites
   dash of nutmeg
½ cup cracker crumbs made
   from stoned wheat crackers*
½ cup minced fresh parsley
   no-salt catsup or tomato sauce*
   (optional)

Steps:

1. Heat oil in a large heavy skillet over medium high heat. Add garlic and saute for 1 minute to release flavor. Add celery, onion and pepper and saute for 3 minutes or until vegetables are soft.
2. Preheat oven to 375°F. Bring a kettle of water to a boil.
3. Add mushrooms to vegetable mixture and place cover on skillet until mushrooms give up their liquid, about 5 minutes. Remove cover and saute vegetables until all liquid has evaporated, about 5 minutes. Remove from heat.
4. In large bowl, combine the turkey meat, egg whites, nutmeg, cracker crumbs and parsley. Add the vegetables and mix well. Turn mixture into glass loaf pan and place loaf pan into large baking dish.
5. Pour enough boiling water into baking dish to measure about 1 inch. Bake at 375°F. for 1 hour. Let baked loaf rest for 15 minutes before slicing.

Yield: 6 servings

This product is available from Health Valley.

Serving Suggestion: For added zest and moistness, serve with catsup or heated tomato sauce.

Turkey Meatballs with Yogurt-Cilantro Sauce

Preparation Time: 20 minutes   Cooking Time: 12 minutes

Hors d'oeuvres are always a problem when you want to eat healthier. You want to be a host or hostess who can throw an enjoyable party, but so many of the so-called "finger foods" are just plain unhealthy to serve. This is one recipe that guests will enjoy that is very nutritious and below 30% of calories from fat.

¾ pound ground turkey (white meat only)
½ cup cracker crumbs made from herb crackers*
⅓ cup finely chopped scallions grated peel of 1 lime

2 teaspoons finely chopped cilantro
¼ teaspoon chili powder
1 egg white
2 tablespoons whole wheat pastry flour
1 teaspoon safflower oil

Yogurt-Cilantro Sauce

1 cup plain nonfat yogurt
1½ teaspoons finely chopped cilantro

2 teaspoons honey
1 tablespoon lime juice dash of cayenne

Steps:

1. In a medium bowl, combine turkey meat, cracker crumbs, scallions, lime peel, cilantro, chili powder and egg white. Mix well. Form mixture into small balls and dust lightly with flour.

2. Combine ingredients for the sauce in a small serving bowl and set aside.

3. Heat ½ teaspoon oil in a heavy skillet over medium high heat. Place as many balls as possible without crowding into heated skillet and brown on all sides, about 6 minutes. Drain on paper towel and arrange on a warmed serving platter. Repeat until all turkey balls are browned and serve them with the sauce.

Yield: 30 hors d'oeuvres

This product is available from Health Valley.

"One of My Favorites"

George Mateljan

Turkey Patties with Red Beet Sauce

Ground turkey is an excellent alternative to ground beef because it is substantially lower in fat. For example, most ground beef contains between 20 to 30% fat by weight. In contrast, the dark meat of turkey without the skin contains a little over 7% fat by weight. And turkey breast without the skin has less than 1% fat by weight!

This particular recipe is a real favorite of mine. Although the turkey patties are very tasty by themselves, I always serve them with the Red Beet Sauce. This sauce not only complements the flavors perfectly, it makes the patties moist, and even more nutritious.

The **nutritional highlight** of this recipe is that it is high in protein, yet contains only 28% of calories from fat.

Turkey Patties

Preparation Time: 20 minutes	Cooking Time: 30 minutes

1 tablespoon olive oil
2 cups finely shredded beet greens, mustard greens, or swiss chard
4 cloves garlic, minced
1 pound ground turkey
3 medium potatoes, boiled, mashed and chilled (2 cups)
1 cup soft tofu, drained in a strainer for 30 minutes

1 cup chopped scallions
2 tablespoons prepared mustard
1½ tablespoons chicken seasoning
(recipe in Condiment section)
1 tablespoon dried basil or ¼ cup chopped fresh basil
¾ cup cracker crumbs made from herb crackers*

Steps:

1. Heat the oil in a medium saucepan over medium high heat. Add the shredded greens and sprinkle with minced garlic. Cover pan and reduce the heat to low. Wilt the greens for 2 minutes, stir and set aside to cool.
2. Preheat oven to 375°F.
3. In a mixing bowl, combine turkey meat, mashed potatoes, tofu, scallions, mustard, chicken seasoning, basil, ½ cup cracker crumbs and beet greens.
4. Form the mixture into 4-inch round and ½-inch thick patties and sprinkle them with remaining ¼ cup of cracker crumbs. Place patties on lightly oiled cookie sheet and bake at 375°F. until lightly browned, about 30 minutes.

Yield: 12 patties

This product is available from Health Valley.

Red Beet Sauce

Preparation Time: 20 minutes	Cooking Time: 20 minutes

1 cup chicken broth
(recipe in Soup section)
2 large beets, peeled and julienned
2 teaspoons prepared Dijon style mustard

2 teaspoons apple cider vinegar
1 teaspoon honey
½ cup sliced scallions
1 teaspoon arrowroot
2 tablespoons water

Steps:

1. In a medium saucepan, heat 2 tablespoons of the chicken broth over medium high heat. Add the beets and saute for 5 minutes. Add the rest of the chicken broth and boil mixture until beets are tender and liquid has been reduced by one-third, about 10 minutes.
2. Add mustard, vinegar, honey and scallions. Combine arrowroot with the water in a small bowl and stir slowly into beet mixture. Bring to a boil, lower heat, and simmer sauce until thickened, about 2 minutes.

Yield: 2 cups

Curried Turkey and Green Peas

Preparation Time: 20 minutes   Cooking Time: 2 hours

One of the most important minerals that our bodies require, and one of the most neglected, is *zinc*. It is essential for cell division, cell repair and growth, and bone growth. Oysters and herring are two of the richest sources of zinc, but many people don't eat these fish. Wheat germ, yeast, sesame seeds and molasses are also good sources, but we can't eat them in sufficient quantities to cover our needs. The most commonly enjoyed food that is rich in zinc is turkey, and it's just one more good reason to eat this nutritious bird more often than Thanksgiving and Christmas. One serving of Curried Turkey provides 18% of the U.S. RDA for zinc.

2 tablespoons safflower oil
2 small yams, peeled and
    cut into ½-inch cubes
2 cups chopped onion
1 rib celery, chopped
3 cloves garlic, minced
¼ teaspoon ground ginger
⅛ teaspoon thyme

1½ pounds turkey meat, skinned
    and cut into 1-inch cubes
    and blanched
1½ tablespoons curry powder
¼ cup lemon juice
3 cups chicken broth
    (recipe in Soup section)
¼ cup raisins
1 10-ounce package frozen
    green peas, defrosted

Steps:

1. In a large heavy skillet, heat 1 tablespoon of the oil over medium high heat. Add the yams and cook them until they are tender and browned, stirring often, about 25 minutes. Puree the cooked yams in a food processor or blender. Set aside.

2. Heat the remaining oil in the same skillet and add the onion, celery, garlic, ginger, and thyme. Cook until onions begin to brown, about 15 minutes.

3. Combine onion mixture with turkey meat, curry, lemon juice, and chicken broth. Bring to a simmer. Cover and simmer for 45 minutes.

4. Add raisins and yam puree. Replace cover and simmer for 30 minutes, stirring occasionally. Remove from heat and stir in the peas. Let stand for 5 minutes. Serve immediately.

Yield: 6 servings

Ginger Turkey Breast

Preparation Time: 30 minutes
Plus Marinating Time: 8 to 24 hours

Cooking Time: 30 minutes

The ginger family includes three popular spices, ginger, cardamom and turmeric. Its name is from the Sanskrit stingavera, which means "horn-shaped" or "horn-root." The Chinese were using ginger as early as the 6th century B.C., and it has been popular throughout history. Ginger is steeped in mythology, and is reputed to have the power to tame a tiger and dispel the incubus (an evil spirit which descends on people in their sleep). You will enjoy the hot-sweet taste of ginger in this recipe even if you don't have a wild tiger around the house.

¼ **cup chicken broth**
(recipe in Soup section)

2 **teaspoons chicken seasoning**
(recipe in Condiment section)

¾ **teaspoon cinnamon**

2 **tablespoons fresh, grated ginger**

3 **cloves garlic, minced**

1 **1½-pound turkey breast, skinned and boned**

1 **tablespoon safflower oil**

Steps:

1. For the marinade, combine chicken broth, chicken seasoning, cinnamon, ginger and garlic in a shallow bowl just large enough to hold the turkey breast. Place turkey breast in the marinade after making a few ½-inch deep slits into thick parts of the meat with a sharp knife. This allows the marinade to penetrate the meat. Cover and refrigerate for at least 8 hours or up to 24 hours. Turn the meat occasionally.
2. Preheat oven to 350°F.
3. Remove the turkey breast from marinade, making sure all clinging ginger and garlic are scraped off the meat and returned to the bowl with marinade. Reserve marinade for basting. Allow the meat to come to room temperature, about 1 hour.
4. Heat oil in a heavy ovenproof skillet over medium high heat. Saute turkey until golden brown on all sides.
5. Put skillet into preheated 350°F oven and bake for 20 minutes or until turkey feels springy to the touch, basting once with the reserved marinade. Remove turkey from the oven and cool for 5 minutes before slicing.

Yield: 6 servings

"One of My Favorites"

George Mateljan

Turkey Bean Casserole

Making your own baked beans isn't that much work, but it does require a lot of time. The beans must be soaked overnight, and then cooked for hours the next day. But the results are worth it: rich baked beans without the pork you find in so many recipes and commercial canned varieties.

If you don't have the time to prepare your own baked beans, Health Valley has a healthy alternative for you. Just open a can of Health Valley Boston Style Baked Beans, or Health Valley Vegetarian Beans with Miso. They're both delicious, and both vegetarian.

Turkey Bean Casserole

Preparation Time: 1 hour
Plus overnight soaking of beans

Cooking Time: 4 hours

1 pound white navy beans
9 cups water
1 pound ground turkey
1 cup finely chopped onions
½ teaspoon dry mustard
2 tablespoons apple cider vinegar
½ cup molasses
2 cups grated carrots

½ cup diced celery
2 cups peeled, finely chopped tomatoes
6 teaspoons chicken seasoning
(recipe in Condiment section)
2 teaspoons all purpose seasoning
(recipe in Condiment section)
½ teaspoon garlic powder

Steps:

1. Wash beans. Soak overnight in 9 cups of water. In the morning, boil the beans in same liquid until the skins are tender but not broken (about 1 hour).

2. In large pan or Dutch oven, brown ground turkey, add onions and saute until soft. Add remaining ingredients except beans and cook for 10 minutes.

3. Add cooked navy beans with liquid. Mix well. Simmer 4 hours or until liquid has evaporated.

Yield: 10 servings

13

Vegetarian Entrees

The latest research on the relationship between nutrition and health indicates that the typical American diet contains too much fat, especially saturated fat, from too much red meat.

These same studies show that the best sources for essential vitamins, minerals and fiber without saturated fats, come from vegetables, fruits, grains and beans.

For this reason, it is strongly recommended that at least once a week, you avoid meat, especially red meat, altogether. So even if you are not a vegetarian per se, on one or even two days a week, you should enjoy the infinite variety of flavors, textures and nutrients found only among vegetables, grains, beans and fruit.

This chapter has been especially created to show you how to prepare vegetarian recipes that provide the nutritional balance you need to look and feel your best. For a long time, it was felt that you needed to eat meat and eggs to get complete protein. But you can also get complete protein by combining grains and legumes. In fact, grains and beans are among the most nourishing and economical sources of protein.

If you've always been a person who eats meat every night, it will probably take you two or three weeks before you become accustomed to not having it. But you'll also find that when you cut out all that fat, you'll start feeling so much more alert and energetic. And whether or not you're a vegetarian, we think you'll find recipes here that you'll want to use. All of these entrees offer hearty, satisfying flavor, as well as an abundance of nutrients – without a lot of fat, calories, sodium or cholesterol.

For example, the Stuffed Green Peppers provide 28% of your requirement for iron and 300% of the daily requirement for vitamin C. Overall, you'll find that the recipes in this section are good sources of calcium, and they are all below 30% of calories from fat.

The only drawback of preparing grains and bean dishes is that they can require long cooking times, which are not always convenient when you're in a hurry.

That's why Health Valley prepares a variety of bean and grain products for your convenience and enjoyment. Health Valley offers three varieties of meatless chilis, two varieties of baked beans, and an exclusive Amaranth Minute Meal™ vegetable pilaf. This pilaf is unique because it combines high-protein Amaranth with a perfect balance of other grains to provide "complete" meatless protein. All of these products are carefully prepared the healthier way, using the finest whole natural ingredients, without animal fats of any kind. So they make a tasty and convenient main dish all by themselves.

"One of My Favorites"

George Mateljan

Garden Veggies Casserole

I was a vegetarian for many years, and I still believe that it's healthy for everyone to plan vegetarian dinners in their weekly menus.

Rice is a natural choice as a staple ingredient in vegetarian dishes because it's nutritious and filling. It's important to use brown rice, which retains both the bran and germ. White rice, like white bread, has been milled and processed – discarding the most nutritious parts – while retaining the white starchy endosperm. Brown rice has a heartier flavor than white rice, in the same way that whole wheat bread is heartier than white bread.

This recipe is a favorite of mine because it's so tasty that you don't even notice the absence of meat. In fact, I've often served it to my non-vegetarian friends, and they think it's delicious.

The **nutritional highlights** of this recipe include the fact that it contains only 29% of calories from fat, and it also provides almost 3 grams of dietary fiber per serving. The vegetables in the recipe are especially rich in vitamin A and C.

Garden Veggies Casserole

Preparation Time: 20 minutes   Cooking Time: 30 minutes

2 cups cooked brown rice
1 cup grated cheddar cheese
(about 4 ounces)
½ cup chopped onion
1 cup cauliflower flowerettes
1 cup chopped broccoli
½ cup sliced celery

½ cup sliced carrots
½ cup sliced zucchini
2 cups pasta sauce (recipe in Dressings and Sauces section)
1 clove garlic, minced
2 teaspoons dried basil

Steps:

1. Preheat oven to 350°F.
2. Combine rice and half of cheddar cheese. Mix well. Place in bottom of 10 x 6 x 2-inch baking dish.
3. Meanwhile, steam the vegetables 5-7 minutes until tender crisp. Spoon vegetables over rice-cheese mixture.
4. Combine pasta sauce, garlic, and basil. Pour over vegetables. Top with remaining cheese.
5. Bake at 350°F for 30 minutes.

Yield: 8 servings

Millet Stuffed Peppers

Preparation Time: 45 minutes   Cooking Time: 30 minutes

1 cup whole millet
3 cups water
5 medium green peppers, halved
    lengthwise and seeded
1 tablespoon safflower oil
2 cups chopped onion
1½ teaspoons minced garlic
8 ounces sliced mushrooms
3 tablespoons chopped parsley

1 teaspoon dried basil
½ teaspoon oregano
4 teaspoons vegetable seasoning
    (recipe in Condiment section)
3 teaspoons all purpose seasoning
    (recipe in Condiment section)
2 lightly beaten egg whites
3 ounces grated cheddar cheese
2 cups pasta sauce (recipe in
    Dressings and Sauces section)
2 teaspoons honey

Steps:

1. Put millet and water in saucepan, bring to a boil, lower heat, cover and simmer until tender, about 30 minutes.
2. Steam the pepper halves over boiling water for 5 minutes.
3. Preheat oven to 350°F.
4. Meanwhile, in a large skillet, heat oil and saute onions until tender. Add garlic and mushrooms and cook for 2 minutes longer. Add millet, parsley and seasonings, egg whites and 2 ounces grated cheese. Mix well.
5. Fill pepper halves with millet mixture and put in oiled baking dish. Top each pepper half with grated cheese.
6. Bake at 350°F for 30 minutes.
7. In a small saucepan, combine pasta sauce with honey, heat over medium high heat, and spoon sauce over peppers before serving.

Yield: 5 servings

About Millet

Millet is a nutritious, mild tasting yellow grain that is sold whole or cracked, usually without its tough, inedible hull. Millet and Amaranth are the only grains that are alkaline, making them very easy to digest and non-allergenic. You can use them in cakes, cookies, bread, puddings and as a rice substitute. Millet has almost as much protein as wheat, and is rich in iron, potassium, and B vitamins. Combined with beans, it provides complete protein.

Stuffed Green Peppers

Preparation Time: 25 minutes   Cooking Time: 35 minutes

Christopher Columbus was looking for Asia, the land of pepper, when he wandered into the Caribbean by mistake. When the Indians seasoned his food with hot spice, he mistakenly called it pepper and the name stuck. Actually, it was chili, of the genus *capsicum*. Green and red bell peppers, fiery chilie peppers, yellow banana peppers and pimientos are all from the capsicum family, and are not pepper at all.

¾ cup raw brown rice
4 green peppers
1 cup water
1 teaspoon safflower oil
½ cup chopped onion
½ cup chopped celery
½ cup chopped mushrooms

1 teaspoon vegetable seasoning
(recipe in Condiment section)
½ teaspoon oregano
⅓ cup finely chopped parsley
3 cups tomato sauce*
4 ounces cheddar cheese, shredded
1 tablespoon wheat germ

Steps:
1. Cook rice, according to package directions.
2. Meanwhile, cut green peppers in half lengthwise and remove seeds and stems. Blanch peppers in water until tender but still firm, about 7 minutes; remove from pan and rinse under cold water.
3. Preheat oven to 375°F.
4. In a medium skillet, heat oil and saute onions, then add celery, mushrooms, seasonings and parsley. Add cooked rice, 1 cup of tomato sauce and cheese. Mix well. Stuff peppers with this mixture. Place in oiled shallow casserole. Top with remaining tomato sauce.
5. Sprinkle wheat germ over peppers. Bake at 375°F. for 35 minutes. Spoon tomato sauce from casserole over each pepper and serve.

Yield: 4 servings

This product is available from Health Valley.

About Green & Red Peppers
Red peppers are simply green peppers that have been left on the vine until mature. When choosing either kind, look for bright color, firm and thick fleshed body and glossy skin. Avoid pale peppers or those that are shrivelled or bruised. They'll keep for about a week in the crisper of your refrigerator. Green bell peppers are an outstanding source of vitamin C, and red bell peppers are even better – plus being a fabulous source of vitamin A.

"One of My Favorites"

George Mateljan

Health Valley Rice Surprise

I consider this recipe to be one of the great triumphs of vegetarian cooking. For the first time, here is a vegetarian entree you can serve to guests and nobody will realize it's vegetarian cooking.

It's a beautiful recipe to look at (see color photo), and it's so rich and delicious that it's hard to believe that only 30% of the calories are from fat.

By the way, the topping for this casserole is so rich that we actually adjusted it slightly and use it as a filling for Baked Apples!! (Recipe for Baked Apples with Creamy Filling in Desserts section.)

The **nutritional highlights** of this recipe are that a serving provides over 90% of the U.S. RDA for vitamin A, close to 60% of vitamin C, and 27% of calcium and protein. And there's less than 200 calories in a serving.

Health Valley Rice Surprise

Preparation Time: 30 minutes   Cooking Time: 32 minutes

2 cups cooked brown rice
2 egg whites, slightly beaten
1 teaspoon safflower oil
1 cup diced onions
1 large clove garlic, minced
1 cup sliced mushrooms
1 cup diced zucchini
½ cup diced celery

¾ cup diced red pepper
¾ cup diced carrots
1 cup grated Swiss cheese
¾ cup plain nonfat yogurt
2 egg whites
2 small tomatoes, sliced
   fresh rosemary sprigs,
   basil leaves or parsley sprigs
   for garnish

Steps:

1. Preheat oven to 350°F.
2. Combine rice with the 2 slightly beaten egg whites. Mix well. Press rice mixture into pie plate. Set aside.
3. Heat oil in a large skillet and saute onions until lightly browned. Add garlic and saute lightly for 30 seconds more to release flavor. Add mushrooms, zucchini, celery, red pepper and carrots, and saute until vegetables are tender, about 3 minutes.
4. Sprinkle ¼ cup of Swiss cheese over rice crust. Top with vegetable mixture. Sprinkle with another ¼ cup of cheese.
5. Combine yogurt with the remaining 2 egg whites, and spread carefully over the vegetable-cheese mixture.
6. Sprinkle with another ¼ cup of the remaining cheese. Bake at 350°F for 30 minutes.
7. Remove pie from oven and garnish with tomato slices. Sprinkle remaining cheese over all and return to oven for 2 minutes, or until tomatoes are heated through. Garnish with rosemary sprigs, basil leaves or parsley sprigs just before serving.

Yield: 6 servings

"One of My Favorites"

George Mateljan

Yogurt Noodle Bake

This recipe traditionally calls for sour cream, but we've replaced it with yogurt to make it healthier. One cup of sour cream contains about 48 grams of fat and 100 milligrams of cholesterol, while one cup of plain nonfat yogurt contains only a trace of fat and 4 milligrams of cholesterol.

This delicious casserole is so rich in flavor, it's hard to believe that it can be so healthy too. One of the reasons that it's a favorite of mine is that it's rich in calcium with 20% of the U.S. RDA in a serving, and in iron with 15%. These two minerals are so important to women today, and this is a tasty way to incorporate them in your diet.

The other **nutritional highlights** of this recipe are that it is high in all the important B vitamins, as well as protein and dietary fiber.

Yogurt Noodle Bake

Preparation Time: 30 minutes   Cooking Time: 20 minutes

¾ cup plain low fat yogurt
½ cup sliced green onion
3 cups cooked whole wheat
    elbow pasta*
1 cup chopped onion
1 cup sliced mushrooms
2 tablespoons water
½ teaspoon minced garlic

½ teaspoon oregano
½ teaspoon dried basil
1¼ cups pasta sauce (recipe in
    Dressings and Sauces section)
1½ teaspoons honey
5 ounces cheddar cheese,
    shredded

Steps:
1. Preheat oven to 350°F.
2. In medium bowl, combine yogurt, green onion and cooked pasta. Mix well. Set aside.
3. In medium saucepan, simmer onion and mushrooms in 2 tablespoons water until tender. Add garlic, oregano, basil, pasta sauce, and honey. Mix well.
4. Put pasta mixture in 10x6x2-inch glass casserole. Top with sauce mixture. Sprinkle with cheese.
5. Bake at 350°F. for 20 minutes.

Yield: 8 servings

This product is available from Health Valley.

Summer Stew

Preparation Time: 15 minutes   Cooking Time: 27 minutes

1½ tablespoons olive oil
1 medium onion, sliced
2 cloves garlic, minced
2 small eggplants (about
   1½ pounds), diced
2 medium zucchini, sliced
¼ cup finely chopped parsley
2 tablespoons finely chopped
   fresh basil leaves

1 teaspoon grated lemon peel
1 cup plain nonfat yogurt
1 teaspoon prepared mustard
1 teaspoon prepared horseradish
½ teaspoon honey
3 medium tomatoes, peeled
   and chopped

Steps:

1. Over medium high heat in a large saucepan, heat the oil, then add onion and garlic. Saute for about 2 minutes or until tender. Add eggplant, zucchini, parsley, basil and lemon peel. Reduce heat and simmer covered for 20 minutes or until eggplant is tender.
2. Meanwhile, combine the yogurt, mustard, horseradish and honey in a small bowl. Cover and chill.
3. Add tomatoes to the stew and continue cooking for 5 more minutes.
4. Serve stew hot topped with dollops of yogurt dressing.

Yield: 6 servings

How to Choose & Store Eggplant
Eggplant should be firm, heavy and free of blemishes. The skin should always be smooth, glossy and deep purple with no scars, flabbiness or shriveling. The cap should be bright green. Avoid wrinkled or bruised eggplant, and those with wilted yellow caps. Eggplant will keep in the refrigerator for several days. In Europe, eggplant are also know as aubergine, so if you see that name occasionally in cookbooks you'll know what it is.

Cheese Eggplant

Preparation Time: 30 minutes   Cooking Time: 25 minutes

Eggplant is a member of the nightshade family, which includes tomatoes, red and green peppers, tobacco, the hallucinogenic jimson weed and deadly nightshade. India and the Far East are the largest consumers of eggplant, which has been sadly neglected in the United States. This is too bad because eggplant is a good source of several important nutrients, including iron.

It's an old wives' tale that eggplant has to be peeled, sliced, salted and weighted for a couple of hours to squeeze out the juice. Just slice and use it – it doesn't even have to be peeled unless the skin has been waxed or is quite tough.

1 cup raw brown rice
2 teaspoons olive oil
½ cup coarsely chopped onion
¼ cup coarsely chopped
    green pepper
1 clove garlic, minced or
    ½ teaspoon garlic powder
½ teaspoon dried basil
1 teaspoon vegetable seasoning
    (recipe in Condiment section)

1 medium eggplant, unpeeled
    and cut into ¾ inch cubes
1 medium zucchini, sliced, cut
    each slice into quarters
1 medium tomato, coarsely
    chopped
2 cups tomato sauce*
¼ teaspoon oregano
1 cup shredded mild
    cheddar cheese
¼ cup wheat germ

Steps:

1. Cook rice according to package directions.
2. Meanwhile, in a large skillet, heat oil and saute onion, green pepper, garlic, basil and vegetable seasoning. Add eggplant and stir-fry for 5 minutes. Add zucchini and saute 5 minutes longer. Add tomato and stir just until mixed with other vegetables. Remove from heat.
3. Preheat oven to 350°F. Oil an 8-inch square baking dish.
4. Combine tomato sauce and oregano. Add half of this mixture to the cooked rice. Mix cheese and wheat germ. Add half of this mixture to the rice mixture.
5. Put rice mixture in the bottom of prepared baking dish. Spread vegetable mixture over it. Top with the remaining tomato sauce, then with the remaining cheese mixture.
6. Bake at 350°F for 25 minutes until cheese is melted and browned lightly.

Yield: 6 servings

This product is available from Health Valley.

"One of My Favorites"

George Mateljan

Millet Casserole

Millet is a basic food for half a billion Indians, Chinese, Africans and Russians, but most Americans don't even know what it tastes like. This is a pity because millet is alkaline, making it easy to digest and non-allergenic.

Millet is usually eaten in the form of porridge, and I have to admit, it isn't too terrific because millet itself is so mild tasting. However, this recipe combines it with flavorful vegetables, tangy sauce and cheese for a dish that makes an appetizing vegetarian entree.

The **nutritional highlights** of millet are that it is rich in iron, potassium, and B vitamins.

Millet Casserole

Preparation Time: 20 minutes · · · · · · · · · · · · · · Cooking Time: 45 minutes

1 small eggplant, cut into
½-inch cubes
2 teaspoons safflower oil
1 medium green pepper, chopped
1 medium onion, chopped
1½ cups tomato sauce*
½ cup pasta sauce (recipe in
Dressings and Sauces section)

1 clove garlic, minced
1½ teaspoons all purpose seasoning
(recipe in Condiment section)
1 tablespoon honey
½ cup millet, uncooked
½ cup grated cheddar cheese

Steps:

1. Preheat oven to 350°F.
2. In large skillet, lightly brown eggplant in oil. Remove and set aside.
3. Add green pepper and onion to skillet and saute until tender crisp, about 2 minutes.
4. Add tomato sauce, pasta sauce, garlic, seasoning, honey and uncooked millet. Bring to boil. Lower heat, cover and simmer 15 minutes. Remove from heat.
5. In 1½ quart casserole, layer eggplant and millet mixture. Cover. Bake at 350°F. for 45 minutes or until moisture is absorbed. Remove cover. Sprinkle with grated cheese and bake until cheese is melted.

Yield: 6 servings

This product is available from Health Valley.

14

Tofu

One secret to eating healthy has actually been around for centuries. Although tofu has been a staple food in Asia for thousands of years, it is just being discovered as a "superfood" in the west.

What makes tofu such a "superfood" is the fact that it is rich in calcium, protein and vitamins, low in calories, sodium and saturated fat, and cholesterol free. Eight ounces of tofu provides as much calcium as eight ounces of milk, and more iron than four eggs. And to make it even better, tofu is very economical.

Tofu is derived from nutrition-packed soybeans. Soybeans and purified water are cooked together and pureed into a creamy, healthful soy milk and then curdled with a natural thickener called "nigari" to cause curds to form. This process enhances the nutritional value of the soybeans by improving the quality of the protein so that tofu provides quality protein like that found in meat, fish, poultry and dairy products. That's why in Asia, tofu is referred to as "meat without bones." Sometimes, Asians refer to it as "soy cheese."

We think both of the comparisons are somewhat misleading, because they arouse unrealistic flavor expectations. Tofu by itself is very mild tasting, almost bland. We think the best comparison is with pasta. Pasta by itself isn't very interesting, but you love it when it's topped with sauce and cheese. The same thing happens when you combine tofu with the flavors and textures of other foods, as we do in these exciting recipes.

Health Valley makes two varieties of tofu, "firm" and "soft," using organically grown soybeans. Look for them under the brand name "Tofu-ya®," or for tofu that is made in the same traditional, natural way. Using it in these recipes will quickly help you overcome your concern that tofu is some exotic ingredient primarily applicable to Oriental cooking. It's a healthy ingredient you can use in all kinds of All-American dishes.

Quick Lentil Chili Casserole

Preparation Time: 5 minutes   Cooking Time: 15 minutes

One of the most unique products ever created by Health Valley was canned Vegetarian Chili with Lentils, in which lentils replace the traditional beans. People everywhere liked its lighter taste and texture, as well as the nutritional benefits of lentils.

This recipe is a favorite of mine because it combines lentils with the complementary protein of brown rice and tofu into a healthy vegetarian entree that tastes great, and cooks in only 15 minutes.

The **nutritional highlights** of this recipe are that it provides 6.8 grams of dietary fiber in a serving (about 25% of your daily requirement), and over 30% of the U.S. RDA for protein with only 30% of calories from fat and a negligible 4 mg. of cholesterol.

2 cups cooked brown rice
1 10-ounce package frozen corn, defrosted and drained
1 15-ounce can Health Valley Chili with Lentils

4 ounces firm tofu, drained and cut into ½-inch cubes
¼ cup shredded cheddar cheese

Steps:

1. Preheat oven to 350°F.
2. In a medium bowl, combine rice, corn, chili and tofu. Spoon mixture into a glass casserole. Sprinkle with cheese.
3. Bake at 350°F. for 15 minutes, or until warmed through.

Yield: 6 servings

258

Chili-Cheese Tofu Lasagna

Preparation Time: 25 minutes

This is a recipe we always make whenever we conduct a cooking school. Everyone just loves the idea of a zesty vegetarian lasagna that you can prepare start to finish in 25 minutes. When you see how easy it is to do, and taste the results, you'll add it to your list of staple recipes you make all the time.

We always recommend serving the lasagna with brown rice, as we do here, for complementary protein, and garnish the plate colorfully with red and green peppers.

4 ounces tortilla chips*

2 cups pasta sauce (recipe in Dressings and Sauces section)

4 ounces firm tofu, drained and cut into ¼-inch cubes

5 ounces cheddar cheese, grated

1 15-ounce can spicy vegetarian chili*

2 teaspoons all purpose seasoning (recipe in Condiment section)

1 teaspoon garlic powder

1 green pepper

1 red pepper

6 cups cooked brown rice

Steps:
1. Preheat oven to 400°F. Spread ½ of tortilla chips over bottom of 6x10-inch casserole, reserve other half for topping.
2. Cover chips with ½ of pasta sauce.
3. Add tofu and ½ of grated cheese.
4. Spread chili over all.
5. Cover with remaining pasta sauce. Sprinkle with all purpose seasoning and garlic powder.
6. Sprinkle remaining grated cheese on top. Garnish with the remaining ½ of the tortilla chips, crumbled.
7. Bake at 400°F for 15 minutes.
8. Garnish each person's plate with red and green pepper rings.
9. Serve cooked brown rice on each person's plate to make this a complete and balanced meal, high in protein, fiber, vitamins A and C, and calcuim.

Yield: 8 servings

This product is available from Health Valley.

Tangy Tofu-Veggie Casserole

Preparation Time: 10 minutes　　　　　　Cooking Time: 45 minutes

1 10-ounce package firm tofu,
drained and cut into ½ inch cubes

1 10-ounce package frozen whole
kernel corn, thawed and drained

1 15-ounce can tomato sauce*

½ cup chopped parsley

½ cup chopped green pepper

¼ cup grated cheddar cheese

¼ cup crumbled cheese crackers*

Steps:

1. Preheat oven to 350°F. and oil a 2-quart casserole.
2. Combine tofu, corn, tomato sauce, parsley and green pepper. Spoon mixture into casserole, top with cheese and cracker crumbs.
3. Bake at 350°F. for 45 minutes.

Yield: 6 servings

This product is available from Health Valley.

Choosing, Using and Storing Tofu

There are two primary consistencies in tofu: Firm and Soft. Firm can replace meat, fish, poultry and cheese in recipes. Soft is velvety smooth and creamy, and is ideal for dressings, sauces, custards and light desserts. Tofu will keep in the refrigerator for about a week. If you plan to use the tofu within 24 hours, drain and store without water to preserve the delicate taste. If you plan to use it later, drain and add fresh water daily. If you'd like a meatlike texture for dishes like tofu "cutlets," freeze the tofu first and then thaw overnight. When using tofu, always be sure to drain well and press out all the water to keep the tofu from being too watery.

Far East Tofu-Vegetable Casserole

Preparation Time: 30 minutes   Cooking Time: 30 minutes

1 tablespoon safflower oil
8 ounces firm tofu, drained
   and sliced into ½-inch cubes
2 cups diced celery
1 medium green pepper, diced
1 cup sliced scallions
2 large cloves garlic, minced
1 medium zucchini, diced

4 tomatoes, peeled and chopped
¼ teaspoon cayenne
½ teaspoon oregano
¼ cup finely chopped parsley
1 cup pasta sauce (recipe in
   Dressings and Sauces section)
2 cups cooked brown rice

Steps:

1. Preheat oven to 350°F.
2. In a large skillet, heat the oil over medium high heat. Add the tofu and cook until golden brown. Remove tofu. Drain on paper towel, and set aside.
3. Combine celery, green pepper, scallions, garlic and zucchini in the same skillet. Saute until crisp-tender.
4. Add tomatoes, cayenne, oregano and parsley and cook until tomatoes are warmed through, about 3 minutes.
5. Stir pasta sauce, rice and tofu into the vegetable mixture. Spoon into a glass casserole and bake at 350°F. for 30 minutes.

Yield: 6 servings

How to Make Tofu Taste Good

Tofu is often referred to by Orientals as "soy cheese." This is a misnomer because Westerners expect it to taste like cheese and it doesn't. It's probably more accurate to compare tofu with pasta—it's pretty bland by itself but delicious when combined with other foods. Tofu picks up and heightens the flavors of foods it's with, while adding its own unique "freshness." This is why tofu works so well in a recipe like this where it is combined with strong vegetables like green pepper and scallions, and aggressive seasonings like garlic, cayenne and oregano.

15

Soups

Soup is as basic a food as bread, and it has been the cornerstone of every cuisine in the world since antiquity.

You should include a bowl of soup daily as part of your healthy way of eating. That's because soup provides a variety of benefits: (1) Properly prepared soup can be a source of significant nutrition, especially when the ingredients include fresh vegetables, whole grains, and legumes. (2) Starting your meal with soup gets your digestive system going and wakes up your taste buds so you can really enjoy the meal and digest it properly. (3) Soup takes the edge off your appetite so you won't overeat.

A recent study showed that when people started their meals with soup, they consumed about 20% less calories than what they usually ate. This explains why researchers have found that people who eat soup regularly have an easier time maintaining their ideal weight. But be sure to avoid cheese soups, or cream-based soups like cream of shrimp which can be high in calories and may contain as much as 50% fat.

And eating soup helps make it easy for you to follow the dietary guidelines for healthier eating. Since we use only fresh vegetables in these recipes, most are superior sources of vitamins A and C. For example, our delicious Herbed Chicken Soup supplies more than 10,000 I.U. of vitamin A as beta-carotene per serving. And a serving of Garden Vegetable Soup supplies over 100% of the U.S. RDA for vitamin A and 50% of the U.S. RDA for vitamin C.

Remember that these recipes are only guidelines. So feel free to be creative by using whatever vegetables and herbs are at their freshest and in peak season.

A Healthy Alternative for Extra Convenience
Health Valley offers a complete line of your favorite soups, each prepared like homemade. So when you want a delicious bowl of soup made the healthier way, and you also want the convenience of 5-minute preparation time, open a lead-free can of Health Valley soup. They're lightly salted with 40% less salt than commercial brands, and they're also available with No Salt Added.

Be sure to try Health Valley Chicken Broth, the most versatile of all soups. You can enjoy it by itself with a variety of garnishes, or you can use it to poach fish or chicken, as a liquid to cook brown rice or other grains, or to steam your vegetables. And you can use Health Valley Chicken Broth in many of these recipes to make them even quicker and easier. Health Valley Chicken Broth has only 15 calories in a serving, so you get extra flavor without extra calories.

"One of My Favorites"

George Mateljan

Health Valley Garden Vegetable Soup

Americans are becoming more adventurous in their consumption of vegetables. A decade ago, supermarkets carried 65 produce items. Today, they have 216 produce items to meet consumer demand.*

Many of these recently popular vegetables play an important role in a plan of healthier eating. Along with their nutritional value, they are essential for enhancing flavor when you cook without salt.

In this delicious soup recipe, you will find staples like carrots, onion and celery and you will also find leeks and celery root, which you may not have used so often in the past. They add their distinctive flavors to the other robust vegetables for fresh garden goodness and crunchy texture. Celery root and celery also contain enough sodium to provide a little bit of that "salty" taste you're so used to, but not enough sodium to be of concern to most people.

The **nutritional highlights** of this recipe are that it provides 125% of the U.S. RDA for vitamin A and 51% of the U.S. RDA for vitamin C in a single serving. And while you may not realize that vegetables can be a good source of calcium, this soup provides 8% of the U.S. RDA in a serving.

*Source: USDA Economic Research Service

Health Valley
Garden Vegetable Soup

Preparation Time: 20 minutes   Cooking Time: 1 hour

---

4 cups chicken broth
(recipe in Soup section)

1 cup diced celery root

1 leek, chopped

1 rib celery, chopped

1 medium onion, chopped

1 cup diced carrots

1 cup diced zucchini

1 cup cauliflower flowerettes

1 cup pasta sauce (recipe in
Dressings and Sauces section)

1 teaspoon dried basil

1 tablespoon lemon juice

Steps:

1. In a large saucepan, combine chicken broth, celery root, leek, celery and onion and bring to a boil. Reduce heat and simmer 45 minutes.

2. Add remaining ingredients except lemon juice and simmer 15 minutes. Just before serving, add lemon juice.

Yield: 6 servings

Herbed Chicken Soup

Preparation Time: 20 minutes   Cooking Time: 25 minutes

There are about 2,000 species of mushrooms being eaten worldwide today, but in the United States only one (agaricus bisporus) was offered in restaurants and markets, until recently.

½ teaspoon safflower oil
1 zucchini, sliced
3 medium carrots, chopped
1 small onion, chopped
1 rib celery, chopped
5 cups chicken broth
(recipe in Soup section)

¾ cup sliced mushrooms
3 cups cooked, diced chicken breast
1½ teaspoons lemon juice
4½ teaspoons snipped fresh chives
2 teaspoons minced fresh tarragon

Steps:
1. Heat oil in medium saucepan over medium low heat. Add zucchini, carrots, onion, and celery. Stirring occasionally, cook covered until tender, about 15 minutes. Add broth and mushrooms and simmer 10 minutes, partially covered. Add chicken, lemon juice, chives and tarragon. Stir and serve immediately.

Yield: 6 servings

Choosing and Storing Mushrooms
Fresh mushrooms should be firm and white, with no soft spots. The freshest mushrooms have a closed cap, but many people prefer open mushrooms for their more pungent flavor. Store mushrooms in a brown paper bag in the refrigerator. Paper permits the mushrooms to "breathe" and keeps in the humidity that keeps the mushrooms fresh. To prepare mushrooms, wipe with damp cloth. Do not wash, as mushrooms absorb water while losing nutrients and flavor.

Chicken Broth

Preparation Time: 5 minutes   Cooking Time: 2 hours

If you wish to prepare your own chicken broth from scratch, this is the healthier way to do it without adding salt and skimming off fat. Health Valley also makes canned Chicken Broth for your convenience. Ours is an extra rich broth that works exceptionally well in recipes, and we prepare it two ways: with No Salt Added, or lightly salted with less than other commercial brands.

1 3-pound chicken, cut into serving pieces

6 cups water, or enough to cover chicken

1 medium onion, stuck with 2 cloves

1 carrot, halved

1 rib celery, including leaves, halved

1 bay leaf

3 sprigs parsley

2 teaspoons all purpose seasoning (recipe in Condiment section)

Steps:

1. Place chicken pieces with water in a large soup pot. Bring to boiling, reduce heat, and skim off scum that rises to the surface.

2. Add remaining ingredients and simmer for 2 hours, uncovered.

3. Strain broth through a fine sieve. Cool, refrigerate, and when cold, remove surface fat.

Yield: 3-3½ cups

Note: Skin and bone chicken pieces and reserve for your favorite cooked chicken recipes.

"One of My Favorites"

George Mateljan

Chicken Curry Soup

I like to think that this is a curry recipe even for people who don't normally like curry. The reason is that the curry doesn't overpower the chicken and other ingredients, the way it so often does in Indian cooking.

Curry itself is often misunderstood. It isn't really a spice, it's a blend of spices. There are hundreds of variations, but the most popular curry powders contain ginger, coriander, cardamom, cayenne, turmeric and cumin seed.

The **nutritional highlights** of this recipe border on the amazing. Traditional chicken curry soup recipes include 2-3 tablespoons butter, 1 or 2 cups of cream, egg yolks and sometimes coconut, so they're loaded with fat and cholesterol. Our recipe contains less than 30% calories from fat because it gets its smoothness from potato soup instead of cream. And it's sensationally nutritious with the following U.S. RDA's in a single serving: 60% niacin, 25% B_6, 22% magnesium and phosphorus, 16% calcium and thiamine, 14% riboflavin, 13% iron, 12% vitamin C, and much more.

Chicken Curry Soup

Preparation Time: 25 minutes   Cooking Time: 15 minutes

2 tablespoons chopped onion
½ teaspoon safflower oil
1½ teaspoons curry powder
1½ teaspoons all purpose seasoning
(recipe in Condiment section)
4 tablespoons apple juice
2 cups potato soup*

2 cups chicken broth
(recipe in Soup section)
1⅓ cups cooked, cubed chicken breast
½ teaspoon honey
1 teaspoon lemon juice
thin slices of lemon for garnish

Steps:
1. In a large saucepan over medium heat, saute onion in oil until glossy, add seasonings and apple juice and cook 5 minutes.
2. Add potato soup and chicken broth and cook slowly for 5 minutes.
3. Pour into blender and blend until smooth. Return to saucepan, add chicken. Mix well. Bring to boiling, stir in honey and lemon juice and serve. Garnish with one thin slice of lemon per serving.

Yield: 4 servings

Note: This soup is also delicious served cold. Prepare as above, and chill for several hours.

This product is available from Health Valley

269

Creamy Corn Soup

Preparation Time: 10 minutes   Cooking Time: 10 minutes

Whenever you see a drawing of an ancient Aztec emperor, he always has a stalk of maize (corn) in his hand. Corn was, and is, a primary food of Mexico and with good reason. It is an excellent source of B vitamins, phosphorus and protein. Interestingly, when corn is picked it is a vegetable for the first five days, after which it turns into a starch. Corn that is frozen is still a vegetable because the flash freezing is usually done within 24 hours of harvesting.

This recipe also uses tofu, which adds a creamy consistency as well as high quality protein. If you were to use a cup of light cream in this recipe, you'd be adding almost 50 grams of fat while a cup of tofu contains only 10 grams of fat.

2 cups chicken broth
(recipe in Soup section)
2 10-ounce packages frozen whole kernel corn
2 cloves garlic, minced

1 teaspoon onion powder
⅛ teaspoon dry mustard
1 cup soft tofu, drained
1 cup low fat milk

Steps:

1. In large saucepan, combine chicken broth, frozen corn and seasonings. Bring to boil, lower heat and simmer 5 minutes.
2. Using slotted spoon, measure out 1 cup of corn from soup and set aside.
3. Pour remainder of soup into blender and liquefy.
4. Add tofu and low fat milk and blend until creamy.
5. Return to saucepan and add remaining corn. Mix and serve immediately.

Yield: 6 servings

Golden Squash Soup

Preparation Time: 15 minutes   Cooking Time: 25 minutes

Crookneck squash is one of the summer squashes, which also include zucchini and pattypan, and like the other summer squashes does not have to be peeled. While summer squash isn't as nutritious as the darker winter squashes, it's still a good source of vitamins A and C, and calcium.

1 teaspoon safflower oil
1 large onion, chopped
2 medium tomatoes, chopped
5 medium size yellow crookneck squash (about 1½ pounds), trimmed and chopped
3 cups chicken broth
(recipe in Soup section)

1 cup low fat buttermilk
¼ cup loosely packed minced fresh basil leaves, or 1½ teaspoons dried basil leaves
1½ teaspoons lemon juice
tomato slices for garnish

Steps:

1. Heat oil in large saucepan over medium high heat. Add onion and saute until golden. Add tomatoes and cook until soft, about 5 minutes.
2. Combine squash and chicken broth with onion-tomato mixture and bring to boiling. Cover and simmer mixture for 15 minutes or until squash is tender. Remove from heat.
3. Puree mixture in a blender with the buttermilk. Return soup to pan and stir in the minced basil leaves and lemon juice.
4. Pour into serving dishes and garnish with basil sprig and a thin slice of tomato.

Yield: 8 servings

Note: If you are planning to serve this soup cold, chill covered for up to 24 hours.

"One of My Favorites"

George Mateljan

Zesty Mexican Chicken Soup

The first time I tasted this soup was in Mexico, during a trip I made there searching for Amaranth, the lost grain of the ancient Aztecs. It was a particularly rewarding trip because I not only discovered Amaranth and brought it back, I also brought back this recipe.

It's a favorite of mine because it features such an interesting variety of herbs and spices, including oregano, thyme, basil, tarragon, cumin and cilantro. Usually, soup recipes that are based on chicken need salt to taste good, but because of the blend of spices, this soup is flavorful and lives up to its name as "zesty" without any added salt.

I also like this recipe because it can be a meal in itself. It's a really nourishing soup because of the tomatoes, green onions and red peppers which are outstanding sources of vitamin C and vitamin A. The corn and mushrooms are rich in B vitamins and phosphorus.

The **nutritional highlights** of this recipe, along with the above, are that it provides 40% of the U.S. RDA for protein, while only 24% of calories are from fat.

Zesty Mexican Chicken Soup

Preparation Time: 20 minutes   Cooking Time: 20 minutes

1½ **pounds chicken breast,
   skinned, boned, cubed**
6 **cups chicken broth**
   (recipe in Soup section)
2 **cups sliced mushrooms**
1 **cup sliced celery**
1 **cup peeled diced tomatoes**
½ **cup sliced green onions**
½ **cup diced red or green pepper**
1 **clove garlic, minced**
½ **teaspoon oregano**
½ **teaspoon thyme**

½ **teaspoon dried basil**
½ **teaspoon tarragon**
¼ **teaspoon cumin**
1 **teaspoon chicken seasoning**
   (recipe in Condiment section)
   dash of cayenne
1 **tablespoon finely chopped
   fresh cilantro**
1 **10-ounce package frozen
   whole kernel corn**
2 **tablespoons lemon juice**

Steps:

1. In large saucepan, combine chicken, chicken broth, all vegetables except corn.
   Add seasonings, except lemon juice.
2. Bring to a boil. Reduce heat and simmer 20 minutes.
3. Add corn and stir until heated through, about 2 minutes. Add lemon juice and
   serve in soup bowls.

Yield: 8 servings

273

Chilled Zippy Gazpacho Soup

Preparation Time: 15 minutes   Plus chilling time

Americans tend to drink only hot soups but this chilled gazpacho is a favorite of mine for serving all year long. It's especially refreshing in the summer. The first time I tasted this soup was in Spain, where they have wonderful tomatoes that are plump and full of flavor. Our recipe avoids the common practice of using oil in this soup. We don't think it's necessary and it certainly holds down the calories.

2 cups tomato sauce*
2 medium tomatoes, chopped
1 clove garlic, minced
2 teaspoons apple cider vinegar
½ cucumber, peeled and diced
1 small green pepper, diced
**2 green onions including tops,
   sliced**

1 tablespoon lemon juice
1 teaspoon all purpose seasoning
   (recipe in Condiment section)
**1½ teaspoons prepared horseradish
   dash of cayenne
   chopped parsley for garnish**

Steps:
1. Combine all ingredients. Mix well.
2. Chill several hours or overnight.

Yield: 6 servings

This product is available from Health Valley.

Seafood Chowder

Preparation Time: 10 minutes   Cooking Time: 10 minutes

   Classic fish chowder recipes invariably include large quantities of ingredients like bacon, salt pork, butter, milk and even half & half. In fact, "The Joy of Cooking" defines chowders as: "thick fish, meat and vegetable soups, to which salt pork, milk, diced vegetables, even bread and crackers may be added."

   Our healthy recipe reduces all this fat and sodium to 1 tablespoon of oil. Instead of milk, we get enticing chowder thickness and flavor from potato soup and chicken broth laced with chunks of fish. Now, everyone can give into the temptation of delicious Seafood Chowder without guilt.

**½ cup chopped leeks
  (white part only)**
1 tablespoon safflower oil
2 cups potato soup*
1 cup chicken broth
  (recipe in Soup section)
2 tablespoons chopped parsley
½ teaspoon dried basil

½ teaspoon fish seasoning
  (recipe in Condiment section)
**1 7-ounce halibut steak, cut
  into ¾-inch cubes**
4 ounces cooked shrimp, rinsed
**1 6½-ounce can minced clams,
  drained and rinsed**
1½ tablespoons lemon juice

Steps:

1. In medium saucepan, saute leeks in safflower oil until tender.
2. Add remaining ingredients, except shrimp, clams and lemon juice. Simmer 5 minutes.
3. Add shrimp, clams and lemon juice just before serving.

Yield: 4 servings

This product is available from Health Valley.

Borscht

Preparation Time: 10 minutes   Cooking Time: 25 minutes

There are probably as many different recipes for Russia's famed borscht as there are for the French bouillabaisse or the Italian minestrone. The common ingredient in borscht is always beets, but many recipes include other vegetables and even meat. Our simple version lets you have real Russian borscht in minutes. A word of warning, though: don't plop on a blob of sour cream on serving, like the Russians do. Plain nonfat yogurt is just as good, and much healthier.

6 medium beets
  juice of 1 lemon
  (about 3 tablespoons)
2 tablespoons honey
2 cups water, beet juice or chicken broth (recipe in Soup section)

1 teaspoon vegetable seasoning (recipe in Condiment section)

plain nonfat yogurt and chopped parsley for garnish

Steps:

1. Cover beets with water and boil until tender. Skin and puree.
2. Combine beets, lemon juice, honey, liquid and seasoning.
3. Serve cold or hot, topped with yogurt and parsley.

Yield: 4 cups

Tomato-Split Pea Soup with Yogurt

| Preparation Time: 5 minutes | Cooking Time: 5 minutes |

The booster of yogurt adds protein, calcium, phosphorus, potassium and vitamins to this nutritionally rich soup. Yogurt was the fastest growing food category in the United States in the mid-1970's.

2 cups tomato soup*
2 cups split pea soup*
dash of cayenne
¼ teaspoon garlic powder
½ teaspoon vegetable seasoning
(recipe in Condiment section)

½ teaspoon all purpose seasoning
(recipe in Condiment section)
¼ cup plain nonfat yogurt
1 teaspoon finely sliced green onions
1 teaspoon finely chopped parsley

Steps:

1. In a medium saucepan, combine the two soups and heat over low heat until well blended and smooth. Add seasonings and bring to a boil.
2. Serve very hot, topped with a dollop of yogurt and sprinkled with chopped onions and parsley.

Yield: 4 servings

This product is available from Health Valley.

277

16

Salads

In this section you'll discover delicious new ways to enjoy salads that are low in fat and rich in beneficial nutrients. A salad can consist of an almost endless variety of fresh vegetables and fruits, whole grains, legumes, nuts and seeds, cheese, poultry, and seafood which are wonderful sources of vitamins, minerals, dietary fiber and protein, while being low in calories, fat, and cholesterol.

Best of all, salads can be very versatile. You can enjoy a salad as an accompaniment to a sandwich or soup at lunch, as a tasty prelude to your entree at dinner, as a delicious dessert, or as a light, quick, but completely satisfying meal all by itself. Including delicious salads as part of your program of healthier eating makes it easy for you to cut down on meats that are high in calories, fat, and cholesterol. And it makes it a snap to follow the dietary guidelines for better health and greater resistance to disease.

Many people today still think of a salad as a bowl of iceberg lettuce (the least nutritious variety) covered in high-fat salad dressing. Such a salad provides little nutritional benefit. Another trap in making a salad is to add too much dressing. One ladle of dressing can add 400 to 500 calories to an otherwise low calorie meal.

By choosing your ingredients with the rules of healthier eating in mind, you can transform a simple salad into a nutritionally superior meal. For example, our Morro Bay Seafood Salad is low in calories, fat and sodium and a superior source of protein, fiber, vitamins A and C, all the B vitamins, every key mineral, and vitamin E. Our Three Bean Salad is extremely rich in fiber and iron. And our Tuna – Pasta Salad provides 13% of the U.S. RDA for calcium with only 196 calories per serving. Our delicious fruit-based Healthy Waldorf Salad provides 150% of the U.S. RDA for vitamin C, and only 118 calories per serving.

In creating salads, try to balance the textures, colors and flavors of the ingredients. Mild greens, such as Bibb lettuce should be set off by more assertive ingredients, such as crunchy cucumbers, tangy watercress, or crispy-fresh spinach. Crisp vegetables such as celery and carrots are well complemented by softer ingredients such as plump tomatoes, cooked beets and mild tuna. Almost magically, nature has seen to it that when you combine vegetables of different colors and textures, you invariably create a perfect balance of nutrients as well as flavors.

The main thing to remember in creating salads is to be adventurous and to use your imagination. After all, the whole idea of this guide to healthier eating is to help you to enjoy foods you eat at the same time you are gaining the nutritional benefits of healthier eating.

"One of My Favorites"

George Mateljan

Chicken Salad Oriental

Here is a salad I often use as a complete meal when I want a light lunch, especially during warm weather. It's as nutritious as it is refreshing and tasty. It provides you with plenty of protein from the chicken and cashews, calcium from the nonfat yogurt, and plenty of vitamin C and enzymes from the oranges.

Interestingly, oranges have been cultivated in China for at least 4,000 years. The original wild oranges were probably sour, much like today's Seville orange, which is used to make marmalade. The smaller Mandarin oranges are among the varieties of sweet eating oranges, which include the Navel, Jaffa, and Florida Temple. Valencias are best for juice.

When buying oranges, select firm, heavy ones with the smoothest possible skins and no soft spots. Avoid those that are light, puffy or spongy.

The **nutritional highlight** of this recipe is that only 30% of the calories are from fat, compared to 65% fat in a typical recipe for Chinese Chicken Salad.

Chicken Salad Oriental

Preparation Time: 20 minutes   Plus chilling time

**4 cups cooked diced
chicken breast**
**2 cups mandarin orange
segments**
⅔ cup sliced water chestnuts
2 green onions, sliced thin
¾ cup plain nonfat yogurt

1 tablespoon mayonnaise
1 tablespoon honey
**½ teaspoon ground ginger
salad greens**
**½ cup raw cashew nuts,
chopped**

Steps:

1. In a mixing bowl, combine chicken, orange segments, water chestnuts and green onions. Toss together lightly.
2. In a small bowl, whisk together yogurt, mayonnaise, honey and ginger. Mix well, then pour over chicken mixture. Toss gently. Chill.
3. When ready to serve, spoon onto crisp salad greens and top with cashew nuts.

Yield: 6 servings

Warm Chicken Salad

Preparation Time: 20 minutes   Cooking Time: 20 minutes

Grapes have been cultivated for 6,000 years. Today, there are about 60 species grown on 25 million acres, making the grape one of the most profusely grown of all fruits. Most of these grapes are used for making wine.

This delicious recipe makes a perfect luncheon main dish, because it contains only 175 calories and only 17% calories from fat in a serving. It's also quite nutritious, with almost 60% of the U.S. RDA for niacin and 26% of B_6 in a single serving.

3 cups cooked, cubed chicken breast

½ cup sliced celery

½ cup chopped apple

1 cup seedless green grapes, cut in half

½ cup plain nonfat yogurt

2 tablespoons lemon juice

Steps:

1. Preheat oven to 350°F. and oil a 1-quart casserole.
2. Combine chicken, celery, apple and grapes.
3. Mix yogurt and lemon juice. Pour over chicken mixture, toss gently, then spoon into prepared casserole.
4. Bake at 350°F. for 20 minutes, until all ingredients are heated through and flavors are blended.

Yield: 6 servings

Picnic Salad

Preparation Time: 15 minutes

Leonardo da Vinci invented a spit with a propeller turned in the heat of the fire to roast his chicken. He also sketched his shopping list for his cook, so she would know what to buy.

2 cups torn lettuce leaves (bibb, red leaf)

1 small tomato, cut into thin wedges

1 cup cooked, chopped chicken breast

¼ cup chopped red onion

½ 10-ounce package frozen corn, thawed

¼ cup sliced radishes

¾ cup chopped celery

¼ cup chopped red pepper

Steps:

1. Arrange the lettuce, tomato, chicken, red onion, corn, radishes, celery and red pepper on a large glass serving platter with low fat dressing of your choice.

Yield: 6 servings

"One of My Favorites"

George Mateljan

Health Valley Carrot Orange Salad

This salad is one that I particularly enjoy when the weather turns warm because it is so refreshing. At first glance, you may think that combining orange juice with carrots is a bit unusual, but once you try it, I think this recipe will become one of your favorites, too.

This recipe not only tastes good, it is also very healthy. As you probably know, carrots are an abundant source of beta carotene, which your body can safely use to make vitamin A.

Carrots, like other edible root vegetables, were probably among the earliest foods used by humans. Today, carrots are not only a very popular vegetable, but modern nutritional research has shown that they are nutritionally important as well.

The **nutritional highlight** of this recipe is that it derives only 4% of its calories from fat and contains no cholesterol. This is even more remarkable when you consider that traditional carrot salads contain a cup of sour cream or mayonnaise, and can be over 60% fat! And a single serving of this nutritious salad provides you with over 600% of the U.S. RDA for vitamin A, and over 70% of vitamin C.

Health Valley
Carrot Orange Salad

Preparation Time: 20 minutes   Plus Chilling Time: 15 minutes

**6 large carrots, trimmed,
cleaned, and finely grated**
**1 large navel orange, peeled
and separated into segments**
½ teaspoon grated orange peel

½ cup orange juice
1½ tablespoons apple cider vinegar
**2 tablespoons fresh snipped dill
orange slices for garnish**

Steps:

1. Combine carrots with orange segments, orange peel, orange juice, apple cider vinegar and 1 tablespoon of the dill. Gently toss to mix well.

2. Refrigerate 15 minutes. Before serving, sprinkle with remaining dill and garnish with orange slices.

Yield: 6 servings

Super Carrot Raisin Salad

Preparation Time: 20 minutes   Plus Chilling Time: 2 hours

2 cups grated carrots
½ cup raisins
½ cup plain nonfat yogurt
2 tablespoons low fat milk
1½ tablespoons honey

1½ tablespoons lemon juice
¼ teaspoon cinnamon
¼ cup canned unsweetened
   crushed pineapple

Steps:

1. Grate carrots coarsely, add raisins and mix.
2. In medium bowl, combine yogurt, milk, honey, lemon juice and cinnamon. Mix well.
3. Add carrot-raisin mixture and pineapple to yogurt mixture and mix well.
4. Cover and chill in refrigerator for at least 2 hours.

Yield: 6 servings

Note: Salad will keep well for several days in refrigerator.

Choosing and Using Carrots
Young tender carrots are best for eating raw, as in salads. Choose firm, straight, bright orange carrots with no green or yellow areas at the top. Carrots are rich in carotene, which converts to vitamin A. Store carrots in the bag in which you bought them and refrigerate. Carrots keep well.

Vegetable Carousel Salad

Preparation Time: 30 minutes   Cooking Time: 10 minutes

½ pound fresh green beans, trimmed and broken in half
½ teaspoon olive oil
1 medium red pepper, julienned
1 medium green pepper, julienned

1 small zucchini, julienned
1 medium carrot, julienned
4 ounces radishes, sliced
8 ounces jicama, pared and julienned (optional)

Dressing:
½ cup plain nonfat yogurt
1 tablespoon prepared mustard

2 teaspoons mayonnaise
1½ teaspoons honey

Steps:
1. Steam beans in steamer basket over 1-inch boiling water for 6 minutes or until tender crisp. Drain, rinse under cold water and drain again. Set aside.
2. In heavy skillet over medium high heat, heat ¼ teaspoon olive oil. Add red pepper and saute until limp. Remove from skillet and drain on a paper towel. Repeat same with green pepper.
3. On a large serving platter, arrange beans, zucchini, red pepper, green pepper, carrot, radishes and jicama.
4. In a small bowl, combine yogurt, mustard, mayonnaise and honey. Serve with salad.

Yield: 6 servings

About Jicama
Jicama is a Mexican tuber that has suddenly caught on in parts of the United States. It's very moist and crunchy, and tastes a little like a sweet radish or a sweet turnip. It's a good source of vitamin C, with traces of other vitamins and minerals. If you can find it, use it in this recipe because it adds unique flavor and texture contrasts to the other vegetables.

"One of My Favorites"

George Mateljan

Three Bean Salad

This is our healthy rendition of the old familiar Three Bean Salad recipe. In the typical recipe, the beans get much of their flavor from a dressing that is very high in fat. In this version, we've captured all the zesty flavor, but cut down on fat considerably, as well as making a few other significant nutritional improvements.

Most recipes call for green beans, kidney beans, and wax beans. Instead of wax beans, we use garbanzo beans (also known as chickpeas), because they are an outstanding source of protein and calcium.

The **nutritional highlights** of this recipe are that it contains only 16% of calories from fat, and it is a rich source of dietary fiber. One serving provides almost 6 grams of dietary fiber (about 25% of the recommended daily intake). And the water soluble type of fiber found in beans has been shown to help reduce serum cholesterol levels.

Beans are also an excellent source of vitamin B_6 (pyridoxine), which helps to maintain a healthy nervous system and is essential for the production of antibodies.

Three Bean Salad

Preparation Time: 30 minutes   Plus chilling time

2 cups cooked fresh green beans
2 cups cooked red kidney beans
2 cups cooked garbanzo beans
½ cup chopped green pepper
½ cup chopped red pepper
½ cup chopped celery
¾ cup chopped onion
2 tablespoons honey

4 tablespoons apple cider vinegar
2 teaspoons all purpose seasoning
(recipe in Condiment section)
1 teaspoon vegetable seasoning
(recipe in Condiment section)
¼ teaspoon garlic powder
1 cup herb dressing
chopped parsley

Steps:

1. In large bowl, combine all ingredients except parsley. Mix well, cover and chill for several hours or overnight before serving.
2. To serve, put bean salad in serving bowl. Sprinkle with chopped parsley.

Yield: 8 servings

Note: For best results, chill overnight. Salad will keep well in the refrigerator for one week.

Herb Dressing

Preparation Time: 5 minutes

½ cup water
2 tablespoons apple cider vinegar
2 teaspoons honey
½ teaspoon dried basil
½ teaspoon dried bell pepper

¼ teaspoon oregano
¼ teaspoon thyme
⅛ teaspoon garlic powder
½ teaspoon onion powder
1 tablespoon safflower oil

Steps:

1. In measuring cup, combine water, vinegar and honey.
2. Crush herbs in blender or mortar and pestle and add to vinegar dressing. Stir in oil and pour over salad or vegetables. Store remaining dressing in covered container in refrigerator.

Yield: ¾ cup

Low Fat Cole Slaw

Preparation Time: 5 minutes

   Cole slaw is a great family favorite, and that's why we've included more than one recipe in our cookbook. Most recipes include large amounts of mayonnaise or oil, as well as sugar and salt. Our Yogurt Dill Dressing reduces all this fat to ½ teaspoon of mayonnaise. We think you'll find it's as good as any cole slaw you've eaten, and it's a great deal healthier.

2 cups shredded cabbage   **½ teaspoon celery seed**
½ cup yogurt dill dressing (recipe
    in Dressings and Sauces section)

Steps:

1. Toss cabbage with dressing. Sprinkle with celery seed.

Yield: 2 heaping cups

Bernie's Computer Coleslaw

Preparation Time: 20 minutes   Plus chilling time

Dr. Bernie Landes, our Director of Educational Programs, used a computer to compile the statistical data in this book. When we were searching for a way to create healthy coleslaw, Bernie decided to see how the computer would adjust the numbers to keep it low in fat, calories and sodium. If the computer continues to create tasty recipes like this, it could put "The Joy of Cooking" out of business.

1 pound cabbage, shredded
1 green pepper, diced
1 cup diced celery
¼ cup finely chopped onion
1 ounce pimientos, chopped
⅓ cup plain nonfat yogurt

2 tablespoons mayonnaise
2 tablespoons apple cider vinegar
¼ cup lemon juice
4½ tablespoons honey

Steps:

1. In a large bowl, combine cabbage, pepper, celery, onion and pimientos. Toss well.
2. In a small bowl, stir together yogurt, mayonnaise, vinegar, lemon juice and honey. Pour over vegetable mixture. Toss to mix well.
3. Chill for 1 hour.

Yield: 6 servings

Note: Best if chilled overnight.

Apple Cole Slaw

Preparation Time: 20 minutes   Plus chilling time

Apples have been a symbol of temptation and invention since the beginning of time: Paris gave a golden apple to Aphrodite and thus caused the Trojan War; William Tell shot an apple off his son's head; Snow White's stepmother poisoned her with an apple; and Isaac Newton envisioned gravity while watching a falling apple. By the way, the apple is never mentioned in the story of Adam and Eve — they ate the fruit of the tree of knowledge.

½ cup plain nonfat yogurt
1 teaspoon honey
1 teaspoon prepared horseradish
1 teaspoon prepared mustard
1 medium red delicious apple, cored and chopped

1½ cups shredded cabbage
¼ cup shredded carrots
¼ cup diced celery
1 tablespoon thinly sliced green onions

Steps:

1. Combine yogurt, honey, horseradish and mustard in a medium salad bowl. Add apple pieces and mix to coat well. Add cabbage, carrots, celery and green onion and toss till well coated. Cover and chill for several hours.

Yield: 4 servings

Note: If red cabbage is used, combine with a golden delicious apple.

How to Choose Cabbage

Look for firm heads that are heavy for their size, and with fresh, crisp leaves. Store in the crisper of your refrigerator, where they will last for 1 to 2 weeks. All types of cabbage are excellent sources of vitamin C, and spoon cabbage is also an outstanding source of vitamin A and calcium.

Tangy Apple Vegetable Salad

Preparation Time: 10 minutes

More than 7,000 varieties of apples have been recorded in the United States alone. The brilliant Red Delicious is the most popular of the eating apples, but we feel that Golden Delicious works better in salads such as this.

When buying apples, always look for mature, firm, crisp apples with the stems attached. They should have good color for the variety, and no soft spots, brownish bruises or shriveling.

1 medium golden delicious apple, cored and chopped
1 medium carrot, thinly sliced
1 rib celery, sliced

1 head butter or red leaf lettuce, torn
¼ cup yogurt honey dressing (recipe in Dressings and Sauces section)

Steps:

1. Combine apple and vegetables in medium salad bowl.
2. Pour dressing over salad ingredients and toss gently. Serve immediately.

Yield: 4 servings

"One of My Favorites"

George Mateljan

Healthy Waldorf Salad

Waldorf Salad deserves its reputation as a classic salad recipe. It's a deliciously sweet and crunchy combination of fruit, walnuts and celery in a smooth and creamy dressing.

The only trouble is that the traditional recipe that serves six includes ¾ to 1 cup of mayonnaise, and mayonnaise is virtually 100% fat!

Our Health Valley version of Waldorf Salad is a favorite of mine because we've successfully substituted nonfat yogurt sweetened with honey instead of mayonnaise, so ours is also smooth, creamy and much healthier.

The **nutritional highlights** of this recipe are that it contains only 23% of calories from fat, and provides 20% of the U.S. RDA for vitamin C and 9% of the U.S. RDA for calcium in a serving.

Healthy Waldorf Salad

Preparation Time: 15 minutes
Plus Chilling Time: 30 minutes

**2 medium apples, cored
and chopped**
⅓ cup orange juice
1 tablespoon lemon juice
¾ cup chopped celery

¼ cup raisins
¼ cup chopped walnuts
1 cup plain nonfat yogurt
1 tablespoon honey

Steps:

1. Cover apples with 1 tablespoon orange juice and 1 tablespoon lemon juice. Mix well to prevent discoloration. Add celery, raisins and walnuts.

2. Mix yogurt, honey, and remaining orange juice until smooth.

3. Pour dressing over salad and mix well. Cover and chill for 30 minutes before serving to allow flavors to blend.

Yield: 6 servings

Raw Bulgur Vegetable Salad

Preparation Time: 1 hour including soaking time

1½ cups uncooked bulgur
¾ cup pared, seeded, diced cucumber
½ cup chopped red pepper
½ cup frozen peas, thawed
½ cup frozen green beans, thawed
3 tablespoons sliced scallions
2 tablespoons chopped parsley

½ cup raisins
2 tablespoons chopped walnuts
¾ cup plain nonfat yogurt
1 tablespoon honey
1 teaspoon prepared mustard
2 teaspoons dried mint leaves
1½ tablespoons lemon juice
lettuce leaves for garnish

Steps:

1. Place bulgur in large bowl and cover with lukewarm water. Let soak for 1 hour or until bulgur is tender. Drain.
2. Combine drained bulgur with cucumber, red pepper, peas, green beans, scallions, parsley, raisins and walnuts and toss lightly.
3. In a small bowl, blend together yogurt, honey, mustard, and mint leaves. Pour over bulgur mixture and mix thoroughly. Cover and chill until serving time. Mix in lemon juice just prior to serving. Serve on a bed of lettuce leaves.

Yield: 6 servings

What Is a Whole Grain?

Most of us have never seen grain growing in the field. Every whole grain kernel consists of the bran, germ and endosperm inside an inedible hull. The bran forms the protective inner covering and is an outstanding source of dietary fiber. The germ is actually the embryo of a new plant and a good source of protein, vitamins, minerals, and polyunsaturated fats. The endosperm supplies protein and carbohydrates. When whole grains are processed into white flour, the bran and germ are stripped away, leaving mostly starch. Bulgur is not processed but is simply partially cooked for convenience, and thus retains its full nutritional value.

Bulgur Tuna Salad

Preparation Time: 20 minutes
Plus Chilling Time: 2 hours

Soaking Time: 1 hour

¾ cup chicken broth
  (recipe in Soup section)
¾ cup uncooked bulgur wheat
 2 tablespoons apple cider
   vinegar
   dash of cayenne
½ teaspoon honey
¼ teaspoon oregano

⅔ cup finely chopped celery
⅔ cup frozen peas, thawed and
   drained
¼ cup chopped onion
 1 small tomato, chopped
 1 6½-ounce can solid white tuna
   in water, drained and flaked

Steps:
1. In medium saucepan, bring broth to a boil. Add bulgur. Cover and remove from heat. Let stand 1 hour or until all liquid is absorbed.
2. In small bowl, combine vinegar, cayenne, honey, and oregano; set aside.
3. In large bowl, stir together bulgur, celery, peas, onion, tomato and tuna. Add vinegar mixture and stir well to coat. Cover and chill 2 hours.

Yield: 6 servings

About Bulgur
Bulgur is simply wheat that has been partially cooked, dried and cracked into small pieces for faster cooking. Bulgur has a nutty flavor, and is sold in three grinds: coarse, medium and fine. Bulgur is also known as wheat pilaf, bulghur, burghul and parboiled wheat.

Lentil Salad

Preparation Time: 20 minutes
Plus Chilling Time: 1 hour

Cooking Time: 30 minutes

1½ cups lentils
1 bay leaf
6 cups water
2 large cloves garlic, pureed
1 teaspoon grated lemon peel
1 tablespoon prepared mustard
2 tablespoons lemon juice
1 tablespoon apple cider vinegar

dash of cayenne
½ cup finely minced onion
½ teaspoon dried basil
½ teaspoon thyme
½ teaspoon oregano
1½ tablespoons olive oil
1 medium green pepper, diced
1 medium red pepper, diced

Steps:

1. Wash lentils thoroughly and drain. Bring lentils, bay leaf and water to simmer. Cook for 30 minutes just below simmer (if they simmer, they may disintegrate), partially covered. Drain well.
2. Meanwhile, combine garlic, lemon peel, mustard, lemon juice, vinegar, cayenne, onion, basil, thyme, and oregano. Mix well and slowly, add olive oil. Pour over still warm drained lentils.
3. After lentil and sauce mixture has cooled, gently toss with green and red pepper.
4. Chill for one hour.

Yield: 8 servings

About Lentils

Lentils provide the most protein of all legumes, except for soybeans. Lentils and split peas are the only legumes that don't require soaking before being cooked. Always rinse lentils first, and remove any foreign matter. And remember with all legumes, one cup dry cooks up to 2 to 3 cups in the finished recipe. Do not add salt, lemon, vinegar, tomatoes or any acid ingredients to legumes while cooking, as they hinder softening.

Tuna-Pasta Salad

Preparation Time: 30 minutes

The song "Yankee Doodle went to London just to ride a pony, Stuck a feather in his cap and called it macaroni" was written before macaroni was introduced to the United States. Pasta was the food of the people of Italy, but was favored by the upper classes of England as a delicacy.

6 ounces whole wheat elbow pasta*
1 6½-ounce can water packed albacore tuna

1 cup cooked green peas
1 cup chopped celery

Dressing:

1 cup plain low fat yogurt
2 teaspoons honey
½ teaspoon dill weed
¼ teaspoon celery seed

¼ teaspoon paprika
½ teaspoon all purpose seasoning
(recipe in Condiment section)

Topping:

¼ cup chopped walnuts

½ cup shredded cheddar cheese

Steps:

1. Cook elbow pasta according to package directions.
2. Drain and flake tuna. Put in a large salad bowl. Add cooked pasta, peas and celery. Mix well.
3. Combine dressing ingredients. Mix well. Pour over salad. Toss to mix.
4. Top with walnuts and cheese.

Yield: 8 servings

This product is available from Health Valley.

Morro Bay Seafood Salad

Preparation Time: 20 minutes   Plus chilling time

The key to a great seafood salad is freshness. Lobsters begin to deteriorate in flavor as soon as they are taken from the sea—even when kept in tanks! A tip about shrimp: deveining is not necessary for hygienic reasons, as is commonly thought—but it does cut down the iodine taste that many shrimp possess.

1 small head red leaf lettuce
1 small head butter lettuce
1 cucumber
¼ cup diced onion
½ cup thinly sliced carrot
2 medium tomatoes, sliced

5 ounces medium cooked
  and peeled shrimp
4 ounces cooked crab meat
1 lobster tail (about 4 ounces),
  cooked and chilled
lemon wedges
herb dressing

Steps:

1. In large salad bowl, tear red leaf lettuce and butter lettuce into bite size pieces.
2. Peel cucumber, cut in half lengthwise, remove seeds, cut into slices. Add to lettuce in bowl.
3. Add onion, carrot and tomatoes to salad and toss to mix well.
4. Rinse shrimp and crab in cold water. Remove lobster meat from shell and flake. Add all shellfish to salad.
5. Serve salad on plates garnished with lemon wedges. Squeeze fresh lemon on salad and add 2 tablespoons herb dressing to each serving if desired.

Yield: 4 servings

Note: Always serve seafood salads chilled. Do not keep at room temperature for any length of time.

Herb Dressing

Preparation Time: 5 minutes

½ cup water
2 tablespoons apple cider vinegar
2 teaspoons honey
½ teaspoon dried basil
½ teaspoon dried bell pepper

¼ teaspoon oregano
¼ teaspoon thyme
⅛ teaspoon garlic powder
½ teaspoon onion powder
1 tablespoon safflower oil

Steps:

1. In measuring cup, combine water, vinegar and honey.
2. Crush herbs in blender or mortar and pestle and add to vinegar dressing. Stir in oil and pour over salad or vegetables. Store remaining dressing in covered container in refrigerator.

Yield: ¾ cup

Refreshing Salmon Salad

Preparation Time: 20 minutes

3 cucumbers, peeled and
  coarsely diced
¼ cup diced red pepper
¼ cup diced green pepper
2 tablespoons finely sliced
  green onion
1½ cups flaked salmon
1 cup plain nonfat yogurt
2 teaspoons mayonnaise

1 tablespoon lemon juice
1 teaspoon honey
½ teaspoon celery seeds
1 tablespoon fresh dill, finely
  minced, or ½ teaspoon dried
  dill weed
lettuce, parsley and cherry
tomatoes for garnish

Steps:

1. In a large bowl, combine cucumber, red pepper, green pepper, green onion and salmon.
2. Mix remaining ingredients and gently fold into salad mixture.
3. To serve: line salad bowl with lettuce leaves and spoon salad in center. Ring with a garland of parsley and cherry tomatoes.

Yield: 4 servings

About Canned Salmon

Canned salmon is one of the richest non-dairy sources of calcium. That's because we eat the soft bones too, which will provide about 25% of the U.S. RDA in a 3½-ounce serving. However, canned salmon is also higher in fat then most fish with as much as 14 grams in 3½ ounces of canned chinook salmon. Choose the salmon varieties that are lowest in fat; chum with 5.2 grams per 3½ ounces; coho 7.1 grams; pink 5.9 grams; or sockeye 9.3 grams.

17

Vegetable Side Dishes

Most of the attention at any given meal is paid to the entree, but much of the important nutritional value and a great deal of the flavor variety can and should be supplied by the side dishes served along with the entree.

Vegetable side dishes are extremely important because they make it so much easier to follow the dietary guidelines for healthier eating. The vegetable side dishes in this section are virtually all rich in vitamin A, C, B6, magnesium, iron, phosphorus and dietary fiber. And most are also rich in thiamine, riboflavin, and niacin along with zinc, and potassium. These dishes are low in sodium and none supply more than 30% of their calories as fat. So it's easy to see why vegetable side dishes are an important addition to every healthier eating plan.

The recipes in this section are genuinely exciting. Just look at the names of some of them: "Rosemary Peas with Pine Nuts"..."Glazed Curried Carrots with Raisins"... "Vegetable Pita Pizza"..."Golden Cheese Potatoes"...and many more. Every recipe lives up to its name by combining garden fresh vegetables with interesting sauces, seasonings and complementary flavors. They transform everyday vegetables into gourmet treats that make it a pleasure to eat healthier.

"One of My Favorites"

George Matelian

Glazed Curried Carrots and Raisins

Carrots were known to the Greeks and Romans, although the earliest varieties were red, purple and black. It was much later in the 17th century that the familiar orange carrot, rich in carotene (the precursor of vitamin A), was developed.

Carrots have always been more popular in Europe than in the United States. However, recent medical discoveries that show vitamin A may be effective in fighting cancer have boosted usage. Many restaurants in America, from gourmet to coffee shops, now include carrots, broccoli and cauliflower as the vegetables to accompany their entrees. It's no accident that all three are believed to be cancer fighters.

This recipe is a favorite of mine because it enhances the sweetness of carrots with exciting flavor accents, without drowning them in the usual butter sauce.

The **nutritional highlight** of this recipe is that a single serving provides over 400% of the U.S. RDA for vitamin A.

Glazed Curried Carrots and Raisins

Preparation Time: 15 minutes   Cooking Time: 12 minutes

1½ pounds carrots, washed, halved lengthwise and sliced diagonally into ½-inch thick pieces
2 tablespoons honey

1½ teaspoons prepared mustard
1½ teaspoons curry powder
1½ teaspoons lemon juice
1½ teaspoons safflower oil
½ cup raisins

Steps:

1. Steam carrots in steamer basket over 1-inch of water in medium pan for 8 minutes or until tender crisp. Remove pan from heat and set aside.
2. Meanwhile, combine honey, mustard, curry powder and lemon juice in a small bowl and mix well.
3. In a heavy skillet, heat oil over medium high heat. Add carrots and raisins and saute for 1 minute. Stir in the honey mixture and continue cooking, stirring constantly until carrots are well glazed, about 2 minutes. Serve immediately.

Yield: 6 servings

Asparagus with Orange Sauce

Preparation Time: 20 minutes
Plus chilling time

Cooking Time: 7 minutes

The first great French chef was Pierre Francois de La Varenne, and he created the first elaborate vegetable recipes. He prepared asparagus simply, with a sauce consisting of butter, vinegar, salt, nutmeg and an egg to bind the sauce. Our version is a great deal lower in fat, with only 23% calories from fat.

20 thin asparagus spears, trimmed

⅓ cup orange juice

1 teaspoon lime juice

1 tablespoon finely chopped shallots

1 teaspoon minced garlic

1 tablespoon orange peel cut into thin strips and blanched in boiling water for 30 seconds

1 teaspoon olive oil

1 tablespoon apple cider vinegar

Steps:

1. Steam asparagus in steamer basket for 7 minutes, or until crisp tender. Rinse under cold water to arrest cooking and to preserve their color. Drain and place spears on a paper towel to dry. Refrigerate asparagus until ready to serve.

2. In a small bowl, combine orange juice, lime juice, shallots, garlic and orange peel. Let steep for 10 minutes. Whisk in oil and vinegar and set aside till serving.

3. To serve, arrange asparagus on serving platter. Whisk sauce again and pour over asparagus.

Yield: 4 servings

Orange Glazed Carrots

Preparation Time: 10 minutes   Cooking Time: 20 minutes

Ginger is a richly pungent tuber grown in the tropics, and widely used in Chinese cooking and Indian chutneys. Along with cinnamon, it is a very useful spice when you are trying to cut down on sugar because its hot, clean spiciness adds intense flavor without calories.

Queen Elizabeth I is supposed to have invented gingerbread men by ordering the court chefs to bake ginger-spiced cakes in the likeness of her favorites.

When shopping for ginger, look for firm, plump tubers.

**1 pound young carrots,
 cut about 1-inch thick**
½ cup orange juice
½ teaspoon arrowroot

¼ teaspoon ground ginger
**2 tablespoons finely chopped
 parsley**

Steps:
1. Steam carrots in steamer basket over 1-inch of water for 10 to 15 minutes or until carrots are tender crisp.
2. In medium saucepan, combine orange juice, arrowroot and ginger. Bring to a boil, stirring until mixture thickens. Reduce heat and add steamed carrots and parsley. Mix well and serve.

Yield: 4 servings

"One of My Favorites"

George Mateljan

Rosemary Peas with Pine Nuts

It is now being discovered that peas, along with many other vegetables, are even more nutritionally valuable than was previously thought. New research indicates that foods that are rich in vitamin A can be helpful in reducing the risk of certain forms of cancer, and peas are a good source. This recipe, for example, provides 18% of the U.S. RDA in a serving.

Peas have always been one of America's favorite vegetables, and this recipe is a favorite of mine because adding pine nuts and onions to peas makes for an exciting combination of flavors. It's an unusual and interesting change from the ordinary side dish of plain steamed peas.

The **nutritional highlights** of this recipe are almost too numerous to mention. It's a superior source of vegetable protein, dietary fiber, vitamin A, C, thiamine, riboflavin, niacin and B$_6$, and many minerals including magnesium, iron, zinc and phosphorus.

Rosemary Peas with Pine Nuts

Preparation Time: 5 minutes   Cooking Time: 6 minutes

½ **cup chicken broth**
  (recipe in Soup section)
3 **green onions, chopped**
2 **10-ounce packages frozen**
  green peas or 3 pounds
  fresh peas, shelled
1 **teaspoon safflower oil**

4 **tablespoons pine nuts**
1 **tablespoon minced fresh**
  rosemary or 1 teaspoon
  dried, crumbled
6 **large Boston lettuce leaves**

Steps:
1. In a medium saucepan, bring chicken broth to simmer, add onions and peas. Cover and simmer until just tender, about 3 minutes. Drain, discarding liquid.
2. In a large heavy skillet, heat oil over medium high heat. Add pine nuts, and stir until golden brown, about 2 to 3 minutes. Add rosemary and stir for 1 more minute. Add peas and green onion and stir until hot. Spoon onto a leaf of lettuce and serve.

Yield: 6 servings

Note: If fresh peas are used, increase cooking time to 7 minutes in Step 1.

Green Peas with Spicy Mushrooms

Preparation Time: 20 minutes   Cooking Time: 20 minutes

Peas originated in Southwest Asia, and became an important protein food in Europe in the Middle Ages. Peas are also an outstanding source of vitamins A, C, thiamine, riboflavin, niacin, and iron. Small peas (petits pois) are much tastier than the large ones that look like marbles.

There are three varieties of peas. The most familiar are the common garden or shell peas. In Chinese cooking, you will often find snow peas, which are small, flat and delightfully crunchy. A newer variety is the sugar snap pea, which is plump and can be eaten raw or cooked. We recommend the traditional garden peas in this recipe.

**2 cups shelled fresh peas, or
  2 cups frozen peas, defrosted**
½ cup chicken broth
  (recipe in Soup section)

**2 cups sliced mushrooms
  (about 6 ounces)**
1 onion, chopped
1 teaspoon curry powder
½ cup plain nonfat yogurt

Steps:

1. Steam peas in a steamer basket over 1-inch boiling water in a medium saucepan for about 5 minutes, or until barely tender. Rinse peas under cold running water to refresh them. Drain and set aside.
2. In a medium saucepan, bring the chicken broth to a boil. Add mushrooms, onion and curry powder. Cook over medium heat until almost no liquid remains, about 15 minutes.
3. Add peas to mushroom-onion mixture and heat until warmed through, about 5 minutes. Stir in yogurt and spoon vegetables into a serving dish. Serve immediately.

Yield: 6 servings

Note: When using frozen peas, eliminate Step 1.

How to Choose, Use & Store Peas

Look for fresh, young light green pods that are velvety to the touch and well filled with well developed peas. Avoid pods that are dark green, wilted or swollen, wrinkled or flecked with gray. Refrigerate in the pods, and use as soon as possible. To remove peas from pods, press pods between the thumb and forefinger and push peas out with your thumb. Rinse under running cold water in colander. Peas are an outstanding source of thiamine, niacin, phosphorus and iron.

Saucy Lima Beans

Preparation Time: 5 minutes   Cooking Time: 15 minutes

The sweet blend of onions, red pepper and parsley enhance the buttery taste of lima beans. Lima beans are a good vegetable source of protein, providing about 10% of the U.S. RDA in a ½-cup serving. The protein in lima beans is complemented when served with grain. Serve Saucy Lima Beans over cooked brown rice or millet.

1 tablespoon safflower oil

1 medium onion, coarsely chopped

1 tablespoon chopped red pepper

1 teaspoon vegetable seasoning
(recipe in Condiment section)

1 teaspoon all purpose seasoning
(recipe in Condiment section)

2 tablespoons chopped parsley

2 cloves garlic, minced or
1 teaspoon garlic powder

1 10-ounce package frozen
baby lima beans

½ cup tomato sauce*

Steps:

1. In a large frying pan, heat oil over medium heat. Add onions, red pepper, seasonings, parsley and garlic. Cook until tender.
2. Stir in lima beans and tomato sauce and cook uncovered over medium-low heat for 10 minutes.

Yield: 4 servings

This product is available from Health Valley.

"One of My Favorites"

George Mateljan

Golden Cheese Potatoes

Potatoes have the undeserved reputation for being fattening. The truth is that it is all the fat-rich butter and sour cream people put on their potatoes that is so fattening. A plain baked potato contains fewer than 150 calories, yet it is very filling and satisfying. Of course, it isn't easy to make potatoes taste good without all the high-fat toppings we've all become used to.

The reason this recipe is such a favorite of mine is that it tastes delicious, but it doesn't contain a lot of fat or calories.

The **nutritional highlights** of this recipe are that it contains only 23% of calories from fat. Potatoes are a very good source of vitamin C. Although many people don't think of potatoes as a good source of this vitamin, a medium baked potato with the skin on provides between 35% to 40% of your daily requirement. Potatoes are also an outstanding source of potassium

Golden Cheese Potatoes

Preparation Time: 10 minutes   Cooking Time: 47 minutes

4 medium baking potatoes, washed
   and cut into wedges
1 tablespoon safflower oil
½ teaspoon oregano
½ teaspoon garlic powder

½ teaspoon paprika
½ cup grated Swiss or
   cheddar cheese
cherry tomatoes and parsley
   sprigs for garnish

Steps:
1. Preheat oven to 350°F.
2. Combine oil, oregano, garlic, and paprika in a large bowl. Add potato wedges and mix well to coat potatoes evenly.
3. Arrange potatoes in an ovenproof baking dish and bake at 350°F. for 45 minutes or until potatoes are soft.
4. Remove potatoes from the oven and sprinkle with the cheese. Return them to oven until cheese has melted, about 2 minutes.
5. Before serving, garnish with cherry tomatoes and parsley sprigs.

Yield: 6 servings

Creamy Beets

| Preparation Time: 1 hour | Cooking Time: 20 minutes |

Beets take a long time to cook, but the results are worth it. Beets can have as high as 8% sugar content, which makes them taste very good. Because beets are so naturally sweet, they combine well with the tartness of yogurt and the tanginess of horseradish in this dish.

1 pound medium red beets, cooked, peeled, and cut into ½-inch cubes

¼ cup plain nonfat yogurt
1½ teaspoons prepared horseradish

Steps:

1. Cut the tops from beets. Wash and place in saucepan with enough boiling water to cover them halfway. Cover the pot and cook gently until tender. This will take about 30 minutes for young beets, up to an hour or more for mature beets. Cool beets, peel and cut into ½-inch cubes.
2. Preheat oven to 350°F.
3. Combine beets with yogurt and horseradish and place them in an ovenproof baking dish. Bake at 350°F. for 20 minutes or until heated through.

Yield: 4 servings

Red Beets with Mint

Preparation Time: 20 minutes   Cooking Time: 1 hour

Beets have been eaten since before recorded history, and are native to a broad range of Eurasia. When you shop for beets, look for firm, smooth, globe-shaped ones with firm roots. Avoid those that are flabby, scaly or have soft spots. Beets are a good source of potassium and selenium. If you buy young beets, be sure to use the beet greens too because they are an excellent source of vitamin A and iron.

1 pound beets, peeled and
  cut into ½-inch cubes
1 onion, finely chopped
1 tart apple (pippin, granny smith),
  cored and finely chopped

⅛ teaspoon nutmeg
2 tablespoons chopped fresh mint,
  or 1 teaspoon dried mint
1 tablespoon chopped walnuts

Steps:

1. Preheat oven to 350°F.
2. Combine beets, onion, apple, nutmeg and mint in glass casserole. Mix well. Bake covered at 350°F. for 1 hour or until beets are tender.
3. Remove from oven and sprinkle walnuts over the beets. Serve hot or at room temperature.

Yield: 4 servings

"One of My Favorites"

George Mateljan

Vegetable Pita Pizza

Pizza is one of the most delicious, fattening, high-fat, high-cholesterol, high-sodium foods in the world. It's also one of the most nutritious foods in the world, because it's usually high in protein, calcium and iron too. The problem with most pizza is that it's drenched in heavily salted pasta sauce, thickly coated with high fat cheese, and topped off with meat.

Our recipe is a favorite of mine because it brings you everything that is good and healthy about pizza, without too much fat or sodium. When you look at the ingredients, it doesn't seem possible that this could come out tasting like real pizza, but it does – and it's a lot healthier too!

The **nutritional highlights** of this recipe are that it has only 135 calories per serving (compared to the usual 250-400 in a slice), and only 30% of calories from fat. At the same time, it provides you with 33% of the U.S. RDA for vitamin C; about 10% each of vitamin A, calcium and iron; and all of the B vitamins.

Vegetable Pita Pizza

Preparation Time: 20 minutes   Cooking Time: 5 minutes

1 tablespoon safflower oil
1 small eggplant, cut in 6 slices
1 small green pepper, cut in
  6 slices
1 small red pepper, cut in
  6 slices
1 large onion, sliced
12 mushrooms, sliced

1 cup pasta sauce (recipe in
  Dressings and Sauces section)
½ teaspoon honey
½ teaspoon oregano
½ teaspoon dried basil
6 small pita breads
6 heaping tablespoons grated
  sharp cheddar cheese

Steps:

1. Preheat oven to 400°F.
2. Pour just enough oil into heavy skillet to coat the bottom lightly. Add eggplant slices and brown lightly on both sides. Remove to paper plate.
3. Add slices of green pepper and red pepper to skillet and saute until tender. Remove to paper plate.
4. Add remaining oil, onion slices and mushroom slices and saute until tender. Remove to paper plate.
5. Combine pasta sauce, honey, oregano and basil. Spread sauce evenly over pita breads. Top each pita bread with a slice of eggplant, a slice of red and green peppers, mushroom slices and onions. Sprinkle with grated cheese.
6. Bake at 400°F for 5 minutes or until cheese is melted.

Yield: 6 servings

Nutty Yam Bake

Preparation Time: 10 minutes   Cooking Time: 1 hour

6 medium size yams or
  sweet potatoes
1 20-ounce jar unsweetened
  apple sauce

½ cup chopped cashew nuts
2 egg whites
1 teaspoon honey

Steps:

1. Cook yams in water to cover. Boil until tender, about 30 minutes. Drain, peel and mash yams.
2. Preheat oven to 400°F.
3. Mix apple sauce and cashew nuts with yams. Pour into oiled shallow casserole.
4. Beat egg whites and honey very stiff. Spread on top of yam mixture.
5. Bake at 400°F for 30 minutes.

Yield: 12 servings

Note: This recipe may be cut in half.

How to Choose, Use & Store Yams and Sweet Potatoes:
Choose firm, smooth, even colored tubers with no soft spots. Buy in small quantities, as they don't store well. Scrub, but do not peel, just before using. To boil: cover with boiling water and cook, until fork tender, about 20-30 minutes. To bake: bake unpeeled medium potatoes in 450°F oven for about 1 hour. When baked, cover with damp cloth and allow to steam for a few minutes. Then, the skins will peel off more easily.

Zesty Cauliflower

Preparation Time: 15 minutes	Cooking Time: 15 minutes

Mark Twain once joked that "Cauliflower is nothing but cabbage with a college education," but like many witticisms, it turns out to be true. Cauliflower and broccoli are both members of the cabbage family. There are numerous sub-varieties and colors of cauliflower including white, green and purple. Cauliflower was extremely popular in 17th century Europe, but gradually lost its following until recently when science discovered that it may be effective in combating certain types of cancer, including lung cancer.

1 medium cauliflower separated into flowerettes	2 tablespoons apple cider vinegar
1 teaspoon safflower oil	3 medium tomatoes, peeled and chopped
2 teaspoons olive oil	½ teaspoon oregano
1 medium onion, chopped	1 teaspoon dried basil

Steps:

1. Steam cauliflower for 2 minutes in steamer basket.
2. In heavy skillet, heat oil over medium high heat. Add cauliflower and brown lightly, stirring constantly. Add onions and cook for 3 minutes. Add vinegar and cover the skillet. Cook for 3 minutes over low heat.
3. Add tomatoes, oregano and basil and simmer until cauliflower is tender.

Yield: 6 servings

Dilled Marinated Vegetables

Preparation Time: 1 hour   Plus chilling time

½ cup herb dressing

2 tablespoons picante sauce

4 teaspoons honey

1 teaspoon all purpose seasoning
(recipe in Condiment section)

1 teaspoon vegetable seasoning
(recipe in Condiment section)

1 teaspoon dill weed

⅛ teaspoon garlic powder

1½ cups diced carrots, steamed

1½ cups cauliflower, cut in
flowerettes, steamed

1 pound fresh green peas, or
1 10-ounce package frozen peas

10 ounces fresh green beans, or
1 10-ounce package frozen
green beans

½ cup chopped celery

½ cup chopped onions

chopped parsley for garnish

Steps:

1. In large bowl, combine the first seven ingredients. Mix well.
2. Add remaining ingredients. Toss to coat well. Cover and refrigerate for several hours or overnight. Vegetables will keep for 2-3 days in the refrigerator.

Yield: 12 servings

Herb Dressing

Preparation Time: 5 minutes

½ cup water

2 tablespoons apple cider vinegar

2 teaspoons honey

½ teaspoon dried basil

½ teaspoon dried bell pepper

¼ teaspoon oregano

¼ teaspoon thyme

⅛ teaspoon garlic powder

½ teaspoon onion powder

1 tablespoon safflower oil

Steps:

1. In measuring cup, combine water, vinegar and honey.
2. Crush herbs in blender or mortar and pestle and add to vinegar dressing. Stir in oil and pour over salad or vegetables. Store remaining dressing in covered container in refrigerator.

Yield: ¾ cup

How to Choose, Use & Store Fresh Green Beans

Look for beans that have firm, crisp pods without scars. Bumps on string beans mean that they're tough, so select those with small, well shaped seeds. Length is not important. Store in crisper in your refrigerator and use within 1 or 2 days. To prepare, wash beans and snap off the ends. Any "strings" which adhere to the pod will come off with the end.

Mexican Style Corn

Preparation Time: 5 minutes   Cooking Time: 15 minutes

Corn is a good source of vitamin A, B complex, C, phosphorus and potassium. In using frozen vegetables, be sure to cook them very lightly to retain crunchiness and valuable nutrients. Many frozen vegetables can be thawed, drained and eaten raw. Try it with spinach and broccoli.

1 tablespoon safflower oil
½ cup chopped green pepper
½ cup chopped red pepper
2 tablespoons chopped green onion
1 10-ounce package frozen whole kernel corn, thawed

1 teaspoon vegetable seasoning (recipe in Condiment section)
dash of cayenne (optional)
1 cup pasta sauce (recipe in Dressings and Sauces section)
2 tablespoons chopped parsley

Steps:
1. In a large skillet, heat oil over medium heat.
2. Add green pepper, red pepper and onion and saute for 5 minutes.
3. Add corn, vegetable seasoning, cayenne (if desired) and pasta sauce.
4. Cook and stir for another 8 minutes. Sprinkle with parsley and serve.

Yield: 6 servings

Tips on Selecting Corn on the Cob
Look for fresh green husks and stems, with no signs of decay in the silk ends. The kernels should be bright, plump and milky looking, and yield slightly to the touch. Ideally, corn should be kept cold from the moment it is harvested until used because corn sugar converts into starch very quickly. So, buy the coldest corn and store in crisper for immediate use.

321

Italian Style Zucchini Rounds

Preparation Time: 10 minutes   Cooking Time: 12-15 minutes

The squash family includes cucumbers and pumpkins, as well as winter squash (such as acorn, butternut and Hubbard) and summer squash (zucchini and crookneck). Some of these species have been cultivated for 9,000 years. Zucchini has become increasingly popular in the last few years because it is low in calories, rich in vitamin C and A, and is very versatile.

4 medium zucchini
1 cup tomato sauce*
½ teaspoon honey

1 teaspoon all purpose seasoning
(recipe in Condiment section)
1½ teaspoons vegetable seasoning
(recipe in Condiment section)

Steps:

1. Slice the zucchini into ¼-inch thick rounds.
2. In a small saucepan, mix tomato sauce, honey and seasonings. Add rounds. Simmer covered for 12-15 minutes until heated through.

Yield: 4 servings

This product is available from Health Valley.

How to Choose, Use & Store Zucchini
Small zucchini that are heavy for their size are the best. Look for young, tender and well formed zucchini with bright skin that is free from blemishes. Wash and store in your refrigerator – they'll keep for up to 2 weeks. Zucchini can be enjoyed raw in salads, as well as cooked.

Quick Sauteed Zucchini with Leeks and Tomatoes

Preparation Time: 15 minutes   Cooking Time: 15 minutes

Leeks look like giant scallions, but have a much sweeter and milder flavor than other onions. For centuries, leeks were looked down on as "poor man's asparagus," until the early part of this century when a trendy French chef in New York named Louis Diat created a beautiful and refreshing cold potato-and-leek soup and named it "vichyssoise."

**6 small ripe, firm tomatoes,
   peeled and quartered**

3 teaspoons olive oil

**2 medium leeks (white part only),
   sliced thin**

**1½ pounds zucchini, cut into
   2 x ¼-inch julienne**

dash of cayenne

Steps:

1. Scrape pulp from tomatoes. Drain on a paper towel.
2. In a medium size heavy skillet, heat 2 teaspoons of oil over medium high heat. Add leeks and cook until tender, about 7 minutes, stirring often. Add zucchini and saute until crisp-tender, about 5 minutes. Sprinkle with cayenne and mix well. Using slotted spoon, arrange around the outside edge of a heated serving platter. Cover to keep warm.
3. Add remaining 1 teaspoon oil to skillet, heat on medium high heat and add tomatoes. Toss until just hot, about 2 minutes. Spoon tomatoes into center of serving platter. Serve immediately.

Yield: 6 servings

Curried Garbanzo Beans with Lime

Preparation Time: 25 minutes   Cooking Time: 20 minutes

The Italian word for chick peas is, *ceci.* When the French occupied Sicily in the Middle Ages, the Sicilians would determine if a person was French or Sicilian by asking him to pronounce ceci (the correct pronunciation is "tchay-tchee"). If the person failed to pronounce the word correctly, he was put to death. On the basis of this, we'd have to say that good grammer is as important to your health as nutrition.

1 tablespoon safflower oil
1 large onion, finely chopped
3 cloves garlic, minced
1 tablespoon minced fresh ginger
1 large ripe tomato, chopped
1½ teaspoons ground cumin
1 teaspoon ground coriander

⅛ teaspoon cayenne
½ teaspoon ground turmeric
2 15½-ounce cans garbanzo beans (chick peas), rinsed and drained
¾ cup water
2 large limes, cut in wedges
1 tablespoon chopped cilantro (optional)

Steps:

1. In a large heavy skillet over medium high heat, combine oil, onion, garlic and ginger. Saute until onions are slightly browned. Add tomato and cook until all liquid has evaporated.
2. Add cumin, coriander, cayenne and turmeric. Stir and simmer for 3 minutes. Add garbanzo beans and water and simmer for 15 more minutes.
3. To serve, spoon mixture into serving bowl. Garnish with lime wedges and sprinkle with cilantro.

Yield: 6 servings

Vegetarian Pita Pockets

Preparation Time: 20 minutes

Pita bread is wonderful for a sandwich like this, in which you have a variety of ingredients all cut into small pieces. You can stuff the vegetable filling neatly into the pocket and enjoy it, without fear of everything falling out. Whole wheat pita bread has virtually the same nutrition as whole wheat bread.

2 cups chopped fresh parsley
1 15½-ounce can garbanzo beans, rinsed and drained
1 small green pepper, diced
1 medium tomato, peeled, seeded and chopped

2 scallions, finely chopped
3 tablespoons lemon juice
2 small cloves garlic, minced
3 teaspoons olive oil
6 small whole wheat pita breads, halved
6 ounces alfalfa sprouts

Steps:
1. In a medium bowl, combine the parsley, garbanzo beans, green pepper, tomato and scallions.
2. Mix lemon juice and garlic in a small bowl. Whisk in the olive oil in a slow, steady stream. Pour over vegetables and mix well. Divide mixture among pita breads. Top with alfalfa sprouts.

Yield: 6 servings

Note: Vegetable mixture may be prepared the day before.

18

Pasta & Grain Side Dishes

Whole grains and pastas made from whole grains are among nature's most remarkable nutritional gifts. Within every kernel of grain is the life essence of a plant just waiting to be activated. So important are grains that they are one of the four basic food groups our bodies require every day to stay healthy. Grains are nature's richest source of dietary fiber, and are a storehouse of complex carbohydrates, protein, vitamin E, B vitamins and a variety of important minerals including phosphorus, magnesium, iron and zinc.

In this section, you will find zesty new ways to prepare pasta, rice, and even bulgur and lentils that you might think of as bland into lively side dishes enhanced by a delicious medley of herbs, spices, and delicate sauces. And unlike many grain recipes in other books that use lots of butter and salt to add some taste, ours taste great and are low in fat, cholesterol and sodium.

When you compare a famous Italian dish like Fettucini Alfredo with our Herb Spaghetti, you can readily see that you're consuming 40% less fat with our recipe and no cholesterol. Comparing a slice of typical cheese pizza with our Vegetable Pita Pizza reveals that our recipe contains 25% less fat and virtually no cholesterol.

You may be surprised to see that our recipes are higher in calories, but what you're consuming is more of the complex carbohydrates you need.

FOOD	CALORIES	TOTAL FAT	SATURATED FAT	MONOUN-SATURATED FAT	POLYUN-SATURATED FAT	CHOLESTEROL
Fettucini Alfredo	176	8.14 gm	4.4 gm	2.03 gm	0.25 gm	45.8 mg
Herb Spaghetti	268	4.91 gm	.32 gm	1.7 gm	0.33 gm	0.0 mg
Cheese Pizza	236	9.4 gm	3.0 gm	0.40 gm	6.00 gm	56 mg
Vegetable Pita Pizza*	252	7.0 gm	1.0 gm	0.98 gm	1.94 gm	7 mg

*Recipe in Vegetable Side Dishes

Keep in mind, however, that all pastas are not created equal nutritionally. Many commercial pastas are made from semolina flour, which is durum wheat that has had the nutritious germ and bran removed. If you're looking for the most nutritious whole grain pasta, choose Health Valley Pasta. Health Valley uses seven whole grains that have been sprouted. Sprouting is the natural process of germination that awakens the life essence in the grain seed, and dramatically increases its food value. Health Valley includes high-protein Amaranth as one of these sprouted grains to create a special pasta that is richer in nutrients and flavor. A 2-ounce serving of Health Valley Pasta provides 15% of the U.S. RDA for protein, while most other pastas provide just 10%. So look for Health Valley pastas, or for pastas made with 100% whole grains.

Herb Spaghetti

Preparation Time: 20 minutes   Cooking Time: 15 minutes

Garlic is absolutely essential when you are cooking without salt, because its intense flavor adds zest to many kinds of foods, from poultry to vegetables. The human race seems to be divided between garlic lovers (Aristophanes, Hippocrates, Mohammed, Gandhi and Eleanor Roosevelt) and garlic haters (Plautus, Horace and Count Dracula, who cannot rise from the grave if his mouth is stuffed with garlic and garlic cloves are scattered in his coffin). We like it for its seasoning value, and because garlic appears to be helpful in lowering blood pressure. There is absolutely no truth to the rumor that Count Dracula prefers people with high blood pressure.

8 ounces whole wheat spaghetti*
1 tablespoon olive oil
2 whole garlic bulbs, cloves separated, peeled and minced

¼ teaspoon oregano
⅛ teaspoon cayenne
2 tablespoons chopped cilantro
1 lemon

Steps:

1. Cook spaghetti according to package directions.
2. Meanwhile, heat the oil in a large skillet over medium high heat. Add the garlic and saute for 30 seconds. Add oregano, cayenne and cilantro; stir to mix well. Add the cooked spaghetti and toss well to coat evenly.
3. Serve with lemon wedges immediately on a warmed serving platter.

Yield: 6 servings

Note: You can find bottled minced garlic in many markets in the produce section to reduce preparation time.

This product is available from Health Valley

Spaghetti with Basil and Pine Nuts

Preparation Time: 10 minutes   Cooking Time: 15 minutes

10 ounces whole wheat spaghetti*
1 tablespoon olive oil
2 cloves garlic, minced
1 cup shredded fresh basil leaves

½ cup chicken broth
  (recipe in Soup section)
¼ cup pine nuts, toasted
½ cup shredded Swiss cheese

Steps:
1. Cook pasta according to package directions.
2. While pasta is cooking, heat oil in heavy skillet over medium high heat. Add garlic and saute for 30 seconds. Stir in shredded basil leaves and reduce heat to low. Saute basil leaves until they are wilted, about 30 seconds. Add chicken broth and bring mixture to simmer.
3. Drain pasta and add to the basil mixture in skillet. Coat pasta well with basil mixture. Add pine nuts and Swiss cheese. Toss well and serve immediately.

Yield: 6 servings

This product is available from Health Valley.

Think About Pasta for Protein

Most Americans automatically reach for red meat when they want their protein. But you should know that a 2-ounce serving of Health Valley whole wheat pasta provides about 15% of the U.S. RDA of protein for adults (most commercial pastas provide only 10%). And if you sprinkle on grated cheese as in this recipe, it boosts the protein about 5% more. Pasta is a good way to get your protein while cutting down on all the fat that you consume when you eat meat. And it's a lot cheaper too.

Healthy Pasta Primavera

Preparation Time: 45 minutes	Cooking Time: 25 minutes

Pasta Primavera is a perfect recipe for healthier eating. It combines protein, grain, beans, dairy, and lots of good vegetables into one beautiful dish that is rich in flavor and nourishment. The key to making this recipe is to use only the very freshest vegetables. You can substitute according to what's in season, and to your own taste.

Most recipes for Pasta Primavera include large amounts of oil, so that over 50% of calories are from fat. Our healthy version derives only about 25% of calories from fat.

9 ounces cooked whole wheat spaghetti*
¾ cup chopped onion
4 cloves garlic, minced
1 tablespoon olive oil
½ cup chopped fresh green beans
4 cups broccoli, separated into small flowerettes
1 cup sliced zucchini

½ cup sliced carrots
2 cups sliced mushrooms
½ cup diced green pepper
½ cup diced red pepper
¼ cup cooked kidney beans
¼ cup water
½ teaspoon dried basil
½ teaspoon thyme
½ teaspoon marjoram

Sauce:

3 cloves garlic, minced
1 tablespoon water
1 cup nonfat milk

1 cup shredded Swiss cheese
1½ teaspoons arrowroot
2 teaspoons dried basil

Steps:
1. Cook pasta according to package directions. Drain.
2. In large saucepan, saute onions and minced garlic in olive oil until tender.
3. Add remaining vegetables and kidney beans, and ¼ cup water. Cook, stirring with a wooden spoon 7-9 minutes until broccoli is tender crisp. Add basil, thyme and marjoram. Mix well and set aside.
4. In small saucepan, prepare sauce by cooking 3 cloves minced garlic in 1 table-spoon water until tender. Add milk, cheese and arrowroot. Heat, stirring constantly until cheese is melted. Add dried basil.
5. Add the cooked spaghetti to the vegetable mixture, mix well. Add the cheese sauce, toss to mix well. Serve immediately and top with an additional table-spoon of shredded cheese per serving if desired.

Yield: 6 servings

This product is available from Health Valley.

Peppery Chili Elbows

Preparation Time: 15 minutes   Cooking Time: 30 minutes

This dish is an excellent example of the "meatless protein" principle. It combines whole wheat pasta (grain) with vegetarian chili (legume) and just enough grated cheese to assure the quality of the protein. The flavors are deliciously compatible too.

6 ounces whole wheat elbow pasta*

1 large green pepper, cut into large chunks

1 15-ounce can spicy vegetarian chili*

1 cup plain nonfat yogurt

2 teaspoons honey

3 ounces mild cheddar cheese, grated (about ¾ cup)

¼ cup chopped onion

½ teaspoon garlic powder

½ teaspoon chili powder

1 teaspoon all purpose seasoning (recipe in Condiment section)

Steps:

1. Preheat oven to 350°F. and oil an 8-inch square casserole.
2. Cook elbows according to package directions. While they are cooking, parboil green pepper for 5 minutes.
3. Combine elbows, chili, yogurt, honey, half the grated cheese, onion, seasonings and green peppers. Mix well, then turn into prepared casserole, top with remaining cheese and bake at 350°F. for 25-30 minutes, or until mixture is bubbly and top layer of cheese is completely melted.

Yield: 6 servings

This product is available from Health Valley.

Basic Rice Recipe

Preparation Time: 10 minutes   Cooking Time: 1 hour

If you are accustomed to cooking rice in a pot on the stovetop, you will find that this oven method is both easier and more consistent, producing moist, delicious rice every time.

1 cup raw brown rice, rinsed   **2 cups chicken broth, heated**
and drained   (recipe in Soup section)

Steps:

1. Preheat oven to 350°F.
2. In medium size casserole, combine rice and hot chicken broth. Cover and bake at 350°F for 1 hour.

Yield: 2½ cups

Variations: After rice is cooked:

Risi Bisi—Add 1 cup cooked green peas. Mix well.

Tomato—Add 1 cup finely chopped tomatoes. Mix well.

Confetti—Add ½ cup chopped green pepper and ½ cup chopped red pepper. Mix well.

Parsley—Add ½ cup chopped parsley. Mix well.

Chives or green onion—Add ½ cup chopped chives or green onion. Mix well.

Cashews—Add ½ cup coarsely chopped cashew nuts. Mix well.

Almonds—Add ½ cup toasted slivered almonds. Mix well.

About Rice

Rice is one of the two most important foods in the world (the other is wheat). In our Western culture, rice is a side dish but in the East, it is cherished for its simple nourishment. Rice is primarily carbohydrate, but also provides enough protein, thiamine (B_1), niacin, phosphorus and potassium to be of significance. It is important to use brown rice—not white—in these recipes. White rice, like white flour, has had the nutritious bran and germ removed, leaving mostly starch. We also approve of wild rice which has its nutrition intact, and is a good food.

Green Rice

Preparation Time: 10 minutes   Cooking Time: 35 minutes

There are about 2,500 different varieties of rice, some of which are red, blue and even purple. To grow rice, you need more water than any other cereal crop but the primary purpose of all that standing water is to drown surrounding weeds while the rice seedlings are growing. In the Far East, rice is associated with fertility but don't laugh: just remember, we Westerners always throw rice at the bride and groom.

1 tablespoon olive oil
1 cup finely chopped onion
1 cup raw brown rice
2 cups chicken broth
(recipe in Soup section)
¼ teaspoon thyme

1 10-ounce package frozen chopped spinach, thawed and drained
¼ cup finely chopped parsley
¼ teaspoon garlic powder
lemon wedges

Steps:

1. Heat oil in large skillet over medium heat. Add onion and cook until tender, about 3 minutes, stirring frequently. Add rice, chicken broth and thyme and bring to a boil. Reduce heat and simmer covered for 25 minutes or until rice is tender and all liquid has been absorbed.
2. Stir in spinach, parsley and garlic powder and heat for 5 minutes more or until heated through. Serve with lemon wedges.

Yield: 4 servings

Rice Nutrition

1/2 cup	Calories	Protein g.	Fat g.	Carb. g.	Calcium mg.	Phos. mg.	Potassium mg.	Thiamine mg.	Riboflavin mg.	Niacin mg.	B6 mg.	Folacin mcg.
Cooked brown rice	104	2.2	0.5	22.3	11	64	61	.06	.02	1.2	.16	14
Cooked white enriched rice	112	2.0	0.1	24.9	10	29	29	.11	.07	1	.06	16

Risotto

Preparation Time: 20 minutes   Cooking Time: 1 hour

Rice is said to be the staple food for about 6 out of every 10 people in the world. The people of Japan, China, Thailand and the Philippines do not consider a meal to be complete without rice. Among Europeans, the Italians are the biggest consumers of rice and the creators of numerous risotto dishes.

1½ **cups finely chopped onions**
2 **cups sliced mushrooms**
1 **teaspoon safflower oil**
2 **cups pasta sauce** (recipe in Dressings and Sauces section)
2 **cups raw brown rice, washed**
1½ **cups chicken broth** (recipe in Soup section)

1 **tablespoon lemon juice**
1 **teaspoon honey**
2 **teaspoons all purpose seasoning** (recipe in Condiment section)
½ **teaspoon garlic powder**
¼ **teaspoon nutmeg**
3 **ounces grated jack cheese**

Steps:
1. Preheat oven to 350°F.
2. In medium saucepan, saute onions and mushrooms in oil until glossy, but not brown. Add pasta sauce, cook 2 minutes, stirring often.
3. Add rice, cook 3 minutes until rice begins to get reddish in color. Add chicken broth, lemon juice, honey and seasonings and cook 5 minutes, stirring constantly.
4. Remove from heat, add half of grated cheese. Mix well.
5. Put in lightly oiled casserole dish. Sprinkle with remaining grated cheese. Cover.
6. Bake at 350°F. for 55 minutes. Remove cover and bake 5 minutes longer.

Yield: 8 servings

Risotto Variations
There are many delicious ways to serve Risotto. You can substitute fish stock for chicken broth and add shellfish that has been cooked. Or, try adding cooked peas just before serving.

Brown Rice Pilaf

Preparation Time: 10 minutes   Cooking Time: 55 minutes

The mechanical milling and polishing of rice reduces spoilage, but it also depletes the rice of some protein and vitamins. In the late 19th century, Asia was stricken with the disease called *beriberi*, in which the nerves, digestive system and heart become inflamed and may degenerate. Scientific investigators identified the vitamin thiamine (B_1) as the nutrient whose deficiency causes beriberi. By feeding rice bran to the sick, the disease could be reversed. When Asians went back to eating whole grain brown rice instead of milled white rice, the disease diminished. A serving of Brown Rice Pilaf provides 14% of the U.S. RDA for thiamine.

1 tablespoon safflower oil	**3 cups chicken broth** (recipe in Soup section)
1½ cups raw brown rice	**2 tablespoons finely chopped parsley**
1 small onion, chopped	
½ cup celery, chopped	

Steps:

1. In large saucepan, heat the oil over medium high heat. Add brown rice, onion and celery. Cook for 5 minutes or until vegetables are tender, stirring frequently. Remove from heat.
2. Add chicken broth. Return to heat and bring rice-vegetable mixture to a boil. Cover and lower heat to simmer for 50 minutes or until all liquid has been absorbed.
3. Remove from heat and let stand for 10 minutes before stirring in parsley.

Yield: 6 servings

Italian Style Broccoli and Brown Rice

Preparation Time: 15 minutes	Cooking Time: 20 minutes

Rice is one of the oldest food crops known. Chinese records of rice cultivation go back 4,000 years. It was first introduced to the American colonies in the mid 17th century. Rice has been a staple crop since that time, although the average annual consumption here is only about 6 to 10 pounds per person, compared to 200 to 400 pounds per person in the Orient.

1 medium onion, chopped
8 ounces mushrooms, sliced
1 teaspoon olive oil
2 cups cooked brown rice
1 pound fresh broccoli,
 steamed for 5 minutes,
 or 1 10-ounce package
 frozen broccoli, thawed
 and drained

1 cup pasta sauce (recipe in
 Dressings and Sauces section)
½ teaspoon dried basil
½ teaspoon oregano
1 teaspoon garlic powder
4 ounces Swiss cheese, grated

Steps:

1. Preheat oven to 350°F.
2. Saute onions and mushrooms in olive oil until tender. Combine with cooked rice.
3. Place rice-mushroom mixture in bottom of 10 x 6 x 2-inch casserole. Top with broccoli.
4. Combine pasta sauce with basil, oregano and garlic powder and pour over broccoli. Top with grated cheese.
5. Bake at 350°F for 20 minutes.

Yield: 8 servings

How to Choose, Use and Store Broccoli
Look for broccoli plants with firm, tight clusters of closed flower buds that are dark green to purplish green, and tender, light green stalks. Avoid open yellow buds and soft wet spots. Broccoli can be eaten raw or lightly steamed. To store broccoli, wash and wrap in plastic and refrigerate. Broccoli should be used within 2-3 days.

Spanish Bulgur Chili

Preparation Time: 15 minutes   Cooking Time: 40 minutes

½ cup chopped onion
½ cup chopped celery with leaves
¼ cup chopped green pepper
2 teaspoons safflower oil
½ cup uncooked bulgur wheat
2 15-ounce cans tomato sauce*
3 teaspoons garlic powder
1½ teaspoons ground cumin
1 teaspoon chili powder

1 teaspoon vegetable seasoning
(recipe in Condiment section)
¼ teaspoon cayenne
1 15-ounce can spicy
vegetarian chili*
3 teaspoons all purpose seasoning
(recipe in Condiment section)
grated cheese for garnish
tortilla chips*

Steps:
1. In large skillet over medium high heat, saute onions, celery, and green pepper in oil until soft. Add bulgur and saute 5 minutes, stirring constantly.
2. Add remaining ingredients except cheese and tortilla chips. Mix well. Bring to a boil, lower heat, cover and simmer 30 minutes, stirring frequently to prevent sticking to the bottom. Add water if needed.
3. Serve in bowls, sprinkle with grated cheese. Serve with corn tortilla chips.

Yield: 8 servings

This product is available from Health Valley.

Bulgur Lentil Casserole

Preparation Time: 35 minutes   Cooking Time: 30 minutes

Onions are so ancient and so widespread a cultivated plant that their origins are lost in prehistory. An early Turkish legend describes how after Satan was expelled from heaven, on his way down to hell he touched down on the earth. Where his left foot touched down, garlic grew, and where his right foot touched down, onions grew. In any event, in ancient times, onions were so abundant and cheap that they were considered food for the poor. It wasn't until much later that onions acquired any respectability.

Today, we recognize that onions can add a distinctive flavor and valuable nutrition to recipes.

1 cup lentils, uncooked
4 cups chicken broth
(recipe in Soup section)
2 cups boiling water
1 cup uncooked bulgur wheat

½ cup finely chopped red onion
1 cup finely chopped fresh parsley

Dressing:

¼ cup chicken broth
1 tablespoon prepared Dijon mustard
3 tablespoons apple cider vinegar
1 teaspoon oregano

½ teaspoon dried basil
¼ teaspoon ground cumin
⅛ teaspoon cayenne
1 tablespoon olive oil
½ cup thinly sliced scallions

Steps:

1. In a medium saucepan, bring the lentils to a boil in chicken broth. Cover and simmer for 30 minutes. Drain and set aside.
2. Meanwhile, put the bulgur into a medium bowl. Pour boiling water over it and let soak for about 15 minutes or until all liquid is absorbed.
3. In a large bowl, combine lentils, bulgur, onion and parsley.
4. For the dressing, whisk together chicken broth, mustard, vinegar, oregano, basil, cumin and cayenne in a small bowl. Slowly whisk in the oil. Pour dressing over lentil-bulgur mixture. Toss to mix well.
5. Before serving, add the scallions and toss again.

Yield: 6 servings

Vegetable Bulgur Pilaf

Preparation Time: 15 minutes   Cooking Time: 15 minutes

Traditional Middle Eastern pilaf consists of rice steamed in broth, sometimes with poultry, meat or fish, and flavored with herbs and spices. However, you can actually make pilaf with any grain you can prepare in this manner.

Our recipe combines bulgur with lima beans for outstanding complementary protein, as well as interesting flavor and texture contrasts. It's a very hearty dish you can enjoy as an entree or as a side dish.

4 cups chicken broth
   (recipe in Soup section)
1 tablespoon curry powder
8 cloves garlic, minced
2 medium carrots, coarsely
   shredded

2 10-ounce packages frozen
   baby lima beans
2 cups uncooked bulgur
½ cup sliced green onions
   plain nonfat yogurt

Steps:

1. In a medium saucepan, combine chicken broth, curry powder, garlic, carrots and lima beans. Bring to a boil. Remove from heat and stir in the bulgur. Cover and bring to a boil; reduce heat and simmer for 12 minutes or until all liquid is absorbed and bulgur is tender.
2. Reserve 2 tablespoons green onions and mix the remainder into bulgur-vegetable mixture.
3. Sprinkle with remaining 2 tablespoons green onions and serve with dollops of plain nonfat yogurt.

Yield: 8 servings

Note: If you want to make this recipe strictly vegetarian, you may substitute water for chicken broth, and eliminate the yogurt topping. The recipe will still be tasty, if not quite as rich.

19

Desserts & Snacks

Desserts and snacks can be a nutritional disaster. Just look at the calories, fat and sodium you're consuming in an average serving of some typical desserts:

FOOD (1 serving)	CALORIES	FAT	CHOLESTEROL	SODIUM	PERCENT OF CALORIES FROM FAT
Chocolate Cake	366	17.2 gm	33 mg	294 mg	over 40%
Ice Cream	260	14.1 gm	53 mg	84 mg	almost 50%
Coconut Custard Pie	510	30.0 gm	70 mg	394 mg	over 53%

So you can see why the best dessert is fresh fruit, which is low in calories, high in vitamins, minerals and fiber, and which also contains enzymes to aid your digestion.

But when you crave something sweet or want to serve something fancy, it can be done the healthy way. Our Poached Pears with Yogurt and Almonds are a truly elegant party dessert; our Frozen Peach Dessert is very much like ice cream (and it's a superior source of protein, calcium, and vitamins A, C, riboflavin, and B_{12}). Our Chewy Amaranth Brownies are tempting, and they're made with the super high protein grain of the Aztecs instead of white flour. You can really feel good about indulging yourself in these desserts because they're so healthy:

FOOD (1 serving)	CALORIES	FAT	CHOLESTEROL	SODIUM	PERCENT OF CALORIES FROM FAT
Poached Pears	235	6.2 gm	2 mg	30 mg	under 24%
Frozen Peach Dessert	99	.2 gm	1 mg	47 mg	under 2%
Chewy Amaranth Brownies	113	3.7 gm	0 mg	27 mg	29.4%

After you've mastered the recipes in this section, you should use it as a blueprint for making all of your own dessert recipes healthier. For example, these luscious recipes frequently use fruit or fruit juices as sweeteners instead of sugar, and nonfat yogurt with a dash of honey instead of butter and cream.

A Healthy Alternative for Extra Convenience.

At Health Valley, we believe that dessert doesn't have to be the part of your meal you always feel guilty about eating. So Health Valley offers a wide variety of healthy cookies and snacks that are made using only the finest fruits, nuts, and whole grains as ingredients, and sweetened with pure fruit juice or a touch of honey.

So when you're in a hurry and don't have time to prepare these recipes, try Health Valley Apple Bakes® or Raisin Bakes® snack bars, Fruit Jumbos® Cookies, or any other of the many Health Valley healthier snack foods. They're as good tasting as they are good for you!

"One of My Favorites"

George Mateljan

Health Valley Jumbo Lemon Delight

This is one of the lightest, easiest, most deliciously satisfying desserts you'll ever have the pleasure of preparing and serving. It's a particular favorite of mine because it takes only a few easy minutes to fix and you can enjoy it so many different ways.

I like it best as a smooth and creamy topping for our Health Valley Fruit Jumbos™ Cookies, because its tangy sweetness blends so well with these juice sweetened cookies.

But it also tastes great on almost all kinds of fresh fruit. And because it contains only 12 calories per tablespoon, you can indulge in almost as much as you want without gaining pounds or inches.

The **nutritional highlight** of this recipe is that it contains almost no fat.

Health Valley
Jumbo Lemon Delight

Preparation Time: 15 minutes   Plus chilling time

¼ cup lemon juice

¼ cup water

3 tablespoons honey

1 tablespoon arrowroot

1 teaspoon grated lemon peel

1 cup plain nonfat yogurt

1 medium banana, finely chopped

1 egg white

Health Valley Fruit Jumbos® cookies

Steps:

1. In small saucepan, combine lemon juice, water, honey, arrowroot and lemon peel. Cook over medium high heat until sauce is thick and smooth. Remove from heat. Cool slightly.
2. Fold in yogurt and banana and chill for 2 hours.
3. Beat egg white until stiff peaks form. Fold into lemon-yogurt mixture. Chill.
4. Spoon a generous tablespoon of Jumbo Lemon Delight onto each Fruit Jumbo Cookie.

Yield: 2 cups

Serving Suggestion: You can make this recipe really attractive by topping it with sliced strawberries or kiwi fruit, or both.

Banana Creme Bars

Preparation Time: 5 minutes   Plus chilling time

Bananas are not actually a fruit at all, but a giant herb. The Koran identifies the forbidden fruit of the Old Testament as the banana, and not the apple; and early Hindu Christians envisioned Adam and Eve as covering themselves with banana leaves and not fig leaves.

In the 1920's, a young American black singer named Josephine Baker was having a tough time breaking into show business in the United States so she went to Paris. She appeared in the Folies Bergere wearing a girdle of bananas, which she peeled onstage. Needless to say, she was an immediate hit.

Josephine Baker became one of the legendary stars of the Folies, and returned to the United States in triumph in the 1950's where her legend grew even brighter as an entertainer and leader in the civil rights movement.

1 cup plain nonfat yogurt   **2 tablespoons honey**
2 medium size ripe bananas

Steps:

1. Puree ingredients in a food processor or blender. Pour into mold and freeze until firm.

Yield: 6 bars

Note: Fresh strawberries, raspberries, peaches, or apricots may be used.

Frozen Peach Dessert

Preparation Time: 10 minutes   Plus chilling time

A healthy dessert doesn't have to be a piece of plain fresh fruit, or one bite of something sinful. This refreshing chilled dessert is a delicately delicious replacement for ice cream or sherbet, with just 100 calories and a trace of fat in a serving. You can really feel good about eating it, because it provides 12% of the U.S. RDA for calcium and vitamin A.

1 16-ounce can sliced peaches in unsweetened juice, well drained

1 cup plain nonfat yogurt
2½ tablespoons honey

Steps:

1. Place peach slices on a baking sheet, making sure that slices are not touching. Freeze for 1½ hours or until hard.
2. Remove frozen peach slices from freezer and place in a chilled food processor or blender. Add yogurt and honey and process until smooth. Spoon into chilled dessert cups and sprinkle with your favorite topping. Serve immediately.

Yield: 4 servings

"One of My Favorites"

George Mateljan

Poached Pears with Yogurt and Almonds

Pears break the usual rule that tree-ripened fruits are best. Pears are picked full grown but still green and achieve their best flavor and texture off the tree. The Bartlett pear is bell shaped and yellow with a red blush when ripe, and is excellent for poaching, canning or eating raw. The ruddy Comice is a delicious winter pear that is highly perishable. The Bosc is another juicy winter pear. Pears should be ripened at room temperature until they yield to slight pressure. Avoid pears that are dull, shriveled or soft around the stem.

This is a favorite recipe of mine because it is not only delicious but very beautiful. You can serve this dessert at a formal dinner party, and your guests will "ooh" and "aah" as it is served, never realizing that you are starting them on the road to healthier eating.

The **nutritional highlights** of this recipe are that it is rich in vitamins A and C, and the luscious yogurt sauce even provides 7% of the U.S. RDA for calcium.

Poached Pears with Yogurt and Almonds

Preparation Time: 20 minutes   Cooking Time: 30-45 minutes

6 firm, ripe pears
¼ cup honey
1 tablespoon lemon juice
  dash of ginger or cloves

1 cup unsweetened apple juice
  or white grape juice
½ cup slivered almonds
1 cup plain low fat yogurt
6 fresh, ripe strawberries

Steps:

1. Core pears but do not peel.
2. In a large saucepan which has a tight-fitting lid, combine honey, lemon juice, ginger or cloves, and fruit juice. Bring to boiling over medium heat, then place pears upright in the boiling liquid. Cover saucepan, lower heat and simmer for 30-45 minutes, until tender.
3. Remove pears carefully to dessert serving dish. Stir almonds and yogurt into sauce, spoon over pears and allow to cool. Garnish with fresh, ripe strawberries.

Yield: 6 servings

Orange Pears

Preparation Time: 10 minutes   Cooking Time: 35 minutes

There are thousands of varieties of pears, varying greatly in size, color, texture, flavor and shape. The most popular pear in America is the Bartlett, which accounts for about three-quarters of the pear crop in the country. It is a summer pear with the familiar bell shape, and is ideal for poaching, canning, or eating raw. In the winter, the Bosc and Comice are popular eating pears.

4 medium ripe pears   **1 cup orange juice**
1 teaspoon grated orange peel   **2 tablespoons honey**

Steps:
1. Preheat oven to 375°F.
2. Wash pears, cut into halves and core. Place cut side down in a glass baking dish.
3. Combine orange peel, orange juice and honey and pour mixture over pear halves. Bake at 375°F for 35 minutes or until pears are tender, basting several times. Serve at room temperature or chilled.

Yield: 8 servings

Baked Apples

Preparation Time: 10 minutes   Cooking Time: 45 minutes

There are over 7,000 varieties of apples, but only a handful are readily available in the United States. The most popular apple in the world is the Red Delicious, which is an eating apple. The most popular baking apple is the Rome Beauty, but you can also use the all-purpose Winesap or McIntosh. Apples are an excellent source of fiber, proving once again that there's usually a good scientific basis for old sayings, like "An apple a day keeps the doctor away."

4 medium baking apples   **creamy yogurt filling**

Steps:
1. Preheat oven to 350°F.
2. Wash and core apples. Place in glass baking dish.
3. In small bowl, prepare creamy yogurt filling. Divide into 4 portions and fill each apple hole with 1 portion.
4. Cover and bake at 350°F for 45 minutes.

Yield: 4 servings

Creamy Yogurt Filling
  1 egg white, slightly beaten   ¼ **teaspoon vanilla**
  ¼ **cup plain nonfat yogurt**   **dash of cinnamon (optional)**

Steps:
1. In a small bowl, combine all ingredients. Stir until fluffy.

Yield: enough filling for 4 apples

Note: When you core apples, make sure you do not cut all the way to the bottom so the filling will remain inside.

"One of My Favorites"

George Mateljan

Raspberry-Filled Melon

This lovely dessert is a favorite of mine because it's so refreshing, delicious, low in calories, and it's elegant enough to serve to guests.

I know that raspberries are sometimes hard to find because they have a short peak season, being at their best in June and July. They're also expensive, but they are crucial to the success of this recipe. While you can substitute fresh strawberries or blackberries, you will not achieve the flavor and rich sauce texture that you do with raspberries. I also recommend canteloupe as the melon in this recipe, for taste and color contrasts, as well as its superior nutrition.

The **nutritional highlights** of this recipe are that it is extremely high in vitamins A and C.

Raspberry-Filled Melon

Preparation Time: 15 minutes

2 cups fresh raspberries, divided
1 tablespoon honey
1 tablespoon lemon juice

2 small melons, or
1 medium-sized
mint sprigs for garnish

Steps:
1. Wash berries gently and place on paper towels to dry.
2. Measure ½ cup berries into a small saucepan. Add honey and lemon juice. Bring to boiling, lower heat, then simmer for about 5 minutes until sauce starts to thicken. Stir sauce through strainer.
3. Cut small melons into halves or medium-sized melon into quarters. Remove seeds.
4. Pour sauce over remaining 1½ cups uncooked berries, then spoon berry mixture into cavities in melon. Garnish with mint leaves and serve at room temperature.

Yield: 4 servings

"One of My Favorites"

George Mateljan

Fruit and Almond Crumble

This is a favorite recipe of mine because it's like the old fashioned and beloved crumbly fruit pies of a century ago, but without the butter-laden pie crust and cups of sugar. The refreshing flavors of the fruit really come through.

Fresh pineapple simply does not work well in baking, so canned pineapple must be used. Fortunately, pineapple loses very little nutrition in the canning process and is readily available packed in its own juice. Hawaii supplies most of the canned pineapple used in the world.

The **nutritional highlights** of this recipe are that it is high in vitamin C, and rich in digestive enzymes.

Fruit and Almond Crumble

Preparation Time: 15 minutes   Cooking Time: 30 minutes

1 15-ounce can mixed fruit in unsweetened juice

1 20-ounce can pineapple chunks in unsweetened juice, drained

1 tablespoon grated orange peel

1 cup Health Valley Fruit Jumbos® cookies, crumbled (about 6 cookies)

1 tablespoon safflower oil

¼ cup chopped or slivered almonds

plain low fat yogurt

Steps:

1. Preheat oven to 350°F.
2. Combine mixed fruit with drained pineapple chunks and orange peel in oiled 9-inch pie pan.
3. Combine remaining ingredients except yogurt and work into crumbs. Spread over top of fruit to cover completely.
4. Bake at 350°F for 30 minutes until crumbs are crisp and golden brown. Serve topped with yogurt.

Yield: 8 servings

Healthy Ambrosia

Preparation Time: 10 minutes

Wheat germ adds not only a pleasant nutty flavor to this dessert but it adds a high amount of protein. Wheat germ contains major amounts of the B vitamins and vitamin E, and minerals.

1 cup plain nonfat yogurt

2 medium oranges, peeled and cut into bite-size pieces

1 8-ounce can pineapple chunks packed in unsweetened juice, undrained

1 medium banana, sliced

2 Health Valley Fruit Jumbos® cookies

4 tablespoons wheat germ

Steps:

1. In a small bowl, combine all ingredients except the cookies and wheat germ, and toss to mix.

2. Crumble the cookies and sprinkle over ambrosia. Sprinkle on wheat germ just before serving.

Yield: 4 servings

Orangeola®-Oat Bran Bars

Preparation Time: 15 minutes　　　　　　Cooking Time: 20 minutes

Orangeola is Health Valley's unique orange-flavored cereal that is so sweet and crunchy, kids eat it as a snack right out of the package. And juice sweetened Oat Bran Flakes have the same irresistible effect on people. Each of these delicious bars contains about 1 gram of dietary fiber and no cholesterol.

1 cup Health Valley
　Orangeola® Cereal
1 cup crumbled Health Valley
　Oat Bran Flakes
½ cup finely ground walnuts
　or pecans

dash of nutmeg
4 tablespoons honey
½ teaspoon vanilla
2 egg whites, beaten stiff
1 teaspoon grated orange peel

Steps:
1. Preheat oven to 275°F. and oil a 6½ x 11 x 2-inch baking pan.
2. In a mixing bowl, combine Orangeola, Oat Bran Flakes, nuts and nutmeg. Add honey and vanilla and mix thoroughly (it might be necessary to use your hands to do this). Then fold in egg whites and allow mixture to stand 2 to 3 minutes.
3. Spread or press into prepared pan and sprinkle with grated orange peel. Bake at 275°F. for 20 minutes.
4. Remove from oven, cut into bars and transfer immediately to glass or china plate to cool.

Yield: 20 bars

Amaranth Cereal Cookies

Preparation Time: 35 minutes   Cooking Time: 15 minutes

Health Valley Amaranth Cereal is widely available in health food stores everywhere, and Amaranth flour can now be found in many stores that carry bulk grains.

If they don't have Amaranth flour, then whole wheat flour is acceptable but you won't be getting quite the flavor, moistness or nutritional value that you enjoy with Amaranth.

2 cups Health Valley Amaranth Cereal
1 cup orange juice
½ cup honey
2 egg whites, slightly beaten

1 teaspoon vanilla
⅓ cup safflower oil
1 cup raisins
1¼ cups Amaranth flour
½ teaspoon cinnamon

Steps:

1. Soak cereal in orange juice for 30 minutes.
2. Preheat oven to 350°F. and oil a large baking sheet.
3. Combine honey, beaten egg whites, vanilla and oil. Add to cereal mixture, then stir in raisins, flour and cinnamon.
4. Drop by teaspoonful onto prepared baking sheet and bake at 350°F. for about 15 minutes, until lightly browned. Remove from sheet and cool on wire rack.

Yield: about 8 dozen

Note: For a tangy flavor variation, substitute 1 teaspoon grated orange peel instead of cinnamon.

Chewy Amaranth Brownies

Preparation Time: 35 minutes   Cooking Time: 25 minutes

One of the pleasures of working with Amaranth flour is that Amaranth contains more natural oil than whole wheat flour. Because of this, these brownies are genuinely moist and rich without using any butter or egg yolks. For the first time, you can enjoy sinfully sweet brownies with only 113 calories in a brownie, only 30% of calories from fat, and no cholesterol.

3 egg whites	**¾ cup Amaranth flour**
¾ cup honey	**⅓ cup carob powder**
¼ cup safflower oil	**½ teaspoon baking soda**
2 cups Health Valley	**1 teaspoon cream of tartar**
Amaranth Cereal	**¼ cup slivered almonds**

Steps:

1. Beat together egg whites, honey and oil. Add cereal and allow to stand for 30 minutes.
2. Preheat oven to 350°F. and oil an 8x12-inch baking pan.
3. Sift together flour, carob powder, soda and cream of tartar. Add to soaked cereal mixture, then stir in almonds.
4. Spread batter evenly into prepared baking dish and bake at 350°F. for 25 minutes. Cool 5 minutes, then cut into squares.

Yield: 24 brownies

Note: Both of these recipes call for the original crunchy Amaranth Cereal, or Amaranth Crunch™ cereal. Do not substitute Health Valley Amaranth Flakes.

20

❧ℤ

Dressings & Sauces

Of all the recipes in this book, these were among the most challenging to create. Traditionally, the best tasting salad dressings and sauces all use large amounts of oil or butter, cream, eggs, and salt. It's a lot worse than you might think:

FOOD	CALORIES	FAT	CHOLESTEROL	SODIUM	PERCENT OF CALORIES FROM FAT
Bleu Cheese (1 Tbsp.)	75	7.7 gm	1 mg	149 mg	92.4%
Italian Dressing (1 Tbsp.)	75	8.1 gm	0 mg	362 mg	97.2%
Spaghetti Sauce (¼ cup)	105	6.0 gm	0 mg	500-1100 mg	51.4%

As you can see, dressings and sauces are probably the highest calories-fat-sodium foods in existence. And how many people do you know who use only one tablespoon of salad dressing, or just ¼ cup of pasta sauce as a serving?

In the following pages, you will find recipes for light and lively salad dressings, sauces for pasta, poultry and vegetables, and even dessert sauces. They will enhance your foods with more flavor interest and more nutritional value. These recipes are easy to prepare, and they're all low in total fat, saturated fat, cholesterol, sodium and calories. And they're rich in key minerals like calcium, magnesium, phosphorus, iron and zinc, and important vitamins like vitamin A, C, and the B complex.

These are all delicious recipes, and you can see how dramatically lower they are in calories, fat and sodium:

FOOD	CALORIES	FAT	CHOLESTEROL	SODIUM	PERCENT OF CALORIES FROM FAT
Yogurt Honey Dressing (1 Tbsp.)	11	0.1 gm	0.2 mg	16 mg	8.2%
Mock Russian Dressing (1 Tbsp.)	11	0.3 gm	0.3 mg	16 mg	24.5%
Pasta Sauce (¼ cup)	30	0.1 gm	0.0 mg	27 mg	3%

With these recipes, you can continue to enjoy the pleasures of delicious dressings and sauces on your food...and without worrying if you should happen to use a little bit extra.

"One of My Favorites"

George Mateljan

Health Valley Yogurt Honey Dressing

The secret is that most of our dressings and sauces have a base of nonfat yogurt instead of oil. This recipe is a favorite of mine because it contains only 12 calories per tablespoon and only 3.7% of calories from fat. Yet it brings rich and zesty flavor to all kinds of vegetable salads.

Now, for the first time, you can enjoy salad dressings that taste really good without a lot of fat or calories. Every recipe in this section contains less than 30% calories from fat, and less than 30 calories per tablespoon.

So, when you toss your salads, you can use generous amounts of salad dressing without guilt.

Health Valley
Yogurt Honey Dressing

Preparation Time: 5 minutes

½ cup plain nonfat yogurt   1 teaspoon prepared mustard
2 teaspoons honey

Steps:
1. Combine ingredients. Mix well.
2. Serve over salad. Store remaining dressing in covered container in refrigerator.

Yield: ½ cup

Yogurt Dill Dressing

Preparation Time: 5 minutes

½ cup plain nonfat yogurt

½ teaspoon mayonnaise

2 teaspoons honey

½ teaspoon dill weed

Steps:

1. Combine ingredients. Mix well.
2. Serve over salad. Store remaining dressing in covered container in refrigerator.

Yield: ½ cup

Mock Russian Dressing

Preparation Time: 5 minutes

½ cup plain nonfat yogurt

1 tablespoon mayonnaise

2 tablespoons no salt catsup

2 teaspoons honey

Steps:

1. Combine ingredients. Mix well.
2. Serve over salad. Store remaining dressing in covered container in refrigerator.

Yield: ¾ cup

Creamy Mustard-Dill Sauce

Preparation Time: 5 minutes

¾ cup plain nonfat yogurt
¼ cup prepared mustard
2 teaspoons dill weed

1 teaspoon dry mustard
½ teaspoon honey

Steps:

1. Mix ingredients together well in a small mixing bowl.

2. Serve on vegetables or fish.

Yield: 1 cup

Light Curry Sauce

Preparation Time: 15 minutes   Cooking Time: 8 minutes

This sauce is especially delicious on chicken and steamed cabbage. You should make the sauce ahead of time so that the flavors have a chance to blend.

Most people don't think about sauces in terms of nutritional value, but this one is really healthy. Just ¼ cup of Light Curry Sauce provides over 100% of the U.S. RDA for vitamin A, 13% of your daily requirement for iodine, and 9% of calcium.

2 carrots, sliced
1½ cups plain nonfat yogurt
3 teaspoons curry powder

1 tablespoon olive oil
½ teaspoon cinnamon
1 tablespoon honey

Steps:

1. In a small saucepan over medium high heat, cook the carrots in 1 cup of water until tender, about 8 minutes. Drain the carrots and transfer them to a food processor or blender.

2. Add 3 tablespoons of yogurt, 1 teaspoon curry powder, olive oil, cinnamon and honey, and puree the mixture. Add the remaining yogurt and curry powder and puree again.

3. Pour sauce into serving dish and keep warm until ready to serve.

Yield: 2 cups

Pasta Sauce

Preparation Time: 15 minutes   Cooking Time: 1 hour

You will notice that this recipe includes no fats of any kind, so if you make your own sauce, you can assure yourself of making pasta dishes with the least amount of fat.

If you wish to save time by buying bottled pasta sauce in the store, there are a number of acceptable brands. Just be sure to read the ingredients carefully to be certain they are prepared the natural way, and look for those with no salt added.

1 cup chopped onions	1 tablespoon oregano
1 cup chopped mushrooms	½ teaspoon rosemary
½ cup finely chopped carrots	½ teaspoon thyme
6 cups tomato sauce*	½ teaspoon marjoram
5 cloves garlic, minced	½ teaspoon dry mustard
2 tablespoons dried basil	

Steps:

1. In large saucepan over medium heat, cook onions, mushrooms and carrots until tender, about 5 minutes, stirring occasionally.
2. Add remaining ingredients. Simmer uncovered 1 hour, stirring occasionally.
3. Flavors will be well blended if made a day ahead of serving.

Yield: 5 cups

This product is available from Health Valley.

364

Yogurt Tomato Sauce

Preparation Time: 10 minutes

This sauce is delicious on chicken.

1 cup plain nonfat yogurt
1 tablespoon apple cider vinegar
½ teaspoon honey
1 ripe tomato, peeled, seeded and finely chopped

5 large basil leaves, finely chopped
dash of cayenne (optional)

Steps:

1. Combine yogurt, vinegar, honey, tomato, basil, and cayenne into a small serving bowl and mix well.

Yield: 2 cups

"One of My Favorites"

George Mateljan

Fresh Berry Topping

You might think that healthier eating means giving up pancakes and waffles forever, but this isn't so. Our Sunday Brunch menu includes pancakes with this delicious topping.

This simple recipe is a favorite of mine because it turns an ordinary pancake into a beautiful and tempting crepe. It's easy to prepare in minutes, and it's nutritious.

The **nutritional highlights** of this recipe are that it is low in calories with only about 40 calories in 2 tablespoons, and if made with strawberries, this serving provides 18% of the U.S. RDA for vitamin C, and 6% of calicium.

Fresh Berry Topping

Preparation Time: 5 minutes

This is a delicious and healthier topping to replace syrup on pancakes or waffles.

1 cup fresh or frozen
  unsweetened berries
  (strawberries, blueberries,
  raspberries or blackberries)

2½ tablespoons honey
1 cup plain nonfat yogurt

Steps:

1. In a medium bowl, crush the berries and add honey. Mix well.
2. Combine berry mixture with yogurt.

Yield: 2 cups

Salsa

Preparation Time: 20 minutes   Plus chilling time

This salsa is a zesty dip for tortilla chips, and is good on salads, cold chicken and cold fish.

3 medium tomatoes, peeled
  and chopped

½ cup finely chopped onions

1 large green pepper, finely
  chopped

2 fresh jalapeno chili peppers,
  seeded and finely chopped

2½ tablespoons finely chopped
  fresh cilantro

Steps:

1. In a small bowl, combine all ingredients and mix well. Cover and chill for several hours or overnight.

Yield: 1¾ cups

Buttermilk Yogurt Dressing

Preparation Time: 10 minutes

This dressing can be used for chicken or turkey salad.

¼ cup low fat buttermilk
¼ cup plain nonfat yogurt
2 tablespoons apple cider vinegar
1 tablespoon lemon juice
½ teaspoon honey

2 cloves garlic, minced
2 scallions, finely chopped
   dash of cayenne
½ teaspoon celery seeds

Steps:
1. In a jar or bowl with tight fitting lid, combine all ingredients and mix well.

Yield: about 1 cup

Orange Yogurt Sauce

Preparation Time: 5 minutes

This versatile sauce is delicious served over steamed carrots or beets, and it's just as good as a topping for rice pudding and fruit.

¼ cup nonfat yogurt
2 tablespoons orange juice

1 teaspoon honey

Steps:
1. Combine all ingredients in a small bowl, and mix well.

Yield: ¼ cup

21

Condiments

There are many good reasons for cutting down on salt in your diet. In people who are salt sensitive, salt is a major contributor to high blood pressure. And even if you are not salt sensitive, salt can contribute to excessive fluid retention and may even contribute to obesity by increasing the rate at which your body takes up calories from food. And salt adds absolutely nothing to your food except sodium and chloride...no vitamins, no fiber.

When most people decide to cut down on salt in their diets, they simply take the salt shaker off the table and eliminate salt from their cooking.

If you're used to using a lot of salt, and try to cut it out all at once, your meals are going to seem bland and uninteresting. And if you're really addicted to salt, it will take 3 to 6 weeks before you lose your taste for salt.

In this book, we have not added salt to any recipe. Nor will you find any black pepper which can be irritating to the digestive tract. And yet these recipes are all delicious tasting. In fact, many of these recipes have been served at dinner parties without informing the guests that they were eating low sodium cooking, and nobody reached for the salt shaker.

The secret lies in the imaginative use of herbs and spices. There is literally a world of flavors to be enjoyed with seasonings other than ordinary salt and pepper.

Earlier in this book, there was a chapter which listed the most popular herbs and spices with a guide on how to use them. This chapter makes it even easier for you by providing recipes for four basic herb blends to be used in cooking. One herb blend is for Fish, one is for Chicken or Turkey, one is for Vegetables, and the last is for All Purpose Seasoning. You can use this All Purpose seasoning in your cooking, and also at the table to replace salt.

Each of these recipes takes only 10 minutes to make, and they enhance both the flavor and the nutritional value of the foods in which they are used. They make it much easier to eat healthier without sacrificing flavor. Each of these recipes provides a high density of vitamin A, calcium, magnesium, potassium and iron as well as lesser amounts of zinc, and thiamine, riboflavin, and niacin. And there's even a small amount of dietary fiber present in these recipes.

A Healthy Alternative for Extra Convenience.

Health Valley makes it convenient for you to enjoy these zesty and exciting spice blends even if you don't have the time to blend them yourself. They're available at nutrition-conscious stores under the name of Health Valley "Instead of Salt.®"

You'll find one or more of these seasoning blends as an ingredient in the majority of the recipes in this Healthier Eating Guide. So be sure to have them handy, and use them freely for more exciting, enjoyable and nutritious meals.

All Purpose Seasoning

Preparation Time: 10 minutes

This is possibly the most important recipe in this entire book.

Without seasoning, your meals will be bland and lifeless. But with this All Purpose Seasoning, your foods will be enhanced with zesty flavors that make eating without salt much easier.

You can use this versatile seasoning in all your cooking, and at the table too. In fact, we recommend that you fill a shaker with All Purpose Seasoning and have it on the table at all times to shake on your foods instead of salt.

Health Valley has bottled this particular blend of herbs under the trademark name "Instead of Salt® All Purpose Herb Seasoning." You will find it in many health food stores and supermarket nutrition centers. So if you want to save time, you can buy Instead of Salt seasoning and add flavor to your foods in just a shake.

2 tablespoons minced dehydrated onion	1 teaspoon dried basil
2 tablespoons sesame seeds	1 teaspoon spearmint
2 tablespoons parsley flakes	1 teaspoon bay leaf powder
2 teaspoons oregano	½ teaspoon dill seed
2 teaspoons garlic powder	½ teaspoon thyme
1 teaspoon celery seed	½ teaspoon coriander
1 teaspoon marjoram	½ teaspoon dry mustard
	½ teaspoon rosemary

Steps:

1. In blender, blend dehydrated onion into finer pieces.
2. Add remaining herbs. Blend to mix well, but do not make into a powder.
3. To keep herbs fresh, store in shaker top bottle with tight fitting lid.

Yield: 1¾ ounces, or
9¾ tablespoons, or
29½ teaspoons

Note: For your convenience, the Yield for this recipe lists all of the equivalents you may need for measuring.

Fish Seasoning

Preparation Time: 10 minutes

Of all foods, fish is probably the easiest to learn how to enjoy without salt. This is because almost all of us have become accustomed to squeezing lemon on our fish, so we don't miss the salt so much. Several of the herbs in this recipe also provide flavors with which we have become familiar when eating fish.

This is the most perfect blend of herbs you can have for seasoning fish. So when you make the fish recipes in this book, be sure to use this seasoning as specified. It makes a world of difference in the finished dish.

2 tablespoons minced dehydrated onion	2 teaspoons thyme
2 tablespoons plus 2 teaspoons dill weed	1 teaspoon paprika
	1 teaspoon bay leaf powder
4 teaspoons garlic powder	½ teaspoon tarragon
4 teaspoons parsley flakes	½ teaspoon dill seed
	½ teaspoon savory

Steps:

1. In blender, blend dehydrated onion into finer pieces.
2. Add remaining herbs. Blend to mix well, but do not make into a powder.
3. To keep herbs fresh, store in shaker top bottle with tight fitting lid.

Yield: 1½ ounces, or
9¼ tablespoons, or
27½ teaspoons

Note: For your convenience, the Yield for this recipe lists all of the equivalents you may need for measuring.

Chicken Seasoning

Preparation Time: 10 minutes

When you stop using salt on chicken or turkey, you really miss it. That's because so many of us have become dependent on salt for seasoning poultry.

So it's especially important to use this seasoning in all of your poultry recipes. This aromatic blend includes a variety of herbs with very distinctive flavors you need to heighten the relatively mild taste of chicken and turkey.

If you want to save time, there are a number of bottled poultry seasonings on the market that are acceptable. Just be sure to check the ingredients carefully to be certain the one you're buying contains no questionable ingredients. However, we cannot guarantee that the recipes in this book will turn out the same with a prepared poultry seasoning. So we recommend that you take 10 minutes to prepare our easy recipe.

All of the herbs in this recipe are also used in some of our other herb seasoning recipes, so it will be easy and economical to blend all of your own herb seasonings.

2 teaspoons dehydrated minced onion

2 tablespoons plus 2 teaspoons rosemary

2 tablespoons paprika

4 teaspoons oregano

2½ teaspoons garlic powder

2 teaspoons dried basil

2 teaspoons parsley flakes

Steps:

1. In blender, blend dehydrated onion into finer pieces.
2. Add remaining herbs. Blend to mix well, but do not make into a powder.
3. To keep herbs fresh, store in shaker top bottle with tight fitting lid.

Yield: 1½ ounces, or
8¾ tablespoons, or
26½ teaspoons

Note: For your convenience, the Yield for this recipe lists all of the equivalents you may need for measuring.

374

Vegetable Seasoning

Preparation Time: 10 minutes

It's relatively easy to stop using salt on raw vegetables. At first, they taste flat but you soon discover that many vegetables when they are raw have full, assertive flavors. You begin to enjoy the natural tastes of raw carrots, tomatoes, cabbage, celery, cauliflower and broccoli.

Cooked vegetables are another story. It's almost impossible to make potatoes taste good without salt. And string beans, corn, asparagus and peas are almost as bad.

That's why this tangy blend of sharply flavored natural herbs is so valuable in seasoning all your vegetables. It brings out the taste in all kinds of vegetables, so you won't have to depend on salt, pepper and butter to do it for you.

4 teaspoons oregano	1 tablespoon thyme
2 teaspoons garlic powder	1 tablespoon dill weed
2 teaspoons minced dehydrated garlic	1 tablespoon parsley flakes
1 tablespoon tarragon	2 teaspoons bay leaf powder

Steps:

1. Place all ingredients in blender. Blend to mix well.
2. To keep herbs fresh, store in shaker top bottle with tight fitting lid.

Yield: 1.1 ounces, or
7⅓ tablespoons, or
22 teaspoons

Note: For your convenience, the Yield for this recipe lists all of the equivalents you may need for measuring.

375

Breakfast

Nutritionists call breakfast the "most important meal of the day." It provides our first nutrition after 8 to 12 hours without food, and should supply the protein, vitamins, minerals and energy we need to start off our day in a positive, energetic way.

But while a good breakfast can start you off the right way, a poorly selected breakfast that doesn't follow the rules of healthier eating can ruin your day. High fat breakfasts full of meat, eggs, butter and cholesterol can leave you feeling sluggish all morning. And while a typical "quick breakfast" is lower in calories, fat, cholesterol and sodium, it's still far too high – and it provides almost no nutrition!

BREAKFAST	CALORIES	FAT	CHOLESTEROL	SODIUM	PERCENT OF CALORIES FROM FAT
2 Scrambled Eggs	220	16.6 gm	526 mg	328 mg	67.9%
3 Slices Bacon	120	11.0 gm	18 mg	368 mg	82.5%
2 Slices Whole Wheat Bread	130	1.8 gm	0 mg	272 mg	12.5%
2 Tbsp. Butter	200	22.6 gm	70 mg	276 mg	100%
TOTALS	670	52.0 gm	614 mg	1244 mg	70%
QUICK BREAKFAST					
2 Doughnuts	280	13.4 gm	20 mg	320 mg	43%
Coffee with Cream	33	3.1 gm	10 mg	6 mg	93%
TOTALS	313	16.5 gm	30 mg	326 mg	47.4%

Clinical studies have shown that people who eat a good breakfast not only perform better than those who eat an unhealthy breakfast, but that they're likely to be healthier and live longer. Start your day with high energy foods rich in fiber and complex carbohydrates, along with fresh fruit and juice, and low fat dairy foods.

This section includes recipes for delicious, healthy muffins and bread. For mornings when you're in a hurry, try one of the refreshing blender breakfasts.

A Healthy Alternative for Extra Convenience.
One of the healthiest breakfasts you can have is a bowl of Health Valley Cereal with nonfat milk or Soy Moo® soy drink. All of our cereals are made with 100% whole grains, and no refined sugar or salt. So have a breakfast featuring recipes in this section, or Health Valley Cereal. You can see how much healthier you'll be:

FOOD	CALORIES	FAT	CHOLESTEROL	SODIUM	PERCENT OF CALORIES FROM FAT
Super Bran Muffin	72	2.4 gm	1 mg	78 mg	30%
Strawberry Yogurt Pick-Up	161	2.5 gm	9 mg	85 mg	14%
Health Valley Oat Bran Flakes with Nonfat Milk	153	2.2 gm	2 mg	68 mg	12.9%

"One of My Favorites"

George Mateljan

Strawberry Yogurt Pick-Up

Strawberries can be kept in the refrigerator longer than you might realize. The secret is to store them in a colander, which permits the cold air to circulate around the strawberries. Don't hull strawberries until after you wash them, or they'll absorb water and become mushy.

We created this recipe specially for people who are always in a hurry. If you tend to run out the door without eating breakfast, take 5 minutes to blend this breakfast instead (or make it the night before). It will get you off to a good start in the morning, and it also is a refreshing afternoon pick-me-up.

This recipe is a favorite of mine because it tastes so good, and it provides an outstanding balance of nutrients you need to start your day with a burst of energy. Strawberries are a rich source of vitamin C, while milk and yogurt provide solid protein and calcium.

The **nutritional highlights** of this recipe are that a serving provides 60% of the U.S. RDA for vitamin C, 22% of calcium and 14% of protein.

Strawberry Yogurt Pick-Up

Preparation Time: 5 minutes

1 cup sliced strawberries
3 tablespoons honey
2½ tablespoons lemon juice

1 cup plain low fat yogurt
¾ cup cold low fat milk

Steps:
1. Place all ingredients in blender. Blend until foamy.
2. Serve garnished with fresh strawberries.

Yield: 3 servings

Note: Beverage will keep for several days in refrigerator.

Nectarine Frosty

Preparation Time: 5 minutes

Nectarines, like peaches, are available in cling and freestone varieties with white or yellow flesh. Choose plump, orange-yellow to red fruit that is slightly soft along the seam. Avoid hard, dull, shriveled or green nectarines. Nectarines are very high in vitamin A as well as C, so this quick shake provides you with a balanced breakfast high in protein, calcium, vitamins A and C in one delicious drink.

**3-5 nectarines, pitted
but not peeled**
**⅓ cup frozen orange juice
concentrate, thawed**
2 tablespoons honey

½ teaspoon vanilla
2 cups plain low fat yogurt
2 cups cold low fat milk
mint for garnish

Steps:

1. Pit and slice nectarines to measure about 3 cups.
2. Place juice concentrate, honey, vanilla and yogurt in blender. Add nectarine slices, a few at a time and puree. Add milk. Mix well.
3. Serve at once in tall chilled glasses. Garnish each with a nectarine slice and a mint sprig.

Yield: 4 servings

Note: Stir a little milk into each glass if you prefer it less thick. Beverage will keep well for a day or two in the refrigerator.

Peachy Frost

Preparation Time: 5 minutes

The easy way to peel peaches is to dip them in boiling water for 15 seconds, then dip them in cold water. The skin will slide right off. Dipping them in the cold water is important to prevent the peach from cooking.

1 cup peeled, stoned and
   chopped peaches
1 egg white
1 tablespoon lemon juice

½ cup plain low fat yogurt
1 teaspoon honey
6 ice cubes
   mint for garnish

Steps:

1. Combine all ingredients except mint in blender and blend until smooth.
2. Pour into tall glass and serve. Garnish with mint leaf.

Yield: 1 serving

Note: Makes a quick pick-up snack or a quick breakfast.

About Peaches

There are two types of peaches: "freestone" with soft, juicy flesh that breaks away from the stone easily; and "cling" with firmer flesh. Choose moderately firm peaches with a red blush against a cream to yellow background. Avoid hard, greenish fruit, or very soft bruised fruit. Peaches are an outstanding source of vitamin A and niacin.

Freezing Peaches:

Peaches are only in season for a short time, but when they are available, they're often abundant. You can make the most of their juicy sweetness by buying extra, peeling and stoning them, and freezing in plastic bags. When you make this frosty drink, you don't even have to thaw the peaches. Put them directly in the blender and add a little water, instead of the ice cubes called for in the recipe.

Fresh Melon Slush

Preparation Time: 5 minutes

The best tasting cantaloupes won't have any greenish cast to the skin. When choosing cantaloupe, smell it – a ripe one will have a pleasant melony scent. Press the blossom end of the melon (the end opposite to the stem) – a ripe melon will yield to the touch.

2 cups melon cubes (cantaloupe, crenshaw or honeydew)
1 cup low fat milk

6 tablespoons frozen orange juice concentrate, thawed
2 cups crushed ice
lime slices for garnish

Steps:

1. Place all ingredients in blender. Blend until slushy.
2. Pour into tall glasses. Garnish with lime slices.

Yield: 4 servings

Note: Will keep in refrigerator for 1 to 2 days.

Fat Content in Milk		
	Fat	Non-Fat Milk Solids
Non-Fat Milk	under .5%	at least 8.25%
Low Fat Milk	.5-2%	at least 8.25%
Whole Milk	at least 3.25%	8.25%

Fresh Fruited Buttermilk Shake

Preparation Time: 5 minutes

Plums are not as great a nutritional powerhouse as some other fruits but they are still good sources of several essential vitamins, and they're low in calories. They're one of the most easily available of the stone fruits, because there are varieties that can grow in almost any climatic condition. Choose slightly soft plums, and avoid the hard, dull ones.

1 cup low fat buttermilk	1 tablespoon lemon juice
1 cup sliced fresh plums, pitted but not peeled	¼ cup clover honey
	lemon slices for garnish

Steps:

1. Combine all ingredients except lemon slices in blender. Blend until smooth.
2. Pour into glasses and serve. Garnish with lemon slices if desired.

Yield: 2 servings

Note: Makes a refreshing after school snack or a quick breakfast.

Super Bran Muffins

Preparation Time: 20 minutes　　　　　　Cooking Time: 20 minutes

Egg whites contain no cholesterol but the yolks are extremely high, with 250 milligrams of cholesterol in one large egg yolk. When you realize that all of the leading health organizations recommend that you consume not more than 300 milligrams of cholesterol a day, you can readily see why we've eliminated egg yolks from this book.

So be very careful about how many eggs you eat, but have all the egg whites you want. There's only 18 calories in a large egg white, and it provides 8% of the U.S. RDA for protein and 6% of the U.S. RDA for riboflavin.

1½ cups unprocessed miller's
　bran flakes
⅔ cup raisins
½ cup boiling water
⅔ cup honey
2 tablespoons safflower oil

2 egg whites
1 cup low fat buttermilk
⅔ cup whole wheat flour
1¼ teaspoons baking soda
½ cup chopped walnuts

Steps:

1. Preheat oven to 400°F. Place 1 cup bran flakes and raisins in bowl and pour boiling water over mixture. Set aside to cool.
2. Put honey in a large bowl and stir in one at a time: oil, egg whites, buttermilk and remaining bran flakes.
3. Combine flour and baking soda and add to bran-egg-buttermilk mixture.
4. Add bran-raisin mixture and walnuts, mix well. Fill paper muffin baking cups ⅔ full.
5. Bake at 400°F. for 20 minutes.

Yield: 18 muffins

Oat-Nut-Apple Bread

Preparation Time: 20 minutes   Cooking Time: 1 hour

Grains were the first cultivated food. Once man learned how to plant crops, he became a farmer instead of a wandering nomad. The local grain became the staple food of the region: rice in the Orient, oats in Scotland and wheat in the United States, for example. The major grains of the world are wheat, oats, rye, corn, millet, rice, barley and amaranth. Buckwheat is not actually a grain but a member of the rhubarb family.

1½ cups whole wheat pastry flour
2 teaspoons cinnamon
½ teaspoon nutmeg
2 teaspoons cream of tartar
1 teaspoon baking soda
¼ cup safflower oil
⅓ cup honey

½ cup apple juice
1¼ cups unsweetened chunky applesauce
1 cup old-fashioned rolled oats
½ cup chopped walnuts
1 cup raisins
plain nonfat yogurt (optional)

Steps:

1. Preheat oven to 350°F. and oil a 9 x 5 x 3-inch loaf pan.
2. Sift together flour, cinnamon, nutmeg, cream of tartar and baking soda.
3. Whisk together oil and honey, then add juice and applesauce. Mix well.
4. Stir in the flour mixture; add oats, nuts and raisins.
5. Pour batter into prepared pan and bake at 350°F. for 1 hour. Cool in pan for about 10 minutes, then turn out onto wire rack. Serve warm or cold. Top with a dollop of yogurt, if desired.

Yield: 1 loaf (12 servings)

Apple-Carrot Corn Muffins

Preparation Time: 15 minutes   Cooking Time: 20 minutes

Corn was first recognized as a grain, long before it was thought of as a vegetable. Grain products such as cornmeal are made with field corn, which has more starch and less sugar than sweet corn, which is the variety eaten as corn on the cob. Field corn and sweet corn are both raised in yellow and white varieties. Yellow corn is richer in vitamin A, but otherwise both varieties are nutritionally similar.

1 cup yellow cornmeal
1 cup whole wheat flour
½ teaspoon baking soda
2 teaspoons cream of tartar
1½ cups low fat buttermilk
3 tablespoons honey

¼ cup safflower oil
½ cup raisins
1 apple, cored, peeled and
  chopped fine
1 carrot, grated

Steps:

1. Preheat oven to 400°F.
2. In a large bowl, mix together dry ingredients.
3. In another bowl, combine buttermilk, honey and oil. Stir in raisins, apple and carrot. Add this mixture to dry ingredients.
4. Divide batter into paper muffin baking cups and bake at 400°F for 20 to 25 minutes, until golden brown.

Yield: 12 muffins

Part Six

Nutritional Analyses of Healthier Eating Recipes

23

Nutritional Analyses of Healthier Eating Recipes

The Charts and How to Use Them

To provide you with the specific nutritional information you want about the recipes in this "Healthier Eating Guide" we have created the two sets of easy to use charts in this section.

The first set of charts provides a complete nutritional profile for each recipe by section and in alphabetical order. Twenty-two values are given for each recipe.

All of the recipes in this book are a superior source of one or more nutrients. The nutrients for which each recipe is a superior source is highlighted in red type. In designating a recipe a superior source of a nutrient, we compared the level of the nutrient to the level of calories. For comparison purposes we chose 2000 calories as the standard level per day.

If a recipe provides a greater percentage of the U.S. RDA of a nutrient than it does of calories, then it is a superior source of that nutrient. For example, Health Valley Super Light Halibut Casserole provides 13% of the daily requirement of calcium per serving. And since it only provides 8% of the 2000 calories daily standard, it is a superior source of calcium.

In the second set of charts we have looked at each nutrient individually, showing which recipes contain the most, or in some cases, the least amount of that nutrient per serving. We have also included a brief discussion of the nutritional role of each nutrient.

We believe that these charts will make it easy for you to find the specific nutritional information you want and to select recipes based on your own personal wants and needs.

How the Data Was Derived

The data presented in the following charts was derived from several nutritional data bases and processed with the aid of a highly sophisticated computer program specifically designed for nutritional analysis.

The actual nutrient values for the foods incorporated in the recipes in this book were obtained from the following primary sources:

1. AGRICULTURAL HANDBOOKS 8-1 THROUGH 8-12 U.S.D.A., 1977-1985

2. INDEPENDENT LABORATORY ANALYSIS

3. McCANCE AND WIDDOWSON'S "THE COMPOSITION OF FOODS," FOURTH EDITION, HER MAJESTY'S STATIONERY OFFICE, 1985

4. FOOD VALUES OF PORTIONS COMMONLY USED, 14TH EDITION, BOWES AND CHURCH, HARPER AND ROWE, 1985

Fish Recipes Nutritive Values

	Calories	Protein g	Carbohydrate g	Fat g	Cholesterol mg	Dietary Fiber g	Vitamin A I.U.	Beta Carotene I.U.	Vitamin C mg	Calcium mg	Sodium mg	Potassium mg	Magnesium mg	Iron mg	Zinc mg	Phosphorous mg	Thiamine mg	Riboflavin mg	Niacin mg	Vitamin B6 mg	Vitamin B12 µg	Vitamin E I.U.
Brown Rice w/Curried Shrimp	266	12	49	2.5	43	5.5	17	5440	19.6	84	166	665	62.0	2.6	1.0	220	0.24	0.10	4.4	0.33	0.29	0.6
Creamed Salmon & Broccoli	144	15	10	4.8	21	3.4	205	1335	80.9	258	293	587	54.0	1.3	1.3	301	0.15	0.31	4.2	0.32	3.28	3.4
Easy Fish Stew	69	7	6	1.6	14	0.5	58	970	21.5	48	187	505	47.2	1.3	0.4	97	0.05	0.06	1.9	0.12	0.17	0.8
Halibut Fillet In Tomato Sauce	218	34	16	2.0	76	2.1	666	1086	22.5	91	96	1087	40.0	2.4	1.6	397	0.23	0.17	13.4	0.73	1.50	0.6
Halibut Steak w/Avocado Dill Sauce	273	44	9	5.3	100	0.4	878	188	6.4	125	142	1119	22.6	2.8	1.8	492	0.16	0.21	17.0	0.90	2.15	0.6
Health Valley Super Lite Halibut Casserole	159	22	4	5.1	45	0.0	398	34	0.8	132	171	497	14.0	0.9	1.0	251	0.07	0.25	6.4	0.35	1.07	3.0
Orange Fish Fillets	165	25	7	4.4	57	1.4	40	98	19.1	105	139	448	54.3	2.0	0.5	339	0.13	0.11	4.2	0.02	1.13	2.4
Poached Fish w/Dill Sauce	250	44	10	2.4	100	0.0	1000	90	10.2	132	143	1054	17.4	2.6	1.7	496	0.16	0.23	16.7	0.90	2.20	0.1
Quick Bouillabaise	193	23	9	6.3	22	0.9	108	2548	24.6	83	172	663	74.8	2.4	0.5	273	0.12	0.14	4.3	0.13	0.15	1.4
Salmon Salad Sandwich Spread	81	9	5	2.4	15	0.2	28	76	2.7	121	250	223	17.0	0.5	0.5	145	0.03	0.12	3.1	0.13	2.72	1.3
Spaghetti w/Garlic & Shrimp	277	19	29	8.7	74	5.9	120	468	12.4	258	111	265	74.5	3.0	2.7	378	0.17	0.16	4.8	0.17	0.66	3.5
Tuna Pita Sandwich	175	11	18	5.8	3	3.8	26	196	34.8	80	78	267	23.0	2.1	0.5	107	0.16	0.12	5.0	0.21	0.91	4.3

Chicken Recipes Nutritive Values

	Calories	Protein g	Carbohydrate g	Fat g	Cholesterol mg	Dietary Fiber g	Vitamin A I.U.	Beta Carotene I.U.	Vitamin C mg	Calcium mg	Sodium mg	Potassium mg	Magnesium mg	Iron mg	Zinc mg	Phosphorous mg	Thiamine mg	Riboflavin mg	Niacin mg	Vitamin B6 mg	Vitamin B12 µg	Vitamin E I.U.
Bombay Chicken	398	21	50	13.4	51	6.1	141.0	428	34.7	85	134	689	111	2.8	1.8	274	0.27	0.31	9.8	0.32	0.30	3.6
California Chicken	429	39	34	14.2	93	5.1	127.0	1981	22.9	297	221	1384	167	4.3	3.1	509	0.28	0.33	16.5	0.80	0.65	3.5
Cheddar Chicken	380	37	31	10.5	88	5.8	108.0	746	10.0	175	224	619	101	3.6	2.7	445	0.41	0.31	16.1	0.74	0.41	3.8
Chicken Vegetable Stew	389	37	47	5.2	87.5	5.5	21	12960	29.0	72	162	1246	112.0	4.1	1.8	378	0.31	0.24	18.9	1.25	0.40	1.8
Chicken Apple Sandwich	296	23	30	8.6	38	7.2	19.2	41	3.3	79	373	293	110	3.4	1.5	521	0.20	0.22	7.5	0.43	0.20	9.9
Easy Skillet Chicken	183	28	5	4.4	73	1.4	18.0	5265	23.2	31	101	473	61	1.6	1.1	247	0.13	0.19	14.2	0.62	0.34	0.9
Healthy Valley Sesame Chicken w/Broccoli	190	19	21	4.5	37	4.6	11.3	2429	149.0	97	66	791	75	2.6	1.3	235	0.31	0.23	7.3	0.57	0.14	5.0
Healthy Roast Chicken w/Herb Stuffing	306	36	17	10.2	101	2.6	33.5	280	11.1	47	185	498	69	2.5	2.5	315	0.16	0.24	13.4	0.65	0.41	3.5
Herbed Chicken	259	39	3	8.4	107	0.0	83.5	735	1.9	117	184	450	71	1.8	1.6	353	0.11	0.24	17.5	0.70	0.58	0.9
Lemon Chicken on Spinach Leaves	296	35	27	6.3	75	7.7	18.0	13330	62.5	219	265	1579	227	6.9	2.2	355	0.27	0.53	17.2	0.94	0.40	8.6
Mustard Chicken	211	28	9	6.7	73	0.0	18.3	1	3.7	42	336	266	27	1.3	0.8	226	0.06	0.10	11.9	0.51	0.29	3.3
Orange Honey Glazed Chicken	188	27	9	4.0	73	0.1	18.0	195	22.8	23	64	342	33	1.1	0.9	209	0.10	0.11	12.0	0.53	0.29	1.1

Turkey Recipes Nutritive Values

	Calories	Protein g	Carbohydrate g	Fat g	Cholesterol mg	Dietary Fiber g	Vitamin A I.U.	Beta Carotene I.U.	Vitamin C mg	Calcium mg	Sodium mg	Potassium mg	Magnesium mg	Iron mg	Zinc mg	Phosphorous mg	Thiamine mg	Riboflavin mg	Niacin mg	Vitamin B6 mg	Vitamin B12 µg	Vitamin E I.U.
Curried Turkey & Green Peas	351	40	28	8.1	96	3.3	0.0	343	19.5	64.8	173	944	115.0	3.8	2.8	382	0.29	0.29	12.9	0.88	0.54	3.4
Ginger Turkey Breast	183	34	1	3.3	94	0.0	0.0	197	1.1	27.7	65	373	40.3	2.1	2.0	263	0.05	0.16	8.8	0.63	0.44	1.3
Spinach Cheese Turkey Meatloaf	276	35	19	7.1	80	5.1	103.0	10690	40.8	394.0	229	1191	170.0	6.4	3.6	445	0.24	0.54	7.6	0.73	0.61	7.0
Turkey Bean Casserole	185	18	25	1.0	37	3.5	0.0	6876	12.1	180.0	134	1054	30.0	5.6	1.4	217	0.16	0.16	4.7	0.64	0.17	1.8
Turkey Patties w/Red Beet Sauce	157	15	15	4.1	31	2.1	0.0	1545	13.8	64.3	161	600	56.5	2.0	1.1	150	0.12	0.15	4.2	0.39	0.16	1.3
Turkey Meatballs w/ Yogurt-Cilantro Sauce	37	4	2	1.0	8	0.3	0.4	98	0.9	19.3	23	68	7.5	0.2	0.3	46	0.02	0.04	0.8	0.07	0.08	0.4
Turkey Vegetable Loaf	206	25	10	6.7	57	2.5	0.0	582	48.4	46.7	126	548	42.7	2.9	2.8	239	0.15	0.33	5.8	0.48	0.28	2.3

Tofu Recipes Nutritive Values

	Calories	Protein g	Carbohydrate g	Fat g	Cholesterol mg	Dietary Fiber g	Vitamin A I.U.	Beta Carotene I.U.	Vitamin C mg	Calcium mg	Sodium mg	Potassium mg	Magnesium mg	Iron mg	Zinc mg	Phosphorous mg	Thiamine mg	Riboflavin mg	Niacin mg	Vitamin B6 mg	Vitamin B12 µg	Vitamin E I.U.
Chili Cheese Tofu Lasagna	428	15	57	14.9	18	6.2	112.0	1804	34.0	177	169	798	62.5	2.9	1.1	270	0.28	0.22	3.4	0.15	0.14	2.2
Far East Tofu Casserole	171	7	26	4.6	0	3.9	0.0	1836	45.5	60	76	702	48.3	1.9	0.4	99	0.18	0.10	1.8	0.16	0.00	2.7
Quick Lentil Chili Casserole	186	14	20	6.3	4	6.8	30.0	921	6.4	62	159	207	33.3	1.4	0.4	91	0.09	0.11	1.4	0.11	0.03	1.4
Tangy Tofu-Veggie Casserole	131	8	16	4.4	5	1.6	53.0	961	30.3	124	79	356	62.8	2.2	0.5	138	0.11	0.11	1.4	0.11	0.04	1.0

Vegetarian Entree Recipes Nutritive Values

	Calories	Protein g	Carbohydrate g	Fat g	Cholesterol mg	Dietary Fiber g	Vitamin A I.U.	Beta Carotene I.U.	Vitamin C mg	Calcium mg	Sodium mg	Potassium mg	Magnesium mg	Iron mg	Zinc mg	Phosphorous mg	Thiamine mg	Riboflavin mg	Niacin mg	Vitamin B6 mg	Vitamin B12 µg	Vitamin E I.U.
Cheese Eggplant	264	10	35	9.0	19	4.0	128.0	1044	25.0	182	151	559	87.3	2.3	1.7	262	0.27	0.18	2.9	0.21	0.15	2.4
Garden Veggies Casserole	155	6	20	5.1	14	2.9	89.8	2962	30.1	160	141	575	52.3	1.5	0.7	122	0.11	0.12	1.4	0.13	0.11	2.0
Health Valley Rice Surprise	198	12	23	6.7	18	3.6	98.6	4609	34.2	271	126	495	33.4	1.1	1.3	247	0.17	0.31	1.9	0.17	0.50	1.2
Millet Casserole	168	6	25	5.4	9	3.5	59.8	871	28.2	107	95	523	96.3	2.6	0.6	146	0.21	0.16	1.4	0.15	0.07	1.5
Millet Stuffed Peppers	185	8	29	5.4	8.9	4.5	54	978	58.8	119	99	660	86.7	3.8	0.8	192	0.28	0.29	2.2	0.18	0.08	1.8
Stuffed Green Peppers	369	16	49	11.9	29.8	4.5	183	2948	135.0	317	300	1355	196.0	5.1	2.1	353	0.35	0.34	4.9	0.45	0.23	2.1
Summer Stew	118	4	18	4.0	1	5.7	2.0	1217	24.4	115	62	736	48.2	1.4	0.8	133	0.20	0.17	1.4	0.24	0.23	1.4
Yogurt Noodle Bake	201	10	24	6.7	20	3.7	127.0	455	7.2	201	150	436	62.4	2.7	1.7	252	0.28	0.24	2.8	0.19	0.26	2.1

Soup Recipes Nutritive Values

	Calories	Protein g	Carbohydrate g	Fat g	Cholesterol mg	Dietary Fiber g	Vitamin A I.U.	Beta Carotene I.U.	Vitamin C mg	Calcium mg	Sodium mg	Potassium mg	Magnesium mg	Iron mg	Zinc mg	Phosphorous mg	Thiamine mg	Riboflavin mg	Niacin mg	Vitamin B6 mg	Vitamin B12 μg	Vitamin E I.U.
Borscht	67	3	9	2.2	1	0.8	0.2	50	5.4	21	84	261	64.3	0.6	0.3	57	0.04	0.08	3.5	0.03	0.14	0.1
Chicken Curry Soup	229	23	16	7.3	49	1.6	11.8	429	6.9	151	166	576	85.5	2.1	1.0	211	0.24	0.24	12.0	0.50	0.31	1.4
Chicken Broth	30	2	1	1.0	1.8	0.0	0.0	0.0	0.0	3	61	111	48	0.2	0.1	37	0.02	0.06	3.3	0.01	0.11	0.1
Zippy Gazpacho Soup	31	1	6	0.3	0	1.3	0.0	977	31.8	23	31	290	35.6	1.0	0.2	31	0.06	0.05	0.7	0.09	0.00	0.5
Creamy Corn Soup	148	9	23	3.9	4	1.9	83.0	234	3.0	105	68	287	55.3	1.2	0.6	158	0.13	0.19	3.5	0.12	0.22	1.0
Golden Squash Soup	93	4	13	3.2	2	2.4	10.0	3433	17.4	65	82	625	53.8	0.8	0.5	90	0.13	0.13	3.3	0.14	0.15	0.9
Garden Vegetable Soup	95	5	12	3.1	2	2.0	0.0	5768	25.7	59	127	643	108.0	1.7	0.4	102	0.11	0.14	5.2	0.15	0.15	0.5
Herbed Chicken Soup	224	31	7	7.3	75	1.4	17.8	10223	6.3	40	183	615	117.0	1.8	1.2	303	0.15	0.28	18.0	0.60	0.47	1.4
Seafood Chowder	254	26	18	8.2	97	2.2	235.0	510	14.3	217	189	719	64.3	4.4	1.8	309	0.24	0.23	7.7	0.38	9.58	2.6
Tomato-Split Pea Soup w/Yogurt	38	2	5	0.7	0	0.5	0.7	1323	3.5	11	24	149	18.4	0.4	0.1	21	0.03	0.03	0.3	0.03	0.02	0.3
Zesty Mexican Chicken Soup	294	35	16	10.1	77	2.2	17.8	1382	35.3	56	265	869	191.0	3.1	1.6	366	0.22	0.45	23.3	0.63	0.62	1.7

Pasta & Grain Side Dish Recipes Nutritive Values

	Calories	Protein g	Carbohydrate g	Fat g	Cholesterol mg	Dietary Fiber g	Vitamin A I.U.	Beta Carotene I.U.	Vitamin C mg	Calcium mg	Sodium mg	Potassium mg	Magnesium mg	Iron mg	Zinc mg	Phosphorous mg	Thiamine mg	Riboflavin mg	Niacin mg	Vitamin B6 mg	Vitamin B12 µg	Vitamin E I.U.
Basic Rice Recipe	189	5	34	3.0	1	3.1	0	0	0.0	18	65	204	48.0	0.9	0.1	133	0.16	0.08	5.3	0.01	0.11	0.1
Brown Rice Pilaf	216	5	36	5.3	1	3.5	0	82	3.0	27	75	261	51.2	1.1	0.1	140	0.18	0.09	5.4	0.03	0.11	1.6
Bulgur Lentil Casserole	294	14	48	6.1	2	9.4	45	575	12.1	71	156	606	76.7	4.9	1.3	283	0.21	0.19	6.6	0.67	0.15	3.7
Green Rice	231	6	41	5.0	0	5.5	0	5729	15.9	136	83	422	66.9	2.3	0.6	154	0.22	0.16	3.2	0.17	0.02	4.1
Healthy Pasta Primavera	256	13	33	8.7	18	8.3	310	4501	126.0	316	139	763	76.3	3.5	2.2	359	0.26	0.40	4.2	0.44	0.47	3.1
Herb Spaghetti	158	4	28	2.9	0	7.6	0	26	14.3	27	8	191	47.1	1.9	1.1	158	0.16	0.08	4.0	0.15	0.00	3.3
Italian Broccoli w/Brown Rice	159	8	21	5.1	13	4.6	72	1231	41.7	230	64	450	63.4	1.7	0.9	160	0.14	0.32	2.5	0.19	0.24	2.5
Peppery Chili Elbows	302	15	37	9.8	15	7.1	91	1307	20.0	196	141	622	56.3	3.7	1.9	289	0.36	0.35	3.4	0.23	0.34	3.0
Risotto	159	6	21	5.3	1	2.0	101	774	12.3	126	121	576	65.9	1.6	0.7	171	0.12	0.19	3.5	0.11	0.04	1.9
Spaghetti w/Basil & Pine Nuts	268	9	35	9.0	9	7.3	50	89	0.8	124	44	287	70.0	2.8	2.0	296	0.27	0.15	5.8	0.17	0.17	4.1
Spanish Bulgur Chili	176	7	25	5.0	0	4.2	0	1805	28.4	48	57	694	80.1	3.0	0.5	105	0.14	0.16	2.1	0.18	0.00	1.6
Vegetable Bulgur Pilaf	286	11	54	3.2	1.9	8.9	1	5188	7.9	67	94	634	95.4	4.1	0.6	296	0.23	0.18	5.9	0.14	0.15	9.2

Salad Recipes Nutritive Values

	Calories	Protein g	Carbohydrate g	Fat g	Cholesterol mg	Dietary Fiber g	Vitamin A I.U.	Beta Carotene I.U.	Vitamin C mg	Calcium mg	Sodium mg	Potassium mg	Magnesium mg	Iron mg	Zinc mg	Phosphorous mg	Thiamine mg	Riboflavin mg	Niacin mg	Vitamin B6 mg	Vitamin B12 µg	Vitamin E I.U.
Apple Cole Slaw	56	2	11	0.3	1	1.8	1.4	2036	19.6	82	68	246	14.0	0.4	0.3	62	0.04	0.08	0.2	0.07	0.17	1.3
Bernie's Computer Cole Slaw	79	1	14	2.6	1.9	1.4	9	198	42.0	48	45	225	13.0	0.6	0.2	34	0.04	0.05	0.3	0.08	0.05	4.1
Bulgur Vegetable Salad	259	7	54	2.4	1	7.9	2.9	634	26.1	99	49	422	32.4	3.3	0.7	241	0.29	0.17	2.5	0.14	0.17	3.7
Bulgur Tuna Salad	150	12	23	1.5	11	4.0	24.9	396	7.2	23	57	297	31.9	2.0	0.4	174	0.15	0.08	6.0	0.16	0.46	2.3
Chicken Salad Oriental	341	40	19	11.4	98	2.8	31.6	1664	46.5	125	125	725	79.5	2.7	2.1	398	0.22	0.30	16.3	0.75	0.56	5.6
Health Valley Carrot Orange Salad	51	1	12	0.2	1	2.6	0.0	20340	28.7	33	26	322	16.3	0.5	0.2	40	0.10	0.05	0.8	0.13	0.00	0.7
Healthy Waldorf Salad	118	3	20	3.2	1	2.3	1.8	88	12.1	92	44	297	25.2	0.5	0.6	99	0.06	0.11	0.2	0.06	0.23	2.2
Lentil Salad	114	6	17	2.8	0	4.1	0.0	140	27.0	33	49	258	5.1	2.1	0.8	102	0.07	0.05	0.5	0.49	0.00	2.1
Low Fat Cole Slaw	39	2	6	0.5	1	0.9	3.2	57	21.5	77	31	182	13.2	0.4	0.3	51	0.02	0.05	0.1	0.04	0.14	1.5
Morro Bay Seafood Salad	168	21	12	4.3	138	3.8	21.0	5535	24.3	118	293	686	61.2	2.0	2.9	258	0.27	0.15	2.6	0.19	3.30	3.4
Picnic Salad	79	9	8	1.1	21	1.8	5.3	831	27.7	28	39	297	21.6	1.0	0.4	90	0.08	0.09	4.1	0.23	0.09	1.1
Refreshing Salmon Salad	192	18	16	6.2	27	4.4	54.3	1695	47.8	296	399	927	66.2	2.2	1.8	339	0.18	0.36	6.3	0.38	4.74	5.4
Super Carrot Raisin Salad	86	2	20	0.2	1	2.1	12.9	10320	6.6	63	32	287	15.9	0.5	0.3	63	0.07	0.09	0.5	0.10	0.13	0.3

Salad Recipes, continued

	Calories	Protein g	Carbohydrate g	Fat g	Cholesterol mg	Dietary Fiber g	Vitamin A I.U.	Beta Carotene I.U.	Vitamin C mg	Calcium mg	Sodium mg	Potassium mg	Magnesium mg	Iron mg	Zinc mg	Phosphorous mg	Thiamine mg	Riboflavin mg	Niacin mg	Vitamin B6 mg	Vitamin B12 µg	Vitamin E I.U.
Tangy Apple Vegetable Salad	49	1	10	0.3	0	2.0	0.7	5489	7.6	54	37	269	14.3	0.3	0.2	47	0.05	0.07	0.3	0.08	0.09	1.2
Three Bean Salad	187	6	35	3.4	0	5.9	0.0	555	56.0	66	332	478	31.6	3.3	1.0	136	0.10	0.09	1.0	0.38	0.00	2.8
Tuna Pasta Salad	196	13	22	5.8	9	3.9	63.6	247	3.3	131	113	332	57.4	2.7	1.6	249	0.28	0.19	4.8	0.22	0.82	3.1
Vegetable Carousel Salad	62	2	9	2.1	7	2.1	5.3	3833	42.8	70	69	350	24.8	1.0	0.4	69	0.08	0.11	0.6	0.12	0.12	1.7
Warm Chicken Salad	175	27	7	3.1	72	0.6	18.7	46	4.1	59	88	355	32.7	1.3	1.0	234	0.08	0.15	11.8	0.52	0.40	0.9

Breakfast Recipes Nutritive Values

	Calories	Protein g	Carbohydrate g	Fat g	Cholesterol mg	Dietary Fiber g	Vitamin A I.U.	Beta Carotene I.U.	Vitamin C mg	Calcium mg	Sodium mg	Potassium mg	Magnesium mg	Iron mg	Zinc mg	Phosphorous mg	Thiamine mg	Riboflavin mg	Niacin mg	Vitamin B6 mg	Vitamin B12 µg	Vitamin E I.U.
Apple-Carrot Corn Muffins	165	3	27	5.4	1	2.1	10	1744	1.5	47	69	192	18.1	0.7	0.4	100	0.12	0.08	0.7	0.10	0.06	3.8
Fresh Melon Slush	116	3	24	1.3	4	1.0	125	131	70.3	90	40	562	26.3	0.2	0.3	87	0.18	0.13	0.8	0.13	0.22	0.5
Fruited Buttermilk Shake	253	5	57	1.9	4	2.8	40	428	17.3	149	131	443	23.3	0.4	0.6	126	0.10	0.33	0.9	0.15	0.26	0.7
Nectarine Frosty	305	12	55	4.9	16	4.0	325	1349	60.0	375	142	1057	62.8	0.5	1.7	327	0.22	0.54	2.2	0.20	1.08	0.2
Oat Nut Apple Bread	220	4	35	8.1	0	3.8	0	25	0.9	39	30	227	38.8	1.3	0.7	117	0.14	0.05	0.9	0.10	0.00	5.2
Peachy Frost	186	10	34	1.9	7	3.9	75	913	19.1	222	131	667	35.2	0.3	1.2	189	0.08	0.41	1.8	0.09	0.66	0.0
Strawberry Yogurt Pick-Up	161	6	29	2.5	9	1.1	175	16	35.2	222	85	380	28.4	0.3	1.0	178	0.07	0.30	0.3	0.10	0.64	0.3
Super Bran Muffins	72	3	12	2.4	1	3.7	4	11	0.3	28	78	155	38.9	1.1	0.7	111	0.08	0.06	1.2	0.07	0.03	1.4

Vegetable Side Dish Recipes Nutritive Values

	Calories	Protein g	Carbohydrate g	Fat g	Cholesterol mg	Dietary Fiber g	Vitamin A I.U.	Beta Carotene I.U.	Vitamin C mg	Calcium mg	Sodium mg	Potassium mg	Magnesium mg	Iron mg	Zinc mg	Phosphorous mg	Thiamine mg	Riboflavin mg	Niacin mg	Vitamin B6 mg	Vitamin B12 µg	Vitamin E I.U.
Asparagus w/Orange Sauce	51	3	8	1.5	0	1.5	0	981	33.7	31	6	414	24.2	0.8	0.6	76	0.13	0.14	1.2	0.16	0.00	3.8
Creamy Beets	44	2	8	0.1	0	2.3	1	15	6.4	41	87	396	44.6	0.7	0.4	49	0.04	0.04	0.3	0.04	0.08	0.0
Curried Garbanzos w/Lime	186	7	29	5.2	0	7.8	0	355	20.6	81	569	418	56.6	4.4	1.4	175	0.06	0.08	0.7	0.05	0.00	8.0
Dilled Marinated Vegetables	59	2	11	1.0	0	2.2	0	4257	16.6	34	52	249	19.9	1.1	0.4	50	0.11	0.06	0.7	0.10	0.00	0.9
Glazed Curried Carrots w/Raisins	111	1	25	1.4	0	5.2	0	20800	4.2	42	86	284	16.4	0.9	0.3	46	0.05	0.05	0.6	0.17	0.00	1.5
Golden Cheese Potatoes	211	5	35	5.6	1	3.6	60	413	21.5	85	71	628	42.6	2.1	0.7	132	0.16	0.09	2.3	0.48	0.07	1.6
Green Peas w/Spicy Mushrooms	70	4	11	0.7	0	2.6	1	360	7.5	57	73	270	31.8	1.3	0.8	113	0.19	0.21	2.3	0.11	0.13	0.7
Italian Zucchini Rounds	48	2	9	0.3	0	1.7	0	919	18.4	43	25	508	70.3	1.5	0.4	64	0.11	0.07	1.1	0.16	0.00	0.0
Mexican Style Corn	94	3	22	0.5	0	2.1	0	1576	100.0	18	19	442	33.5	1.6	0.4	67	0.14	0.12	2.1	0.23	0.00	1.2
Nutty Yam Bake	188	2	39	2.8	0	1.2	0	14	14.3	20	15	831	37.3	0.9	0.5	87	0.12	0.06	0.8	0.28	0.00	0.9
Orange Glazed Carrots	65	1	15	0.3	0	1.7	0	32060	27.8	36	41	446	22.3	0.8	0.2	57	0.13	0.07	1.2	0.18	0.00	1.0
Quick Sauteed Zucchini w/Leeks & Tomatoes	89	3	15	2.8	0	4.8	0	1955	39.0	51	22	634	51.0	2.0	0.3	82	0.18	0.11	1.4	0.16	0.00	1.4

Vegetable Recipes, continued

	Calories	Protein g	Carbohydrate g	Fat g	Cholesterol mg	Dietary Fiber mg	Vitamin A I.U.	Beta Carotene I.U.	Vitamin C mg	Calcium mg	Sodium mg	Potassium mg	Magnesium mg	Iron mg	Zinc mg	Phosphorous mg	Thiamine mg	Riboflavin mg	Niacin mg	Vitamin B6 mg	Vitamin B12 µg	Vitamin E I.U.
Red Beets with Mint	74	1	14	1.3	0	0.8	0	39	10.0	21	57	438	49.0	0.9	0.4	53	0.05	0.02	0.3	0.08	0.00	1.0
Rosemary Peas w/Pine Nuts	122	5	15	4.0	0	3.8	2	908	11.8	32	85	242	30.8	1.9	1.1	126	0.35	0.12	1.7	0.11	0.00	1.5
Saucy Lima Beans	130	6	18	3.8	0	3.1	0	535	16.9	46	34	470	67.4	2.3	0.5	116	0.08	0.06	0.9	0.15	0.00	10.2
Vegetable Pita Pizza	252	10	38	7.0	7	8.6	45	713	42.3	132	74	565	46.6	3.2	0.6	90	0.33	0.14	3.3	0.22	0.05	1.7
Vegetarian Pita Pockets	258	11	41	5.9	0	11.0	0	1573	49.5	110	304	367	45.7	5.5	1.1	116	0.27	0.17	3.1	0.07	0.00	4.7
Zesty Cauliflower	40	2	7	0.6	0	0.7	0	853	50.2	36	24	392	18.8	1.0	0.2	47	0.09	0.07	1.3	0.18	0.00	0.7

Condiments Recipes Nutritive Value (per teaspoon)

	Calories	Protein g	Carbohydrate g	Fat g	Cholesterol mg	Dietary Fiber mg	Vitamin A I.U.	Beta Carotene I.U.	Vitamin C mg	Calcium mg	Sodium mg	Potassium mg	Magnesium mg	Iron mg	Zinc mg	Phosphorous mg	Thiamine mg	Riboflavin mg	Niacin mg	Vitamin B6 mg	Vitamin B12 µg	Vitamin E I.U.
All Purpose Seasoning	7	0.2	1	0.3	0	0	0	33	0.2	9	1	17	4.1	0.3	0.1	8	0.01	0.01	0.1	0.01	0.00	0.00
Chicken Seasoning	5	0.2	1	0.1	0	0	0	331	0.6	12	1	27	3.3	0.4	0.1	4	0.01	0.01	0.1	0.00	0.00	0.00
Fish Seasoning	5	0.2	1	0.1	0	0	0	64	0.2	11	1	24	3.2	0.4	0.1	6	0.01	0.01	0.1	0.01	0.00	0.00
Vegetable Seasoning	5	0.2	1	0.1	0	0	0	48	0.1	14	1	24	3.2	0.6	0.1	10	0.01	0.01	0.1	0.01	0.00	0.00

Dressings and Sauces Recipes Nutritive Value

	Calories	Protein g	Carbohydrate g	Fat g	Cholesterol mg	Dietary Fiber g	Vitamin A I.U.	Beta Carotene I.U.	Vitamin C mg	Calcium mg	Sodium mg	Potassium mg	Magnesium mg	Iron mg	Zinc mg	Phosphorous mg	Thiamine mg	Riboflavin mg	Niacin mg	Vitamin B6 mg	Vitamin B12 µg	Vitamin E I.U.
Buttermilk Yogurt Dressing (1 tbsp)	5	0.3	1	0.1	0.2	0.0	1	34	0.91	13	7	22	1.7	0.1	0.1	10	0.01	0.02	0.1	0.01	0.03	0.1
Creamy Mustard-Dill Sauce (1 tbsp)	11	0.9	1	0.3	0.1	0.0	1	0	0.09	29	59	38	3.3	0.2	0.1	24	0.01	0.02	0.1	0.01	0.06	0.2
Fresh Berry Topping (1/4 cup)	41	1.7	9	0.1	0.5	0.4	3	4	10.80	59	22	107	7.6	0.1	0.3	48	0.01	0.08	0.1	0.02	0.17	0.1
Yogurt Honey Dressing (1 tbsp)	11	0.7	2	0.1	0.2	0.0	1	0	0.10	25	16	33	2.3	0.1	0.1	19	0.00	0.02	0.1	0.00	0.07	0.1
Light Curry Sauce (1 tbsp)	14	0.6	2	0.4	0.1	0.1	1	1268	0.54	23	9	45	3.2	0.1	0.1	19	0.01	0.02	0.1	0.01	0.06	0.1
Mock Russian Dressing (1 tbsp)	27	0.6	4	0.9	0.8	0.0	3	35	0.41	19	25	35	36.9	0.1	0.1	16	0.01	0.02	0.1	0.01	0.05	1.0
Orange Yogurt Sauce (1 tbsp)	16	0.8	3	0.1	0.2	0.1	0	16	4.00	29	11	53	3.6	0.1	0.1	23	0.01	0.03	0.1	0.01	0.08	0.1
Pasta Sauce (1 cup)	120	7.2	21	0.4	0.0	2.2	0	5540	44.40	145	107	1164	221.0	4.4	1.1	118	0.17	0.22	3.8	0.39	0.00	0.3
Salsa (1/4 cup)	16	0.7	3	0.1	0.0	0.5	0	639	27.25	7	4	147	8.5	0.4	0.1	17	0.04	0.03	0.3	0.06	0.00	0.4
Yogurt Dill Dressing (1 tbsp)	15	0.8	2	0.2	0.4	0.0	1	0	0.12	29	12	39	3.1	0.1	0.1	22	0.01	0.03	0.1	0.01	0.08	0.2
Yogurt Tomato Sauce (1/4 cup)	29	2.4	5	0.1	0.6	0.1	2	332	4.80	94	31	174	13.1	0.5	0.4	69	0.03	0.10	0.2	0.03	0.23	0.2

Desserts & Snacks Recipes Nutritive Value

Food	Calories	Protein g	Carbohydrate g	Fat g	Cholesterol mg	Dietary Fiber g	Vitamin A I.U.	Beta Carotene I.U.	Vitamin C mg	Calcium mg	Sodium mg	Potassium mg	Magnesium mg	Iron mg	Zinc mg	Phosphorous mg	Thiamine mg	Riboflavin mg	Niacin mg	Vitamin B6 mg	Vitamin B12 µg	Vitamin E I.U.
Amaranth Cereal Cookies	31	1	5	0.9	0	0.6	0	19	1.5	4	1	36	3.2	0.2	0.1	14	0.01	0.01	0.2	0.01	0.00	0.6
Baked Apple	93	2	22	0.5	0.2	3.3	0.6	74	7.9	39	24	207	9.4	0.3	0.2	33	0.03	0.07	0.1	0.07	0.09	1.4
Banana Creme Bar	79	2	17	0.3	1	0.5	34	0	3.9	78	29	43	18.9	0.2	0.4	67	0.03	0.13	.2	0.25	0.23	0.2
Chewy Amaranth Brownies	113	2	18	3.7	0	1.4	0	0	0.9	22	27	93	18.0	0.6	0.4	56	0.04	0.08	0.7	0.01	0.00	3.2
Frozen Peach Dessert	99	3	21	0.2	1	0.5	11	596	3.8	116	47	264	16.7	0.4	0.6	101	0.03	0.16	0.7	0.05	0.34	0.0
Fruit & Almond Crumble	159	2	28	4.2	1	1.0	0	190	8.3	51	33	226	26.8	0.7	0.3	52	0.15	0.10	0.8	0.01	0.08	1.4
Jumbo Lemon Delight	12	1	2	0.1	1	0.1	1	2	1.1	11	5	31	2.2	0.1	0.1	9	0.00	0.01	0.1	0.02	0.03	0.0
Healthy Ambrosia	194	6	37	2.6	1	3.3	3	219	44.8	157	58	535	61.8	1.2	2.0	209	0.31	0.27	1.1	0.32	0.34	5.5
Orange Pears	36	1	9	0.2	0	1.1	0	38	9.6	6	0	77	3.9	0.1	0.1	6	0.02	0.02	0.1	0.01	0.00	0.1
Orangeola-Oat Bran Bars	74	2	12	2.0	0	1.1	0	9	0.4	8	9	55	21.6	0.4	0.3	61	0.05	0.04	0.2	0.01	0.00	1.2
Poached Pears w/Yogurt & Almonds	235	4	44	6.2	2	5.4	2	59	21.7	117	30	436	48.0	1.0	0.8	128	0.07	0.24	0.6	0.08	0.21	3.6
Raspberry-Filled Melon	101	1	24	0.7	0	1.9	0	5178	110.0	27	15	622	25.2	0.6	0.3	41	0.07	0.08	1.1	0.23	0.00	1.0

KILOCALORIES (CALORIES)

The energy value of food is expressed in terms of a unit of heat, a kilocalorie. A kilocalorie is the amount of heat that is needed to raise the temperature of 1 kilogram of water (a little more than a quart) 1 degree centigrade.

Two tablespoons of sugar, 1 tablespoon of vegetable oil, or 4.5 cups of cabbage provide approximately 100 kilocalories, enough to heat about a quart of water from 0 degrees centigrade (freezing) to 100 degrees centigrade (boiling).

The NATIONAL RESEARCH COUNCIL has established RDA values for calories based on age, sex, weight, and height. The RDA for a 120 pound woman between 23 and 51 years of age with a moderate activity level is 2485 kilocalories per day. The RDA for a 154 pound man between 23 and 50 years of age with a moderate activity level is 2772 kilocalories. Overconsumption of calories is a primary cause of obesity which increases the risk of serious degenerative diseases such as cancer, heart disease, and diabetes.

RECIPES WITH THE HIGHEST NUMBER OF CALORIES PER SERVING

CALIFORNIA CHICKEN. . . . . 429 Kc	PEPPERY CHILI ELBOWS . . . . 302 Kc
CHILI CHEESE TOFU LASAGNA. . . . . . . 428 Kc	CHICKEN APPLE SANDWICH. . . . . 296 Kc
BOMBAY CHICKEN . . . . 398 Kc	LEMON CHICKEN ON SPINACH LEAVES . . 296 Kc
CHICKEN VEGETABLE STEW . . . . 389 Kc	BULGUR LENTIL CASSEROLE . . . . 294 Kc
CHEDDAR CHICKEN . . . . 380 Kc	ZESTY MEXICAN CHICKEN SOUP . . . . . . 294 Kc
STUFFED GREEN PEPPERS . . . . 369 Kc	VEGETABLE BULGUR PILAF . . . . 286 Kc
CURRIED TURKEY AND GREEN PEAS . . . 351 Kc	SPINACH CHEESE TURKEY MEATLOAF . . 276 Kc
CHICKEN SALAD ORIENTAL . . . . 341 Kc	HALIBUT STEAK W/AVOCADO
HEALTHY ROAST CHICKEN	DILL SAUCE . . . . 273 Kc
W/HERB STUFFING . . . . 306 Kc	SPAGHETTI W/BASIL AND PINE NUT . . . . 268 Kc
NECTARINE FROSTY . . . . 305 Kc	

RECIPES WITH THE LOWEST NUMBER OF CALORIES PER SERVING (DRESSINGS AND SAUCES EXCLUDED)

CHILLED ZIPPY GAZPACHO SOUP 29	TANGY APPLE VEGETABLE SALAD 49
CHICKEN BROTH. 30	HEALTH VALLEY CARROT ORANGE SALAD . . . 51
AMARANTH CEREAL COOKIES 31	ASPARAGUS W/ORANGE SAUCE. 51
ORANGE PEARS 36	DILLED MARINATED VEGETABLES 59
TURKEY MEATBALLS W/YOGURT	VEGETABLE CAROUSEL SALAD 62
CILANTRO SAUCE 37	ORANGE GLAZED CARROTS 65
TOMATO SPLIT PEA SOUP W/YOGURT 38	BORSCHT W/YOGURT 67
LOW FAT COLESLAW 39	EASY FISH STEW 69
ZESTY CAULIFLOWER 40	GREEN PEAS W/SPICY MUSHROOMS 70
CREAMY BEETS 44	SUPER BRAN MUFFINS 72
ITALIAN ZUCCHINI ROUNDS 48	

PROTEIN

Protein is a constituent of every living cell. In humans it accounts for half of the dry matter of an adult.

Protein is composed of building blocks called amino acids. Eight of these amino acids must be obtained from the diet since the body is unable to manufacture them. These eight amino acids are called the essential amino acids. They are ISOLEUCINE, LEUCINE, METHIONINE, VALINE, PHENYLALANINE, THREONINE, LYSINE, and TRYPTOPHAN.

Protein is required for growth, with high quality protein such as that found in Amaranth, Dairy Products, Eggs, and Meat, Poultry, and Fish yielding maximum growth on a relatively low intake.

Protein is required for the formation of essential body compounds including hormones, enzymes, and coenzymes. It helps maintain water balance and body neutrality and is necessary for the production of antibodies.

U.S.R.D.A.—65 GRAMS PER DAY (45 GRAMS FOR FOODS PROVIDING HIGH QUALITY PROTEIN SUCH AS MEAT, FISH, POULTRY, EGGS, MILK)

RECIPES WITH THE GREATEST AMOUNT OF PROTEIN PER SERVING

HALIBUT STEAK W/AVOCADO DILL SAUCE . . . . 44 gm	SPINACH CHEESE TURKEY MEATLOAF . . 36 gm
POACHED FISH W/DILL SAUCE . . . . 44 gm	ZESTY MEXICAN CHICKEN SOUP . . . . . . 35 gm
CURRIED TURKEY AND GREEN PEAS . . . . 41 gm	LEMON CHICKEN ON SPINACH LEAVES . . . . 35 gm
CHICKEN SALAD ORIENTAL . . . . 40 gm	GINGER TURKEY BREAST . . . . 35 gm
HERBED CHICKEN . . . . 40 gm	HALIBUT FILLET IN TOMATO SAUCE . . . . 34 gm
CALIFORNIA CHICKEN. . . . . 40 gm	HERBED CHICKEN SOUP . . . . 31 gm
CHEDDAR CHICKEN . . . . 38 gm	EASY SKILLET CHICKEN . . . . 29 gm
CHICKEN VEGETABLE STEW . . . . 38 gm	MUSTARD CHICKEN . . . . 28 gm
HEALTHY ROAST CHICKEN W/HERB STUFFING . . . . 36 gm	WARM CHICKEN SALAD. . . . . 28 gm
	ORANGE HONEY GLAZED CHICKEN . . . . . 27 gm
	SEAFOOD CHOWDER . . . . 26 gm

CARBOHYDRATES

Carbohydrates are either starches or sugars. They are composed of carbon, hydrogen and oxygen and are classified as "monosaccharides" (simple sugars like glucose, fructose, and galactose), "disaccharides" (double sugars like sucrose, lactose, and maltose), and "polysaccharides" (complex carbohydrates like starch, dextrin, and glycogen).

Carbohydrates make up about 46% of the typical American's calorie intake. Unfortunately, about half of these calories come from refined sugars which provide only "empty calories."

Carbohydrates should make up about 55% to 60% of the calories in a healthy diet and should come from fruits, vegetables, legumes, and whole grains, not from refined sugars.

Carbohydrates are the body's primary and best source of energy. They are the only source of energy for the nervous system. They are essential for the proper oxidation of fats.

RECIPES WITH THE MOST CARBOHYDRATES PER SERVING

CHILI CHEESE TOFU LASAGNA	58 gm
FRUITED BUTTERMILK SHAKE	58 gm
NECTARINE FROSTY	56 gm
BULGUR VEGETABLE SALAD	55 gm
VEGETABLE BULGUR PILAF	54 gm
BOMBAY CHICKEN	50 gm
BROWN RICE W/CURRY SHRIMP	50 gm
STUFFED GREEN PEPPERS	50 gm
BULGUR LENTIL CASSEROLE	48 gm
CHICKEN VEGETABLE STEW	47 gm
POACHED PEARS W/YOGURT AND ALMONDS	44 gm
VEGETARIAN PITA POCKETS	41 gm
GREEN RICE	41 gm
NUTTY YAM BAKE	39 gm
VEGETABLE PITA PIZZA	38 gm
HEALTHY AMBROSIA	38 gm
PEPPERY CHILI ELBOWS	38 gm
BROWN RICE PILAF	36 gm
SPAGHETTI W/BASIL AND PINE NUT	36 gm
GOLDEN CHEESE POTATOES	36 gm

FAT

Fats, like carbohydrates, are composed of carbon, hydrogen and oxygen. They are the most concentrated source of food energy supplying 9 calories per gram.

Fats transport the fat soluble vitamins A, D, E, and K and are the source of the essential fatty acids necessary for normal growth. Fats are also necessary for the production of a variety of body compounds including hormone-like substances called prostaglandins which control a vast range of bodily functions.

The typical American derives about 42% of his calories from fat (16% saturated, 19% monounsaturated, 7% polyunsaturated). The American Heart Association and the American Cancer Society recommend that no more than 30% of calories be derived from fat with equal amounts of saturated, monounsaturated, and polyunsaturated fats.

Excessive fat consumption is a primary risk factor for cancer, heart disease, stroke, and obesity.

RECIPES WITH THE GREATEST AMOUNT OF FAT PER SERVING

CHILI CHEESE TOFU LASAGNA	14.9 gm	SPAGHETTI W/BASIL AND PINE NUT	9.0 gm
CALIFORNIA CHICKEN	14.2 gm	HEALTHY PASTA PRIMAVERA	8.7 gm
BOMBAY CHICKEN	13.4 gm	CHICKEN APPLE SANDWICH	8.6 gm
STUFFED GREEN PEPPERS	11.9 gm	SPAGHETTI W/GARLIC AND SHRIMP	8.6 gm
CHICKEN SALAD ORIENTAL	11.4 gm	HERBED CHICKEN	8.4 gm
CHEDDAR CHICKEN	10.5 gm	CURRIED TURKEY AND GREEN PEAS	8.2 gm
HEALTHY ROAST CHICKEN		SEAFOOD CHOWDER	8.1 gm
W/HERB STUFFING	10.2 gm	OAT NUT APPLE BREAD	8.1 gm
ZESTY MEXICAN CHICKEN SOUP	10.0 gm	CHICKEN CURRY SOUP	7.4 gm
PEPPERY CHILI ELBOWS	9.8 gm		
CHEESE EGGPLANT	9.1 gm		

RECIPES WITH THE SMALLEST AMOUNT OF FAT PER SERVING (DRESSINGS AND SAUCES EXCLUDED)

CREAMY BEETS	0.1 gm	MEXICAN STYLE CORN	0.5 gm
FROZEN PEACH DESSERT	0.2 gm	LOW FAT COLESLAW	0.6 gm
ORANGE PEARS	0.2 gm	ZESTY CAULIFLOWER	0.7 gm
HEALTH VALLEY CARROT		RASPBERRY FILLED MELON	0.7 gm
ORANGE SALAD	0.2 gm	GREEN PEAS W/SPICY MUSHROOMS	0.7 gm
BANANA CREME BAR	0.3 gm	TOMATO SPLIT PEA SOUP W/YOGURT	0.8 gm
SUPER CARROT RAISIN SALAD	0.3 gm	AMARANTH CEREAL COOKIES	0.9 gm
CHILLED ZIPPY GAZPACHO SOUP	0.3 gm	TURKEY MEATBALLS	
ORANGE GLAZED CARROTS	0.3 gm	W/YOGURT CILANTRO SAUCE	1.0 gm
ITALIAN ZUCCHINI ROUNDS	0.3 gm	DILLED MARINATED VEGETABLES	1.0 gm
TANGY APPLE VEGETABLE SALAD	0.3 gm	TURKEY BEAN CASSEROLE	1.0 gm

CHOLESTEROL

Cholesterol is a waxy substance found only in animal tissue. It is present in many of the foods we consume but can also be manufactured by the body as needed.

Cholesterol is necessary for the synthesis of important hormones including the sex hormones. It is necessary for the production of bile acids and therefore for the proper digestion of dietary fat. It is also necessary for the production of vitamin D in the body and helps protect the skin from a variety of chemical agents and helps prevent abnormal moisture loss through the skin. Cholesterol is part of the structure of every cell in the body and is found in the circulating blood in combination with triglycerides and protein.

Excessive cholesterol in the blood is a primary risk factor for heart attack and stroke. To modify this risk it is recommended that a healthy diet contain less than 300 milligrams of cholesterol per day.

NOTE: OVER HALF OF THE RECIPES IN THIS BOOK CONTAIN LESS THAN 2 MILLIGRAMS OF CHOLESTEROL PER SERVING. 46 RECIPES CONTAIN NO CHOLESTEROL AT ALL. 19 RECIPES CONTAIN 1 MILLIGRAM PER SERVING AND 6 RECIPES CONTAIN 2 MILLIGRAMS. NONE OF THE RECIPES BELOW CONTAIN AS MUCH CHOLESTEROL PER SERVING AS FOUND IN A SINGLE EGG!

RECIPES HIGHEST IN CHOLESTEROL PER SERVING

MORRO BAY SEAFOOD SALAD . . . . 138 mg	CALIFORNIA CHICKEN . . . . 93 mg
HERBED CHICKEN . . . . 107 mg	CHEDDAR CHICKEN . . . . 88 mg
HEALTHY ROAST CHICKEN	CHICKEN VEGETABLE STEW . . . . 88 mg
W/ HERB STUFFING . . . . .101 mg	SPINACH CHEESE TURKEY MEATLOAF . . 81 mg
POACHED FISH W/DILL SAUCE . . . . 100 mg	ZESTY MEXICAN CHICKEN SOUP . . . . . . 78 mg
HALIBUT STEAK W/AVOCADO	HALIBUT FILLET IN TOMATO SAUCE . . . . 76 mg
DILL SAUCE . . . . 100 mg	HERBED CHICKEN SOUP . . . . 75 mg
CHICKEN SALAD ORIENTAL . . . . 98 mg	LEMON CHICKEN ON SPINACH LEAVES . . 75 mg
SEAFOOD CHOWDER . . . . 97 mg	SPAGHETTI W/GARLIC AND SHRIMP . . . . 75 mg
CURRIED TURKEY AND GREEN PEAS . . . 96 mg	EASY SKILLET CHICKEN . . . . 74 mg
GINGER TURKEY BREAST . . . . 95 mg	MUSTARD CHICKEN . . . . 73 mg

DIETARY FIBER

Dietary Fiber is the portion of plant foods that cannot be digested by the human digestive system. There are two types of dietary fiber, water soluble and water insoluble. Water insoluble fiber adds bulk to the diet and helps prevent constipation. Diets high in this type of fiber are associated with reduced risk of some forms of cancer including cancer of the colon and rectum. Water soluble fiber binds with cholesterol-rich bile acids in the intestinal tract and diets high in this type of fiber have been associated with lowered serum cholesterol levels and lowered risk of heart disease and stroke.

U.S.R.D.A.—NONE ESTABLISHED
THE NATIONAL CANCER INSTITUTE RECOMMENDS A DAILY INTAKE OF
25-35 GRAMS OF DIETARY FIBER

RECIPES WITH THE GREATEST AMOUNT OF DIETARY FIBER PER SERVING

VEGETARIAN PITA POCKETS	11.0 gm	CHICKEN APPLE SANDWICH	7.3 gm
BULGUR LENTIL CASSEROLE	9.5 gm	PEPPERY CHILI ELBOWS	7.1 gm
VEGETABLE BULGUR PILAF	8.9 gm	QUICK LENTIL CHILI CASSEROLE	6.9 gm
VEGETABLE PITA PIZZA	8.6 gm	CHILI CHEESE TOFU LASAGNA	6.2 gm
HEALTHY PASTA PRIMAVERA	8.4 gm	BOMBAY CHICKEN	6.1 gm
BULGUR VEGETABLE SALAD	7.9 gm	SPAGHETTI W/GARLIC AND SHRIMP	5.9 gm
CURRIED GARBANZO BEANS W/LIME	7.8 gm	THREE BEAN SALAD	5.9 gm
LEMON CHICKEN ON SPINACH LEAVES	7.8 gm	CHEDDAR CHICKEN	5.8 gm
HERB SPAGHETTI	7.7 gm	SUMMER STEW	5.7 gm
SPAGHETTI W/BASIL AND PINE NUTS	7.3 gm	GREEN RICE	5.6 gm

FOODS RICHEST IN WATER INSOLUBLE FIBER PER 100 GRAMS

WHEAT BRAN	34.0 gm	LIMA BEANS	9.5 gm
FIGS, DRIED	14.2 gm	PEANUTS	9.2 gm
ALMONDS	12.4 gm	WHOLE WHEAT FLOUR	8.1 gm
BEANS, WHITE	11.5 gm	RASPBERRIES	7.0 gm
PRUNES	11.4 gm	CURRANTS	6.7 gm

FOODS RICHEST IN WATER SOLUBLE FIBER PER 100 GRAMS

CORNMEAL	9.0 gm	BLACKEYE PEAS, COOKED	4.5 gm
BEANS, RED KIDNEY	8.6 gm	PUFFED WHEAT	3.4 gm
CHICK PEAS, RAW	7.7 gm	CABBAGE, CHINESE	3.0 gm
OAT BRAN	7.2 gm	KALE	2.7 gm
OATS, ROLLED	5.0 gm	CAULIFLOWER	2.5 gm

VITAMIN A—BETA CAROTENE

Vitamin A is necessary for the health of the digestive tract, respiratory tract, eyes, skin, and reproductive system. It is necessary for proper night vision. Vitamin A aids in the detoxification of poisons and is essential for resisting infections, allergies, and the effects of air pollution. It is also necessary for growth and the repair and maintenance of cell membranes. Vitamin A is found in food as pre-formed Vitamin A or as Beta Carotene, the non-toxic Vitamin A precursor the body converts to Vitamin A as needed.

U.S.R.D.A.—5,000 INTERNATIONAL UNITS PER DAY
AVERAGE DAILY INTAKE OF AMERICANS—5,200-6,100 I.U. PER DAY

RECIPES WITH THE GREATEST AMOUNT OF PRE-FORMED VITAMIN A PER SERVING

POACHED FISH W/DILL SAUCE	1000 I.U.	NECTARINE FROSTY	325 I.U.
HALIBUT STEAK		HEALTHY PASTA PRIMAVERA	310 I.U.
W/AVOCADO DILL SAUCE	878 I.U.	SEAFOOD CHOWDER	235 I.U.
HALIBUT FILLET IN TOMATO SAUCE	666 I.U.	CREAMED SALMON AND BROCCOLI	205 I.U.
HEALTH VALLEY SUPER LIGHT		STUFFED GREEN PEPPERS	183 I.U.
HALIBUT CASSEROLE	398 I.U.	STRAWBERRY YOGURT PICK-UP	175 I.U.

RECIPES WITH THE GREATEST AMOUNT OF BETA-CAROTENE PER SERVING

ORANGE GLAZED CARROTS	32,060 I.U.	SPINACH CHEESE TURKEY	
HEALTH VALLEY CARROT		MEAT LOAF	10,690 I.U.
ORANGE SALAD	20,340 I.U.	SUPER CARROT RAISIN SALAD	10,320 I.U.
GLAZED CURRIED CARROTS		HERBED CHICKEN SOUP	10,220 I.U.
W/RAISINS	20,080 I.U.	TURKEY BEAN CASSEROLE	6,876 I.U.
LEMON CHICKEN ON		HEALTH VALLEY GARDEN	
SPINACH LEAVES	13,330 I.U.	VEGETABLE SOUP	5,768 I.U.
CHICKEN VEGETABLE STEW	12,960 I.U.		

410

RICHEST FOOD SOURCES OF PRE-FORMED VITAMIN A PER 100 GRAMS

LIVER, BEEF	53,400 I.U.	SWISS CHEESE	514 I.U.
MARGARINE	3,298 I.U.	HALIBUT	441 I.U.
BUTTER	3,057 I.U.	MAYONNAISE	279 I.U.
CHEDDAR CHEESE	635 I.U.	MILK, NONFAT	204 I.U.
EGG, WHOLE	520 I.U.	MILK, WHOLE	126 I.U.

RICHEST FOOD SOURCES OF BETA-CAROTENE PER 100 GRAMS

CARROT, RAW	28,125 I.U.	BROCCOLI, RAW	1,541 I.U.
SWEET POTATO	21,825 I.U.	CHILI PEPPERS	771 I.U.
DANDELION GREENS	11,705 I.U.	GREEN BEANS	666 I.U.
KALE	7,400 I.U.	PEACH	535 I.U.
SPINACH, RAW	6,836 I.U.	SWEET PEPPER	530 I.U.
PARSLEY	5,200 I.U.	LIMA BEANS	371 I.U.
CANTALOUPE	3,224 I.U.	ORANGE	205 I.U.
PUMPKIN	1,600 I.U.	CABBAGE, RAW	126 I.U.

VITAMIN C

Vitamin C is necessary for the formation and maintenance of bones, teeth, and connective tissue. It is required to maintain the strength of blood vessels and is an important anti-oxidant. Vitamin C promotes the absorption of iron, helps maintain a strong immune system and helps the body cope with stress.

U.S.R.D.A.—60 MILLIGRAMS PER DAY
AVERAGE DAILY INTAKE OF AMERICANS—82 TO 87 MILLIGRAMS

RECIPES WITH THE GREATEST AMOUNT OF VITAMIN C PER SERVING

HEALTH VALLEY SESAME CHICKEN W/BROCCOLI . . . . 149 mg	THREE BEAN SALAD . . . . 56 mg
STUFFED GREEN PEPPERS . . . . 135 mg	ZESTY CAULIFLOWER . . . . 50 mg
HEALTHY PASTA PRIMAVERA . . . . 126 mg	VEGETARIAN PITA POCKETS . . . . 50 mg
RASPBERRY FILLED MELON . . . . 110 mg	TURKEY VEGETABLE LOAF . . . . 48 mg
MEXICAN STYLE CORN . . . . 100 mg	REFRESHING SALMON SALAD . . . . 48 mg
CREAMED SALMON AND BROCCOLI . . . 81 mg	CHICKEN SALAD ORIENTAL . . . . 47 mg
FRESH MELON SLUSH . . . . 70 mg	FAR EASTERN VEGETABLE TOFU CASSEROLE . . . . 46 mg
LEMON CHICKEN ON SPINACH LEAVES . 63 mg	HEALTHY AMBROSIA . . . . 45 mg
NECTARINE FROSTY . . . . 60 mg	VEGETABLE CAROUSEL SALAD . . . . 43 mg
MILLET STUFFED PEPPERS . . . . 59 mg	BERNIE'S COMPUTER COLESLAW . . . . . . 42 mg

RICHEST FOOD SOURCES OF VITAMIN C PER 100 GRAMS

ACEROLA CHERRIES . . . . 1000 mg	LEMON JUICE . . . . 46 mg
ROSE HIPS . . . . 500 mg	CANTALOUPE . . . . 42 mg
GUAVA . . . . 183 mg	KALE . . . . 41 mg
GREEN PEPPERS . . . . 128 mg	GRAPEFRUIT JUICE . . . . 38 mg
BROCCOLI . . . . 93 mg	SPINACH . . . . 29 mg
PARSLEY . . . . 90 mg	HONEYDEW MELON . . . . 25 mg
BRUSSELS SPROUTS . . . . 62 mg	BLACKBERRIES . . . . 21 mg
STRAWBERRIES . . . . 57 mg	TOMATO JUICE . . . . 18 mg
ORANGE JUICE . . . . 50 mg	TOMATOES . . . . 18 mg
CABBAGE . . . . 47 mg	BLUEBERRIES . . . . 13 mg

CALCIUM

Calcium is essential for the formation and maintenance of strong bones and teeth. It is involved in the regulation of heart beat, muscle action, and nerve function. It is essential for proper blood clotting.

U.S.R.D.A.—1,000 MILLIGRAMS PER DAY
AVERAGE DAILY INTAKE OF AMERICANS—750 MILLIGRAMS

RECIPES WITH THE GREATEST AMOUNT OF CALCIUM PER SERVING

SPINACH CHEESE TURKEY MEAT LOAF . .	394 mg
NECTARINE FROSTY	375 mg
STUFFED GREEN PEPPERS	317 mg
HEALTHY PASTA PRIMAVERA	316 mg
CALIFORNIA CHICKEN	297 mg
REFRESHING SALMON SALAD	296 mg
HEALTH VALLEY RICE SURPRISE	271 mg
SPAGHETTI W/GARLIC AND SHRIMP . . .	258 mg
CREAMED SALMON AND BROCCOLI	258 mg
ITALIAN BROCCOLI W/BROWN RICE	230 mg
PEACHY FROST	222 mg
STRAWBERRY YOGURT PICK-UP	222 mg
LEMON CHICKEN ON SPINACH LEAVES	219 mg
SEAFOOD CHOWDER	217 mg
YOGURT NOODLE BAKE	201 mg
PEPPERY CHILI ELBOWS	196 mg
CHEESE EGGPLANT	182 mg
TURKEY BEAN CASSEROLE	180 mg
CHILI CHEESE TOFU LASAGNA	177 mg
CHEDDAR CHICKEN	175 mg

RICHEST FOOD SOURCES OF CALCIUM PER 100 GRAMS

PARMESAN CHEESE	1,376 mg
CHEDDAR CHEESE	726 mg
SARDINES	380 mg
NONFAT YOGURT	199 mg
COLLARDS	188 mg
KALE	187 mg
TURNIP GREENS	184 mg
SALMON W/BONES	168 mg
DANDELION GREENS	140 mg
MUSTARD GREENS	138 mg
SKIM MILK	124 mg
WHOLE MILK	120 mg
SHRIMP	117 mg
COTTAGE CHEESE	106 mg
OYSTERS	103 mg
SOUR CREAM	103 mg
BEET GREENS	99 mg
CLAMS	97 mg
RHUBARB	96 mg
SPINACH	93 mg

SODIUM

Sodium is involved in the maintenance of normal water balance of the body. It is also involved in the maintenance of the body's acid-base balance. It is essential for proper nerve function. Sodium is also required for the absorption of glucose and the transport of other nutrients across cell membranes.

An excessive intake of sodium is a risk factor for hypertension which in turn is a primary risk factor for heart attack and stroke. The American Heart Association recommends an intake of no more than 1,000 milligrams per 1,000 calories consumed daily and a maximum daily intake of no more than 3,000 milligrams.

NOTE: THERE ARE 80 RECIPES IN THIS "HEALTHIER EATING GUIDE AND COOKBOOK" THAT CONTAIN LESS THAN 100 MG OF SODIUM PER SERVING!

RECIPES WITH THE GREATEST AMOUNT OF SODIUM PER SERVING

CURRIED GARBANZOS W/LIME	569 mg	SALMON SALAD SANDWICH SPREAD	250 mg
REFRESHING SALMON SALAD	399 mg	SPINACH CHEESE TURKEY	
CHICKEN APPLE SANDWICH	373 mg	MEATLOAF	229 mg
MUSTARD CHICKEN	336 mg	CHEDDAR CHICKEN	224 mg
THREE BEAN SALAD	332 mg	CALIFORNIA CHICKEN	221 mg
VEGETARIAN PITA POCKETS	304 mg	SEAFOOD CHOWDER	189 mg
STUFFED GREEN PEPPERS	300 mg	EASY FISH STEW	187 mg
MORRO BAY SEAFOOD SALAD	293 mg	HEALTHY ROAST CHICKEN	
CREAMED SALMON AND BROCCOLI	293 mg	W/HERB STUFFING	185 mg
ZESTY MEXICAN CHICKEN SOUP	265 mg	HERBED CHICKEN	184 mg
LEMON CHICKEN ON SPINACH LEAVES	265 mg	HERBED CHICKEN SOUP	183 mg

RICHEST FOOD SOURCES OF SODIUM PER 100 GRAMS

PARMESAN CHEESE	1,862 mg	CELERY	88 mg
CHEDDAR CHEESE	620 mg	YOGURT, PLAIN NONFAT	77 mg
SCALLOPS	265 mg	CHICKEN BREAST	73 mg
SWISS CHEESE	264 mg	BEEF	68 mg
LOBSTER	250 mg	HALIBUT	54 mg
BEEF LIVER	184 mg	MILK, NONFAT	51 mg
SHRIMP	140 mg	SALMON	47 mg
EGGS, WHOLE	138 mg		

POTASSIUM

Potassium is necessary for the maintenance of the body's fluid balance and the maintenance of the body's neutrality. It is necessary for normal nerve function and for the proper functioning of all muscles including the heart. It is involved in the release of energy and in the production of glycogen and protein.

U.S.R.D.A.—NONE ESTABLISHED. AN ADEQUATE DAILY INTAKE IS CONSIDERED TO BE 1875 TO 5625 MILLIGRAMS. AVERAGE DAILY INTAKE IN THE AMERICAN DIET—NO DATA AVAILABLE BUT MOST EXPERTS FEEL THAT INTAKE IS TOO LOW.

RECIPES WITH THE GREATEST AMOUNT OF POTASSIUM PER SERVING

LEMON CHICKEN ON SPINACH LEAVES . 1579 mg	CURRIED TURKEY AND GREEN PEAS... 944 mg
CALIFORNIA CHICKEN . . . . 1384 mg	REFRESHING SALMON SALAD . . . . 927 mg
STUFFED GREEN PEPPERS. . . . . 1355 mg	ZESTY MEXICAN CHICKEN SOUP . . . . . 863 mg
CHICKEN VEGETABLE STEW . . . . 1246 mg	NUTTY YAM BAKE. . . . . 831 mg
SPINACH CHEESE TURKEY MEATLOAF . 1191 mg	CHILI CHEESE TOFU LASAGNA . . . . 798 mg
HALIBUT STEAK W/AVOCADO	HEALTH VALLEY SESAME CHICKEN
DILL SAUCE . . . . 1119 mg	W/BROCCOLI . . . . 791 mg
HALIBUT FILLET IN TOMATO SAUCE . . . 1087 mg	HEALTHY PASTA PRIMAVERA . . . . 763 mg
NECTARINE FROSTY . . . . 1057 mg	SUMMER STEW . . . . 736 mg
POACHED FISH W/DILL SAUCE. . . . . . . 1054 mg	CHICKEN SALAD ORIENTAL . . . . 725 mg
TURKEY BEAN CASSEROLE . . . . 1054 mg	SEAFOOD CHOWDER. . . . . 719 mg

RICHEST FOOD SOURCES OF POTASSIUM PER 100 GRAMS

NAVY BEANS, DRY 1300mg	BAKED POTATO. 503mg
PEANUTS 740mg	WALNUTS 450mg
LIMA BEANS 700mg	APRICOTS 440mg
ALMONDS. 690mg	WHOLE WHEAT. 430mg
BRAZIL NUTS 650mg	BROCCOLI 400mg
FILBERT NUTS. 560mg	BANANAS 400mg
HALIBUT 525mg	CAULIFLOWER 400mg

415

MAGNESIUM

Magnesium acts as a catalyst in hundreds of biological reactions. It is essential for cellular respiration and necessary for proper nerve and muscle function. Magnesium is also required for the production of protein within the body.

U.S.R.D.A. — 400 MILLIGRAMS PER DAY
AVERAGE DAILY INTAKE OF AMERICANS — DATA NOT AVAILABLE
BUT BELIEVED TO BE BELOW U.S.R.D.A.

RECIPES WITH THE GREATEST AMOUNT OF MAGNESIUM PER SERVING

LEMON CHICKEN ON		HEALTH VALLEY GARDEN	
SPINACH LEAVES	227 mg	VEGETABLE SOUP	108 mg
STUFFED GREEN PEPPERS	196 mg	CHEDDAR CHICKEN	101 mg
ZESTY MEXICAN CHICKEN SOUP	190 mg	MILLET CASSEROLE	96 mg
SPINACH CHEESE TURKEY MEATLOAF	170 mg	VEGETABLE BULGUR PILAF	95 mg
CALIFORNIA CHICKEN	167 mg	CHEESE EGGPLANT	87 mg
HERBED CHICKEN SOUP	117 mg	MILLET STUFFED PEPPERS	87 mg
CURRIED TURKEY AND GREEN PEAS	115 mg	CHICKEN CURRY SOUP	86 mg
CHICKEN VEGETABLE STEW	112 mg	SPANISH BULGUR CHILI	80 mg
BOMBAY CHICKEN	111 mg	CHICKEN SALAD ORIENTAL	80 mg
CHICKEN APPLE SANDWICH	110 mg		

RICHEST FOOD SOURCES OF MAGNESIUM PER 100 GRAMS

WHEAT BRAN	490mg	PEANUTS	206mg
WHEAT GERM	336mg	FILBERT NUTS	184mg
ALMONDS	270mg	SESAME SEEDS	181mg
CASHEW NUTS	267mg	OATS, WHOLE GRAIN	169mg
SOYBEANS	265mg	MILLET	162mg
BRAZIL NUTS	225mg	CORN, FRESH	147mg

IRON

Iron is essential for the proper transportation of oxygen to the cells of the body. It is required for blood formation, helps bolster the body's resistance to disease and stress.

U.S.R.D.A.—18 MILLIGRAMS PER DAY
AVERAGE DAILY INTAKE OF AMERICANS—12.7 MILLIGRAMS PER DAY

RECIPES WITH THE GREATEST AMOUNT OF IRON PER SERVING

LEMON CHICKEN ON SPINACH LEAVES . . 6.9 mg	VEGETABLE BULGUR PILAF . . . . 4.1 mg
SPINACH CHEESE TURKEY MEATLOAF . . 6.4 mg	CURRIED TURKEY AND GREEN PEAS. . . . 3.8 mg
TURKEY BEAN CASSEROLE . . . . 5.6 mg	MILLET STUFFED PEPPERS . . . . 3.7 mg
VEGETARIAN PITA POCKETS . . . . 5.6 mg	PEPPERY CHILI ELBOWS . . . . 3.7 mg
STUFFED GREEN PEPPERS. . . . . 5.1 mg	CHEDDAR CHICKEN. . . . . 3.6 mg
BULGUR LENTIL CASSEROLE . . . . 4.9 mg	HEALTHY PASTA PRIMAVERA . . . . 3.6 mg
SEAFOOD CHOWDER. . . . . 4.4 mg	CHICKEN APPLE SANDWICH. . . . . 3.5 mg
CURRIED GARBANZO BEANS W/LIME . . . 4.4 mg	THREE BEAN SALAD . . . . 3.4 mg
CALIFORNIA CHICKEN . . . . 4.3 mg	BULGUR VEGETABLE SALAD. . . . . 3.3 mg
CHICKEN VEGETABLE STEW . . . . 4.2 mg	VEGETABLE PITA PIZZA . . . . 3.2 mg

RICHEST FOOD SOURCES OF IRON PER 100 GRAMS

BEEF LIVER 7.8mg	CASHEW NUTS. 5.0mg
LIMA BEANS 7.5mg	OATMEAL. 4.5mg
LENTILS 7.4mg	ALMONDS 4.4mg
CLAMS 7.0mg	PARSLEY 4.3mg
OYSTERS. 5.6mg	TURKEY. 3.8mg

ZINC

Zinc is necessary for the production of insulin which regulates blood sugar levels. It activates enzymes that are needed to break down protein and is required for the transport of carbon dioxide by red blood cells. Zinc is required for normal growth and is necessary for normal wound healing.

U.S.R.D.A.—15 MILLIGRAMS PER DAY
AVERAGE DAILY INTAKE OF AMERICANS—DATA NOT AVAILABLE
BUT BELIEVED TO BE BELOW 15 MILLIGRAMS

RECIPES WITH THE GREATEST AMOUNT OF ZINC PER SERVING

SPINACH CHEESE TURKEY MEATLOAF . . 3.7 mg	CHICKEN SALAD ORIENTAL . . . . 2.2 mg
CALIFORNIA CHICKEN . . . . 3.1 mg	STUFFED GREEN PEPPERS. . . . . 2.1 mg
MORRO BAY SEAFOOD SALAD . . . . 2.9 mg	SPAGHETTI W/BASIL AND PINE NUTS . . . 2.1 mg
CURRIED TURKEY AND GREEN PEAS. . . . 2.8 mg	HEALTHY AMBROSIA. . . . . 2.1 mg
TURKEY VEGETABLE LOAF . . . . 2.8 mg	GINGER TURKEY BREAST . . . . 2.0 mg
SPAGHETTI W/GARLIC AND SHRIMP. . . . 2.7 mg	PEPPERY CHILI ELBOWS . . . . 1.9 mg
CHEDDAR CHICKEN. . . . . 2.7 mg	BOMBAY CHICKEN . . . . 1.9 mg
HEALTHY ROAST CHICKEN	HALIBUT STEAK
W/HERB STUFFING. . . . . 2.5 mg	W/AVOCADO DILL SAUCE . . . . 1.9 mg
HEALTHY PASTA PRIMAVERA . . . . 2.3 mg	CHICKEN VEGETABLE STEW. . . . . 1.8 mg
LEMON CHICKEN ON SPINACH LEAVES . . 2.2 mg	

RICHEST FOOD SOURCES OF ZINC PER 100 GRAMS

OYSTERS. 45.0mg	TURKEY, DARK MEAT 4.4mg
WHEAT GERM 15.4mg	CHEDDAR CHEESE 4.0mg
WHEAT BRAN. 8.4mg	BREAD, WHOLE WHEAT. 1.8mg
BEEF, LEAN 6.2mg	EGGS, WHOLE 1.0mg
LIVER, CALF. 6.1mg	GREEN PEAS 0.8mg

PHOSPHOROUS

Phosphorous is intimately involved in providing energy for bodily functions. It is essential for the calcification of teeth and bones and is part of many essential body compounds including DNA and RNA.

U.S.R.D.A. — 1,000 MILLIGRAMS PER DAY
AVERAGE DAILY INTAKE OF AMERICANS — 1,570 MILLIGRAMS

RECIPES WITH THE GREATEST AMOUNT OF PHOSPHOROUS PER SERVING

CHICKEN APPLE SANDWICH . . . . 521 mg	SPAGHETTI W/GARLIC AND SHRIMP. . . 378 mg
CALIFORNIA CHICKEN. . . . . 509 mg	ZESTY MEXICAN CHICKEN SOUP . . . . . 365 mg
POACHED FISH W/DILL SAUCE . . . . 496 mg	HEALTHY PASTA PRIMAVERA . . . . 359 mg
HALIBUT STEAK	LEMON CHICKEN ON
W/AVOCADO DILL SAUCE . . . . 492 mg	SPINACH LEAVES . . . . 355 mg
SPINACH CHEESE TURKEY MEAT LOAF. . 445 mg	STUFFED GREEN PEPPERS. . . . . 353 mg
CHEDDAR CHICKEN . . . . 445 mg	HERBED CHICKEN. . . . . 353 mg
CHICKEN SALAD ORIENTAL . . . . 398 mg	ORANGE FISH FILLETS . . . . 339 mg
HALIBUT FILLET IN TOMATO SAUCE . . . . 397 mg	REFRESHING SALMON SALAD . . . . 339 mg
CURRIED TURKEY & GREEN PEAS . . . . . 382 mg	NECTARINE FROSTY . . . . 327 mg
CHICKEN VEGETABLE STEW . . . . 378 mg	

RICHEST FOOD SOURCES OF PHOSPHOROUS PER 100 GRAMS

WHEAT BRAN. . . . . 1275 mg	WHOLE WHEAT FLOUR . . . . 372 mg
WHEAT GERM . . . . 1145 mg	GARBANZO BEANS . . . . 331 mg
SUNFLOWER SEEDS . . . . 705 mg	BULGUR . . . . 319 mg
OAT BRAN . . . . 700 mg	SALMON . . . . 286 mg
SESAME SEEDS . . . . 629 mg	CHICKEN BREAST . . . . 228 mg
PINE NUTS. 604 mg	HALIBUT . . . . 211 mg
ALMONDS . . . . 520 mg	EGGS, WHOLE . . . . 180 mg
CHEDDAR CHEESE . . . . 512 mg	YOGURT, NONFAT PLAIN . . . . 156 mg
LIVER, BEEF. . . . . 476 mg	LENTILS, COOKED. . . . . 119 mg
PEANUTS. . . . . 384 mg	MILK, NONFAT . . . . 101 mg

VITAMIN B1—THIAMINE

Thiamine is necessary for the release of energy from carbohydrate foods. It helps maintain healthy nerves and muscles, including the heart. It promotes normal growth and repair of body tissues and promotes a healthy appetite.

U.S.R.D.A.—1.5 MILLIGRAMS PER DAY
AVERAGE DAILY INTAKE OF AMERICANS—1.26 MILLIGRAMS

RECIPES WITH THE GREATEST AMOUNT OF THIAMINE PER SERVING

CHEDDAR CHICKEN	0.42 mg
PEPPERY CHILI ELBOWS	0.36 mg
STUFFED GREEN PEPPERS	0.35 mg
ROSEMARY PEAS W/PINE NUTS	0.35 mg
VEGETABLE PITA PIZZA	0.33 mg
CHICKEN VEGETABLE STEW	0.32 mg
HEALTHY AMBROSIA	0.32 mg
HEALTH VALLEY SESAME CHICKEN W/BROCCOLI	0.31 mg
BULGUR VEGETABLE SALAD	0.30 mg
CURRIED TURKEY AND GREEN PEAS	0.29 mg
YOGURT NOODLE BAKE	0.29 mg
CHILI CHEESE TOFU LASAGNA	0.29 mg
TUNA PASTA SALAD	0.28 mg
CALIFORNIA CHICKEN	0.28 mg
MILLET STUFFED PEPPERS	0.28 mg
BOMBAY CHICKEN	0.28 mg
VEGETARIAN PITA POCKETS	0.28 mg
MORRO BAY SEAFOOD SALAD	0.27 mg
CHEESE EGGPLANT	0.27 mg
LEMON CHICKEN ON SPINACH LEAVES	0.27 mg

RICHEST FOOD SOURCES OF THIAMINE PER 100 GRAMS

BREWERS YEAST	15.61 mg
WHEAT GERM	2.01 mg
SUNFLOWER SEEDS	1.96 mg
SESAME SEEDS	.98 mg
BACON	.92 mg
ALMONDS	.90 mg
PECANS	.86 mg
BUCKWHEAT	.58 mg
PORK LOIN	.49 mg
RYE, WHOLE GRAIN	.43 mg
PEANUTS	.32 mg
WHOLE WHEAT BREAD	.26 mg
KIDNEY BEANS	.11 mg
COLLARDS	.11 mg

420

VITAMIN B2—RIBOFLAVIN

Riboflavin is necessary for the metabolism of protein, carbohydrate, and fat. It is required for the formation of antibodies and red blood cells. In conjunction with vitamin A it helps maintain healthy mucous membranes lining the respiratory, digestive, and excretory tracts and the circulatory system.

U.S.R.D.A.—1.7 MILLIGRAMS PER DAY
AVERAGE DAILY INTAKE OF AMERICANS—1.71 MILLIGRAMS

RECIPES WITH THE GREATEST AMOUNT OF RIBOFLAVIN PER SERVING

SPINACH CHEESE TURKEY MEAT LOAF . 0.55 mg	CALIFORNIA CHICKEN . . . . 0.34 mg
NECTARINE FROSTY . . . . 0.54 mg	FRUITED BUTTERMILK SHAKE . . . . 0.34 mg
LEMON CHICKEN ON	ITALIAN BROCCOLI W/BROWN RICE . . . 0.32 mg
SPINACH LEAVES . . . . 0.54 mg	BOMBAY CHICKEN . . . . 0.32 mg
ZESTY MEXICAN CHICKEN SOUP . . . . . 0.45 mg	CHEDDAR CHICKEN. . . . . 0.31 mg
PEACHY FROST . . . . 0.41 mg	HEALTH VALLEY RICE SURPRISE . . . . . 0.31 mg
HEALTHY PASTA PRIMAVERA. . . . . 0.40 mg	CREAMED SALMON & BROCCOLI . . . . . 0.31 mg
REFRESHING SALMON SALAD . . . . 0.36 mg	STRAWBERRY YOGURT PICK-UP . . . . . 0.31 mg
PEPPERY CHILI ELBOWS . . . . 0.35 mg	CHICKEN SALAD ORIENTAL . . . . 0.31 mg
STUFFED GREEN PEPPERS . . . . 0.35 mg	
TURKEY VEGETABLE LOAF. . . . . 0.34 mg	

RICHEST FOOD SOURCES OF RIBOFLAVIN PER 100 GRAMS

BREWERS YEAST . . . . 4.28 mg	SUNFLOWER SEEDS . . . . .23 mg
LIVER, BEEF . . . . 4.19 mg	BEEF . . . . .22 mg
CHILI PEPPERS . . . . 1.33 mg	COLLARDS .20 mg
WHEAT GERM . . . . .68 mg	KALE . . . . .18 mg
CHEDDAR CHEESE . . . . .46 mg	SKIM MILK . . . . .18 mg
EGG, WHOLE . . . . .30 mg	SALMON . . . . .18 mg
COTTAGE CHEESE. . . . . .25 mg	BEET GREENS . . . . .15 mg
CASHEW NUTS . . . . .25 mg	SPINACH . . . . .14 mg
CREAM CHEESE . . . . .24 mg	TUNA . . . . .12 mg
CHICKEN, DARK MEAT . . . . .23 mg	WHOLE WHEAT BREAD . . . . .12 mg

NIACIN — VITAMIN B3

Niacin is essential for the metabolism of protein, carbohydrate, and fat. It also helps promote good circulation.

U.S.R.D.A. — 20 MILLIGRAMS PER DAY
AVERAGE DAILY INTAKE OF AMERICANS — 18.7 MILLIGRAMS

RECIPES WITH THE GREATEST AMOUNT OF NIACIN PER SERVING

ZESTY MEXICAN CHICKEN SOUP ..... 23.2 mg	EASY SKILLET CHICKEN .... 14.2 mg
CHICKEN VEGETABLE STEW .... 18.9 mg	HALIBUT FILLET IN
HERBED CHICKEN SOUP .... 18.0 mg	TOMATO SAUCE .... 13.4 mg
HERBED CHICKEN .... 17.5 mg	HEALTHY ROAST CHICKEN
LEMON CHICKEN ON	W/HERB STUFFING............ 13.4 mg
SPINACH LEAVES .... 17.2 mg	CURRIED TURKEY W/GREEN PEAS .... 12.9 mg
HALIBUT STEAK	CHICKEN CURRY SOUP .... 12.0 mg
W/AVOCADO DILL SAUCE .... 17.0 mg	ORANGE HONEY GLAZED CHICKEN .... 12.0 mg
POACHED FISH W/DILL SAUCE ...... 16.7 mg	MUSTARD CHICKEN .... 11.9 mg
CALIFORNIA CHICKEN............. 16.5 mg	WARM CHICKEN SALAD........... 11.8 mg
CHICKEN SALAD ORIENTAL .... 16.3 mg	BOMBAY CHICKEN .... 9.8 mg
CHEDDAR CHICKEN.............. 16.1 mg	GINGER TURKEY BREAST .... 8.9 mg

RICHEST FOOD SOURCES OF NIACIN PER 100 GRAMS

BREWERS YEAST .... 37.5 mg	BROWN RICE .... 4.7 mg
WHEAT BRAN .... 21.1 mg	SUNFLOWER SEEDS .... 4.5 mg
PEANUTS .... 14.2 mg	PEACHES, DRIED .... 4.4 mg
CHICKEN BREAST.............. 13.7 mg	WHOLE WHEAT FLOUR .... 4.3 mg
TUNA .... 12.4 mg	BEEF........................ 4.2 mg
HALIBUT .... 8.3 mg	ALMONDS .... 3.4 mg
SALMON..................... 8.0 mg	APRICOTS, DRIED .... 3.0 mg
WHEAT GERM .... 5.6 mg	TROUT....................... 2.5 mg

VITAMIN B6—PYRIDOXINE

Vitamin B6 is necessary for the metabolism of protein and for the conversion of glycogen to energy. Vitamin B6 helps maintain a healthy nervous system and is essential for the production of antibodies and for the conversion of the Amino Acid Tryptophan to Vitamin B3 (Niacin).

U.S.R.D.A.—2 MILLIGRAMS PER DAY
AVERAGE DAILY INTAKE OF AMERICANS—DATA NOT AVAILABLE
BUT BELIEVED TO BE BELOW U.S.R.D.A.

RECIPES WITH THE GREATEST AMOUNT OF VITAMIN B6 PER SERVING

CHICKEN VEGETABLE STEW	1.25 mg
LEMON CHICKEN ON SPINACH LEAVES	0.94 mg
HALIBUT STEAK W/AVOCADO DILL SAUCE	0.91 mg
POACHED FISH W/DILL SAUCE	0.90 mg
CURRIED TURKEY AND GREEN PEAS	0.89 mg
CALIFORNIA CHICKEN	0.81 mg
CHICKEN SALAD ORIENTAL	0.75 mg
CHEDDAR CHICKEN	0.75 mg
HALIBUT FILLET IN TOMATO SAUCE	0.73 mg
SPINACH CHEESE TURKEY MEAT LOAF	0.73 mg
HERBED CHICKEN	0.70 mg
BULGUR LENTIL CASSEROLE	0.68 mg
HEALTHY ROAST CHICKEN W/HERB STUFFING	0.65 mg
TURKEY BEAN CASSEROLE	0.64 mg
GINGER TURKEY BREAST	0.64 mg
ZESTY MEXICAN CHICKEN SOUP	0.63 mg
EASY SKILLET CHICKEN	0.62 mg
HERBED CHICKEN SOUP	0.60 mg
HEALTH VALLEY SESAME CHICKEN W/BROCCOLI	0.57 mg
ORANGE HONEY GLAZED CHICKEN	0.54 mg

RICHEST FOOD SOURCES OF VITAMIN B6 PER 100 GRAMS

BREWERS YEAST	2.50 mg
MOLASSES, BLACKSTRAP	2.49 mg
SUNFLOWER SEEDS	1.25 mg
WHEAT GERM	1.15 mg
LIVER, BEEF	.84 mg
WHEAT BRAN	.82 mg
SOYBEANS	.81 mg
SALMON	.70 mg
CHICKEN BREAST	.68 mg
LIMA BEANS, DRY	.58 mg
BROWN RICE	.55 mg
GARBANZO BEANS	.54 mg
BANANA	.51 mg
TURNIP GREENS	.42 mg
PEANUTS	.40 mg
RAISINS	.35 mg
CRAB	.30 mg
SPINACH	.28 mg

VITAMIN B12—COBALAMIN

Vitamin B12 is necessary for the formation of red blood cells. It is also necessary for normal growth, the production of genetic material, and the maintenance of a healthy nervous system.

U.S.R.D.A.—6 MICROGRAMS PER DAY
AVERAGE DAILY INTAKE OF AMERICANS—DATA NOT AVAILABLE

RECIPES WITH THE GREATEST AMOUNT OF VITAMIN B12 PER SERVING

SEAFOOD CHOWDER	9.58 μg
REFRESHING SALMON SALAD	4.74 μg
MORRO BAY SEAFOOD SALAD	3.30 μg
CREAMED SALMON AND BROCCOLI	3.28 μg
SALMON SALAD SANDWICH SPREAD	2.72 μg
POACHED FISH W/DILL SAUCE	2.20 μg
HALIBUT STEAK W/AVOCADO DILL SAUCE	2.15 μg
HALIBUT FILLET IN TOMATO SAUCE	1.50 μg
ORANGE FISH FILLETS	1.13 μg
NECTARINE FROSTY	1.08 μg
HEALTH VALLEY SUPER LITE HALIBUT CASSEROLE	1.07 μg
TUNA PITA SANDWICH	0.91 μg
TUNA PASTA SALAD	0.82 μg
SPAGHETTI W/GARLIC AND SHRIMP	0.66 μg
PEACHY FROST	0.66 μg
CALIFORNIA CHICKEN	0.65 μg
STRAWBERRY YOGURT PICKUP	0.65 μg
ZESTY MEXICAN CHICKEN SOUP	0.62 μg
SPINACH CHEESE TURKEY MEAT LOAF	0.62 μg

RICHEST FOOD SOURCES OF VITAMIN B12 PER 100 GRAMS

CLAMS	98 μg
LIVER, BEEF	80 μg
OYSTERS	18 μg
SARDINES	10 μg
CRAB	10 μg
HERRING	10 μg
LAMB	2.2 μg
EGGS, WHOLE	2.0 μg
CHEDDAR CHEESE	1.0 μg
SHRIMP	0.9 μg
PORK	0.7 μg
CHICKEN	0.5 μg

VITAMIN E

Vitamin E is an important anti-oxidant. It protects cell membranes from damage caused by pollutants, peroxides, and unstable molecules called "free radicals." It keeps unsaturated fatty acids from becoming rancid, inhibits abnormal coagulation of the blood, and assists in the process of cellular respiration. Vitamin E also helps protect fat soluble vitamins from being damaged by oxidation.

U.S.R.D.A.—30 I.U. (20.2 MILLIGRAMS) PER DAY
AVERAGE DAILY INTAKE OF AMERICANS—DATA NOT AVAILABLE

RECIPES WITH THE GREATEST AMOUNT OF VITAMIN E PER SERVING

SAUCY LIMA BEANS . . . . 10.1 I.U.	HEALTH VALLEY SESAME
CHICKEN APPLE SANDWICH. . . . . 9.9 I.U.	CHICKEN W/BROCCOLI . . . . 5.0 I.U.
VEGETABLE BULGUR PILAF . . . . 9.2 I.U.	VEGETARIAN PITA POCKETS . . . . 4.8 I.U.
LEMON CHICKEN ON	TUNA PITA SANDWICH . . . . 4.3 I.U.
SPINACH LEAVES . . . . 8.6 I.U.	GREEN RICE. 4.2 I.U.
CURRIED GARBANZO BEANS W/LIME. . 8.0 I.U.	SPAGHETTI W/BASIL AND PINE NUTS. . . 4.2 I.U.
SPINACH CHEESE TURKEY MEATLOAF . 7.0 I.U.	BERNIE'S COMPUTER COLESLAW . . . . . . 4.0 I.U.
CHICKEN SALAD ORIENTAL . . . . 5.6 I.U.	CHEDDAR CHICKEN. . . . . 3.9 I.U.
HEALTHY AMBROSIA. . . . . 5.5 I.U.	ASPARAGUS W/ORANGE SAUCE. . . . . . . 3.9 I.U.
REFRESHING SALMON SALAD . . . . 5.3 I.U.	APPLE CARROT CORN MUFFINS . . . . . . 3.7 I.U.
OAT NUT APPLE BREAD . . . . 5.2 I.U.	BULGUR VEGETABLE SALAD . . . . 3.7 I.U.

RICHEST FOOD SOURCES OF VITAMIN E PER 100 GRAMS

WHEAT GERM OIL. . . . . 378.1 I.U.	WHOLE CORN. . . . . 8.6 I.U.
SUNFLOWER SEEDS . . . . 77.5 I.U.	WHOLE WHEAT. . . . . 6.8 I.U.
ALMONDS . . . . 36.4 I.U.	SWEET POTATOES. . . . . 6.8 I.U.
SESAME SEEDS . . . . 33.7 I.U.	GARBANZO BEANS . . . . 4.6 I.U.
PEANUTS. 24.2 I.U.	SPINACH . . . . 4.5 I.U.
LIMA BEANS, DRY . . . . 11.4 I.U.	GREEN PEAS . . . . 4.0 I.U.

Part Seven

Testimonials and Index

24

Testimonials

Here's what people are saying about Health Valley...

About our company in general...

"Health Valley has a genuine, humane concern for the health and well-being of its customers and, furthermore, shows a commitment and a sincerity almost entirely absent in today's marketplace."

M. Correa
San Leandro, California

"When I am eating your product, I feel as if I am doing my body a favor. You have enlightened me with your personal interest."

C. Fitzgerald
La Canada, California

"It's so refreshing to see the personal interest that you take, not only in the care and production of your products, but also the relationship and interest you take in the concerns, needs and opinions of your consumers. It means a lot to the individual, especially in these times of mass-production, fast-foods, and corporate profiteering, that there are still some small, family-owned companies like yours that still have concern about proper nutrition, good health, and care about what is put into the human body. You are doing a great service to the public. Keep up the good work and thank you so much."

J. Moore
Lexington, Virginia

"I love and adore your products primarily because they are low in calories, high in nutrition and fiber and low in salt and sugar. You make a superior product and I always feel that I am doing myself a favor by purchasing them."

K. Flowers

"We applaud you for your sincere commitment to sell only the most healthy products. You are to be specially acclaimed for the 'no-lead' cans, a unique and most appreciated nutritional advance."

H. Lucraft
Hollywood, California

"I can buy your products with my eyes closed, knowing that I can trust the quality."
G. Moussalli
Denver, Colorado

"Just want to compliment you on your great line of good items. You have shown that a big good business company can produce and market natural foods at an affordable price. We are thankful for you and other natural food companies for putting some decent foods on the shelves that don't have so much salt and sugar added to it. We enjoy the varieties too...Keep up the good work."
Mrs. Galen W. Frahm
Denver, Colorado

"Thank you for keeping quality alive in the food world. I consider myself to be a fairly health conscious person and I believe your products reflect a sincere dedication to genuine "good health" consciousness. I have taken much pleasure in cooking with many of your wonderful 'Health Valley' products—

—I guess I like almost anything you do!"
Carla Vajiades
Claremont, California

"...I have been buying Health Valley products at the neighborhood health store and have found myself not only feeling better physically, but mentally and spiritually. They are really made for the human body."
Pat Carbone
Weston, Ontario, Canada

"I really appreciate your product! Many producers make claims of purity of their foods. Then we find that their idea of purity is to add brown sugar or bleached flour. Health Valley foods are a wonderful alternative to that deception. You have managed to make truly healthful foods which are really delicious. Thanks for your honesty and respect for the consumer."
Carol Appenzeller

"I just wanted to inform you that I am very pleased with all of your food products that I have tried. I like the fact that you make lots of foods, such as cereal with no sugar and low salt. And these foods taste very good! None of your food is bland or overwhelming in any way. Your prices are reasonable as well."
Deirdre Burke
Chicago, Illinois

"Thank you for producing foods of such consistent quality and nutritive value. Your company is the greatest."
M. Kywada
Pasadena, California

"I am impressed by the integrity and concern you show for the health and well-being of the people you serve."
M. McElheny
Farmersville, NY

430

"I think that your products are great. The depth of the company's concern for the client and product is excellent. My husband, a confirmed junk food fiend, has at last come to the realization that good-for-you food can taste great thanks to you."

L. Ratzmann
Madison, Wisconsin

"I want to thank you for <u>consistently</u> making high-quality, nutritious foods. I feel good serving your products to my family."

V. Mayer
Everett, Washington

"It is reassuring to know we can count on your company for food that is not only good for us, but good to eat as well."

R. Chapel
Encinitas, California

"I just wanted to tell you how happy I am that there are food products like yours. As a consumer I know that what I'm eating is nutritious for my body when I buy your products. I realize that so many companies today don't care what they put in their foods. As long as it tastes okay, that's all that matters. But you have both taste and nutrition in your products. As a vegetarian I'm very conscious about what I put in my body. So thank you for giving me healthy foods to choose from."

Kimberly A. Bel-Cher
Chatsworth, California

About weight control...

"I've set aside a couple of days to try your 'Week of Healthier Eating' and I must say it made a lot of sense. Not only did I lose weight, but I feel good physically and mentally."

E. A. Williams
Berkeley, California

"I have found that Health Valley foods have such a good flavor—they really taste good—not like some health foods I have bought...When I changed over to them I lost 29 pounds!"

G. Tronsgard
Fullafo, Minnesota

"It was great to find I could eat the right way and still enjoy it! I lost 40 pounds and have kept it off."

C. Stevens
Tulsa, Oklahoma

"I have just recently discovered several of your products on my grocery shelf and wanted to tell you how pleased I am with all of them. The Apple Bakes, Raisin and Date Bakes are the greatest, most satisfying of all your products I have tried. I have recently lost 23 pounds and these products have literally saved my diet!"

Judith E. Brandt
Panama City, Florida

"Thanks to your wonderful Cheddar Lites I have lost 38 pounds and my husband has lost 37 pounds in 3 months."
C. Munn
Munhall, Pennsylvania

About our products for special needs.

"At the age of 48 I had a heart attack. I also discovered that my arteries were very clogged. I have been using your health giving foods, especially cereals and Apple Bakes, and feel great."
M. K. McCauley
St. Petersburg, FL

"Please accept the thanks of my wife and myself for helping fill our requirements for salt-free, low-fat, sugar-free foods."
R. Altgelt
Bloomfield Hills, Michigan

"I am a diabetic and am able to eat many of your products."
E. Krause
Royal Oak, Michigan

"I recently had a triple by-pass surgery. Therefore all of your goodies fit right into my low sodium diet. Thanks for keeping me alive and healthy with the greatest products on the market today."
F. Johnson
Tucson, Arizona

"Three years ago my husband had a temporary loss of eyesight caused by too much cholesterol in the carotid veins. After many agonizing tests, our doctor gave us a choice of an operation or a diet. We were happy to choose the diet.
I have purchased almost everything you have placed on the market...my husband's cholesterol is now normal."
M. Runyan
Alta Loma, California

"Just a note to thank you so much for Health Valley products. I have just found that I have severe allergies to many foods and chemicals...I can use your wonderful products with no side effects! Your enamel-lined cans are okay for me. I use your canned tomato sauce and it's great! I use your frozen vegetables especially lima beans and broccoli when it is difficult to obtain fresh organic. And I can use your bacon and lunch meat. I hadn't used those from commercial sources for a long time because of the chemicals, but I just get so hungry for salami sometimes. Yours is great!...Thank you for your very fine products."
Diana Davis
Alton, Illinois

"We couldn't be more pleased with your delicious and nutritious, wholesome Health Valley All Natural Cereals—No Salt, no sugar or added preservatives in the Stoned Wheat Raisin Bran or Whole Wheat Cereal. Six months ago my husband was put on a no salt diet to reduce his blood pressure. Glad to say the blood pressure is down. Your delicious no salt cereals and whole wheat crackers have been a real help at mealtime and for a lite snack...Thank goodness my husband has seen the light and "come to Health Valley." Thanks for being there and having a hand in bringing wholesome, nutritious and natural food to folks everywhere..."

Mrs. Roger C. Giblon
Gardena, California

"Some months ago, my doctor told me that I needed to keep a watchful eye on my cholesterol and sodium levels. A diet high in fiber and low in animal fats was recommended. I had recollections—none too fond—of my mother's attempts to get me to eat bran cereal when I was young because it was so "good for me," and my resistance to the idea and the only available product.

My local food store...recommended that I try your products, which I did. I feel compelled to write to you and tell you how absolutely delighted I am with the range of products that you produce, but especially with my favorite 100% Bran Cereal with Apples & Cinnamon. Not only do I incorporate it as the principal ingredient of my lunch every day, but I eat it dry from the packet whenever I feel starvation pangs assail me at the office. It's crunchy, chewy and filling, and last but certainly not least, scrumptious!

I have been successful in altering my way of eating, and my digestive tract has never been in such good shape. My cholesterol level has been lowered considerably and the sodium problem has all but abated. I heartily recommend your products as being not only nutritious, but delicious as well..."

Mrs. Merlyn Brown
Falls Church, Virginia

"The other day I purchased two boxes of your Bran Cereal, the Apples and Cinnamon, and Bran with Raisins. Little did I know how delicious your cereal would be. I have hypoglycemia and cannot tolerate nutrasweet...For everyone who can't have sugar, your cereal is a God-Send...Keep up the great work."

Kathleen M. Amerson
Rockton, Illinois

"I was born with heart trouble and have had 3 open heart operations. I am now 30 and live a normal life with restricted dietary guidelines. Your products have made those guidelines bearable."

Thank you,
Dennis Dickson
Vista, California

"For years now I have found great relief from some rather severe allergies by using your products."

D. Townsend
Rochester Hills, Michigan

433

"Your cookies are indeed delicious and full of good flavor, and especially welcome as a treat for me, an insulin dependent diabetic."
J. Burton
Yorktown Heights, New York

"I especially enjoy your Amaranth products. Being a strict vegetarian I sometimes have trouble getting enough protein."
B. Hyer
Weatherford, Texas

"The Great Tofu Cookie is a delicious treat, which contains nothing I am allergic to. Thank you for a great creation."
M. Burke
Champlin, Minnesota

About some of our products.

Cereals

"One of the few rays of sunshine in my life lately has been your Orangeola Cereal. I was hooked from the first mouthful...Thank you for many previous hours of gustatory glee..."
Sera Sacks
Oakland, California

"I am writing this letter to compliment you on your product 100% Natural Stoned Wheat Raisin Bran Flakes. I am not a user of salt or sugar and I have tried other raisin brans, but I have never enjoyed a cereal more than I have yours. I will be sure to try your other products, and I will recommend your products highly to my friends and family."
Jeannette Schrader
Chicago, Illinois

"I would like to commend your company on your Amaranth Cereal. My whole family (including the children) love it. It is nice to know that a natural and healthy cereal can taste good too."
Virginia Cohen

"...The other day I tried your 100% Natural Bran Cereal. It was <u>delicious</u>. I've been looking for a good cereal with no added sugar, salt, artificial ingredients, and no oils. I can't wait to try your other varieties."
Pam Denney
Bowling Green, Kentucky

"GrrrRREAT! Congratulations on the excellent products you make. Recently I have tried three of your cereals: REAL, Orangeola and Sprouts 7. All three really tasted <u>good</u> and were great to eat. I'm glad somebody developed worthwhile, healthful products. Keep up the good work."
Jim Burque
Torrance, California

"I like your cereal a lot. My family has 4 boxes of your cereal in our pantry right now, just like we always do. I like the taste the best. I'm glad there is no sugar in it. Thank you for the recipes on back. I'll try them sometime. I'll eat your cereal even when I get older."

Brad Young
Poway, California

"I have tried all of the fiber cereals on the market today and your Fiber 7 is by far the best."

D. Jacobs
Seattle, Washington

"I want you to know your baby cereals are great. Two of my babies have gotten off to a wonderful start with them—I wish they had been available ten years ago when I had my first two. Your products are so much more convenient to use than my other methods. Those of us who wouldn't feed our babies Gerbers used to really have to work at it!"

Michele McKay
Klamath Falls, Oregon

"I love your natural cereals...Please don't change your cereals. It's wonderful to be able to feed my baby healthy, nutritious foods and you're the only company that understands this. Thanks again."

Susan Hall
Newark, Texas

Crackers and Cookies

"I simply had to drop a line (taking time out of my very busy schedule) to let you know I and my family enjoy completely your delicious 'Herb' Crackers. Thank God, finally, that there is a cracker without all the unnecessary ingredients. The fact that all your ingredients are pure and natural is definitely a plus...Since my first introduction (only a few months ago) to your products, you may be certain that I will continue to use them for entertaining as well. Many of our friends are food conscious. Continued success in all your future endeavors, and of course, thanks again."

Mrs. Lucia Marini

"I just ate my first (and then several more, as they are really delicious) Stoned Wheat Crackers and I was possessed to write this letter immediately. I just couldn't believe that they had no added salt and no sugar. I had to check the box again. I have tried many crackers from health food stores, and all of them had little or no taste, so much so that I often gave up and bought some grocery store crackers, even though I am not supposed to eat salt or sugar. I feel like a great weight has been lifted from my shoulders as I can look forward to healthful snacking with good taste, especially if the rest of your kinds of crackers and soups taste as good. I plan to buy them next time out. Thanks for a delicious and healthful product from a satisfied and grateful customer."

Howard F. Planey
Panama City, Florida

435

"It's not often a guy sits down and writes out a Christmas card to a cracker company, but my family is so in love with your Herb, Stoned Wheat and Sesame Crackers, I thought you ought to know! I think we have purchased so many boxes – well anyway, we appreciate the no preservatives, no sugar, etc....you have a good product – Keep those crackers coming!..."

George Devine & Family
Westwood, New Jersey

"I recently made a trip to Baton Rouge, Louisiana and obtained a box of your Herb Stoned Wheat Crackers. I want you to know that I think this is an excellent and superior product. I have never tasted anything better. I highly commend you for this...I did want you to know that in this age of mediocrity or less, I am appreciative of a company that puts excellence first."

Fr. Richard J. Burns, Jr.
St. Marks Episcopal Church
Crosset, Arkansas

"Although we live in a rural area, I'm willing to drive 22 miles to a store to get your Amaranth Graham Crackers. I love them, and always get 5-6 boxes."

M. Nobe
Colorado Springs, Colorado

"...Have enjoyed your crackers.

We have high cholesterol and triglycerides problems in my family and it's hard to find a cracker with all the proper ingredients. So many have coconut or palm oil – hydrogenated fats and they are no-no's to us. We eat a lot of crackers, as we eat soup a lot for lunch. Your crackers are the only ones we've found able to eat – thank you. Keep up the good work and God Bless."

Mrs. Polli Walsborn
Kennwick, Wisconsin

Soups and Chilis

"I recently purchased and enjoyed some of your Health Valley Tomato Soup and some Bean Soup. These are two of the finest soups I have ever tasted. I am buying these from now on. So often people take things for granted and fail to say please, thank you, or to express any appreciation at all. I wish to say that I have a high regard for your outstanding products and that I will recommend them to all who desire the finest. Thank you again for placing these fine food items on the market."

Val Grimes

"I'm sending you all a heartfelt 'thank you' for marketing such a superlative chili for vegetarians. It was a true delight, my first can, because one of the only meat dishes I've thought of now and then, since becoming a confirmed vegetarian was chili. The list of ingredients is impressive but the test of any product is of course, the taste. And this is where you really get the proverbial "GOLD STAR." We seldom take the time to applaud some product or service – instead we're more apt to complain. So I applaud your group of associates."

Dianne Armstrong

Delanson, New York

"Just a line to let you know how much I enjoy your products, Vegetable and Minestrone—no salt soups. My compliments and continued success!"

R. Horn
Durham, North Carolina

Snacks

"While visiting my daughter in upstate New York, I found Natural Flavor Corn Chips made by Health Valley Natural Foods. I was thrilled to find them and enjoyed them very much. As I have a passion for corn chips, I make them my weekend treat. However, as I have high blood pressure the salt isn't good for me. Sooo—when I found yours with No Salt Added I was happy to have discovered the corn chips I could eat and not worry about...They certainly are delicious..."

Evelyn McCarthy
Yonkers, New York

"I love your Corn Chips with 40% less salt. They are so tasty and crisp and hardly any salt. Can't stand all that salt on things. Now I can taste the corn flavor, not salt. I couldn't believe it when I found them in our Warehouse Food Store. Been looking for a product like this. Hope they keep selling them now that I found them..."

Mrs. Marilyn Reznick
Torrington, Connecticut

Other Health Valley Foods.

"I picked up two quarts of your Soy Moo non-dairy soy milk. I found it delicious and by far the best tasting and finest substitute for cow's milk of all the soy milks on the market."

Sincerely,
J. A. Permenter
Retired Professor and Associate Dean
Memphis State University College of Education
Memphis, Tennessee

"I just tried your Soy Moo and <u>love</u> it! For years I've been looking for an acceptable substitute for cow's milk..."

Maryanne B. Daly
Brookline, Massachusetts

"Instead of Salt is the best salt-free seasoning I have ever tasted. It makes almost anything taste better. In fact, it is delicious..."

Margaret Smith
Santa Monica, California

Healthier Eating Index

441

Footnotes Index

There are a number of footnotes in this book which you may want to refer to frequently because they contain useful tips on how to choose, use, store and cook different foods, as well as nutritional information.

This short index is your handy reference to these notes.

About the Author

GEORGE MATELJAN is a world renowned authority on healthy cooking and nutrition. He is the founder and president of Health Valley Foods, and was personally involved in the development of every one of its 300 products, which include over 100 No Salt Added foods. He is the driving force that has made Health Valley the world's largest producer of healthy foods with no refined white sugar, hydrogenated fats or artificial ingredients. He is widely recognized for his innovative concepts in lowfat, no salt cooking, and for having rediscovered amaranth, the lost grain of the ancient Aztecs. He has held lectures and seminars on healthy eating throughout the world, including Russia, China, Australia, England, Europe and Japan. Born in Split, Yugoslavia, Mateljan studied biology and medicine at the University of Belgrade. He also holds certificates from Ecole de Cuisine, La Varenne, France; Guiliano Bugialli's Cooking School in Florence, Italy; and Gourmet's Oxford, England. He is the author of the "Health Valley Natural Foods Cookbook," published in 1980 with over 60,000 copies in circulation.